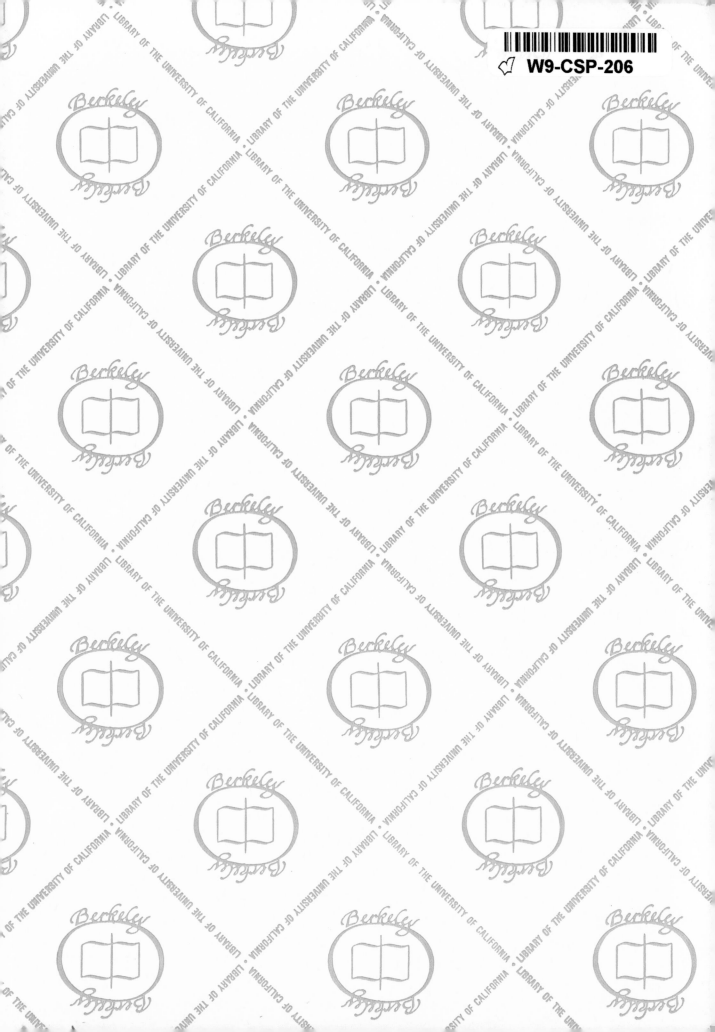

# MICROCHIP FABRICATION

## By
## Peter Van Zant

Mylar
Sep
Chem

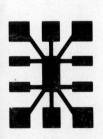

## DEDICATION

This book is dedicated to my father, William D. Van Zant, who would not have understood this subject, but would have been proud as hell that I wrote the book.

Published By:
**Semiconductor Services**
**1155 Meridian Ave., Suite 213**
**San Jose, CA 95125**
**U.S.A.**

Edited By: Mary DeWitt
          Ginny McLaughlin

Illustrated By: John Glare

Typset By: LARC Computing, Inc., Los Altos, California

Printed in the United States of America

## PREFACE

Since 1961, when I joined a solid state microelectronics lab at IBM, I have had some type of training responsibility. Ever since then a constant question of people wanting to know about the industry has been, "Is there a book where I can read about this technology?"

In 1961 there were precious few. Over the years as the industry has come into its own, a number of texts have been written about semiconductor circuits, physics and processing. In general, these books have been written for a technical audience. Few have been written for the nontechnical industry employees, interested lay persons and the many technical professionals in allied fields.

I became acutely aware of this lack while teaching semiconductor processing technical courses for Foothill College in Los Altos Hills, California. Many of the students in the introductory course were NOT engineers. The classes attracted support personnel (Production Control, Personnel, etc.) from semiconductor plants, operators, technicians and many sales and marketing folks from supplier companies.

They were in the course for familiarization with the industry and an understanding of the processes and issues of wafer processing. What was lacking was a book that addressed these needs in a nontheoretical, nonmathematical presentation.

MICROCHIP FABRICATION© was written to meet the needs of all the growing ranks of people described above. As the semiconductor industry becomes more important in the economy, more people will be involved in the industry. It is my intention that MICROCHIP FABRICATION will serve their needs.

# Table of Contents

# The Semiconductor Industry

Chapter 1.

Man has probably been counting and tabulating since the discovery of fingers. While the ten digits were an adequate system at the dawn of civilization, they no longer serve the computational needs of mankind. New systems and machines have developed over the years, keeping pace with our need to compute and manage data. Today the electronic digital computer and its many offspring are the state-of-the-art in counting, calculating and tabulation.

At the heart of a computer and the multitude of "intelligent" machines is the microchip (or, integrated circuit). The manufacturers of microchips and the many suppliers providing high tech materials, services and equipment to them make up the semiconductor industry. This industry began developinng in 1947, away from the public eye. Over the next twenty years, it grew into a multi-billion dollar industry. By the 1970's it had become too large to continue in its anonymity.

Today, the industry continues to grow in size and technical sophistication. More and more people interact with the semiconductor industry and need to understand its products and the methods by which they are manufactured. Within the industry, the manufacturing processes are referred to as "fabrication."

*MICROCHIP FABRICATION*© is an introduction to this intriguing industry, and the steps required to "fabricate microchips."

## 1.1 THE EARLY YEARS

The demands of modern civilization outgrew manual manipulation of data in the late Nineteenth Century. It was predicted that the 1890 U.S. census would take ten years to condense and correlate. The Census Bureau realized that the final tally would be hopelessly out-of-date, and that each succeeding census would be even more outdated.

So they sponsored a contest to solicit a method to reduce and correlate the data faster. The winner was Herman Hollerith whose tabulating machine completed the census tabulation in an amazing six weeks. Hollerith went on to form the Tabulating Machine Company which evolved into the International Business Machines Corporation (IBM).

Hollerith's machine introduced a new driving mechanism for computing machines: electric motors. The technology of computers continued to progress with machines developed in the 'Thirties computing by electrical/mechanical switches. World War II spurred the development of faster and more powerful machines. The result was the world's first electronic computer, switched on at the Moore School of Engineering in Pennsylvania in February, 1947. Named ENIAC (Electronic Numerical Integrator and Calculator), the system was vacuum tube based, weighed 50 tons, occupied 3,000 square feet, had 19,000 tubes, generated a lot of heat, required the power of a small power station and cost one million dollars (1940 value).

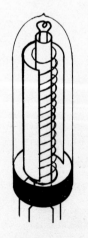

**Vacuum Tube**

In addition to the multitude of vacuum tubes, ENIAC incorporated thousands of solid state devices such as resistors and capacitors. These devices were reliable, compact and generated little or no heat. Vacuum tubes on the other hand were bulky and fragile due to their glass envelopes. They generated a lot of heat, required a lot of power to operate, and were prone to failure from leaks and deteriorated filaments.

These problems were the impetus for finding a replacement for the vacuum tube. On December 23, 1947, working under Bell Labs' ongoing research program, three Bell scientists – Shockley, Brattin and Bardeen – demonstrated a solid state device capable of amplification of an electric current. Dubbed a transfer resistor, the device soon became known as the transistor. This discovery started the microelectronics revolution and earned the inventors a Nobel Peace Prize.

Their invention led to the duplication, twenty years later, of the computing power of ENIAC, on a $3/8''$ square of silicon, drawing less power than a light bulb and costing less than $20.00!

## 1.2 THE DEVELOPMENT DECADE (1951–1960)

The implications of the electrical advantages of the solid state transistor were immediately recognized, although the tremendous advantages of microminiaturization weren't felt until two decades later. During the 1950's, most of the materials and processes used in today's VLSI chip fabrication were discovered and the basics of transistor operation were defined.

Transistor action results from the passage of current across P/N junctions formed in various semiconducting materials. Bell Lab's first transistor was formed in germanium; the junctions were formed at the interface of certain metals alloyed to the germanium. This type of transistor was appropriately called an alloy junction transistor. Another early junction forming technique was the "grown junction". In this method dopants were added as a piece of germanium was "grown" into a single crystal. By choosing the proper dopants, a junction was formed in the crystal.

In 1954 Texas Instruments introduced the first silicon transistor. The issue over which material would be most used was settled in 1956 and 1957 by two developments, again from Bell Labs: Diffused Junctions and Oxide Masking. Both of these techniques favor silicon for reasons explained later. Using these techniques, manufacturers began producing silicon and germanium solid state transistors, diodes and resistors in production quantities. These single electrical function units are called discrete devices.

Diffused Junctions are created in a semiconductor material by the introduction of controlled amounts of dopants (often called impurities) into the wafer. By diffusing an entire layer into the wafer to create a shallow junction, improved electrical performance is gained. Philco, using diffused layers, invented the mesa transistor, named after its mesa-like appearance.

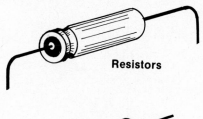
**Resistors**

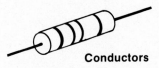
**Conductors**

**Solid State**

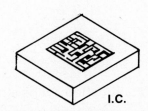
**I.C.**

**Chips**

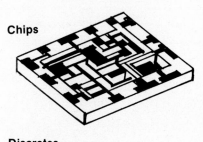

**Discretes**

**Fig. 1.1 Solid State Electrical Devices**

The development of oxide masking ushered in the Silicon Age. Nature's silicon/silicon dioxide system is the perfect system for semiconductor device miniaturization.

Silicon dioxide grows uniformly on silicon and, having a similar index of expansion, allows high temperature processing without wafer warping. The dopants diffused into silicon move (diffuse) much more slowly in $SiO_2$, permitting its use as a diffusion barrier. An additional advantage of the system is its relative ease of selectively removing the oxide (patterning) without disturbing the underlying silicon.

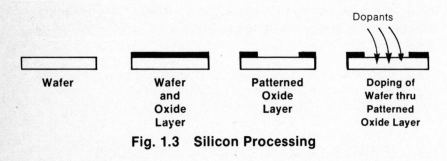

**Fig. 1.3   Silicon Processing**

This ability to remove miniature portions of the oxide and therefore create miniature electrical regions in the wafer has allowed the highly integrated, dense circuits of today. These two developments made silicon literally "King of the Valley." By 1980, 90% of solid state devices and circuits were silicon-based.

Fairchild, the first company to work exclusively in silicon, developed the planar process. Planar technology enables all junctions and thin film formation to take place on or through the top layer of the wafer. Its flattened surface led to the vacuum deposition of thin layers of aluminum to act as surface "wiring." This technique has allowed the production of today's higher density circuits.

Bell Labs conceived of forming the transistors in a high purity layer of silicon that was deposited on the wafer. Called an epitaxial layer, this discovery allowed higher speed devices and closer packing of components in bipolar circuits.

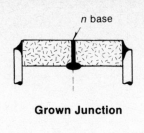

**Grown Junction**

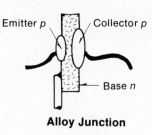

**Alloy Junction**

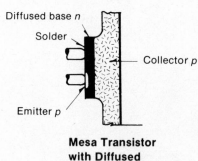

**Mesa Transistor with Diffused Emitter and Base**

**Fig. 1.2   Junction Transistors**

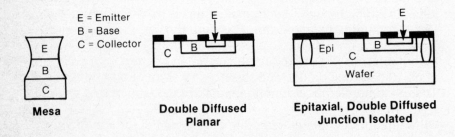

**Fig. 1.4   Solid State Transistors**

Up to 1958 solid state/semiconductor devices (transistors, diodes, capacitors, resistors) were fabricated individually in and on a wafer, separately mounted in a package and wired into a circuit. In 1958 RCA conceived the monolithic circuit technique. They mounted the discrete devices on conductive and resistive paths that had been screened on a thin ceramic substrate (block). The paths terminated at pins on the periphery of the substrate, creating a hybrid circuit. Hybrid circuits expanded the advantages of solid state semiconductor devices to the circuit level. IBM's famous 360 computer series utilized hybrid circuitry. Hybrid technology was touted as the breakthrough to the densification of circuits, but it was a very short-lived dream.

In 1959 Jack Kilby leapfrogged the advantages of hybrid circuitry with his invention of the integrated circuit at Texas Instruments. He connected a Mesa transistor to a thin film capacitor on the same chip of germanium. Using the natural resistance of the substrate, he thus formed a circuit of several components integrated in one chip.

In a little over a decade, the new semiconductor industry obsoleted tube circuitry, moved from discrete devices to integrated circuits and developed the basic techniques for miniaturization.

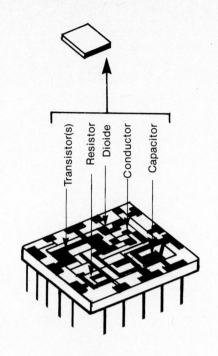

**Fig. 1.5**
**Hybrid and Integrated Circuit**

## 1.3 THE PROCESSING DECADE (1961–1970)

The 1960's was the decade of the process engineer. In Silicon Valley, on the Texas plains and around Route 128 in Boston, process improvements and new device and circuit designs were cranked out. New companies were formed by dropouts from Fairchild, Texas Instruments and others. In 1963 RCA informed the world that it had developed the insulated gate field effect transistor (or, MOS transistor). This new technology joined bipolar technology and twenty years later surpassed the latter in device volume. RCA again boosted semiconductor fortunes with the introduction of CMOS (N and P channel MOS transistors on the same chip).

The new MOS devices, featuring lower power requirements and higher packing densities, were a natural device for computer memories. MOS growth came at the expense of core memories, not bipolar devices. In this decade, the industry expanded and refined new processes to yield increasingly sophisticated devices and circuits at lower and lower prices.

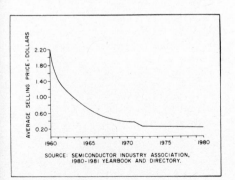

**Fig. 1.6    Semiconductor Prices**

In fact, semiconductor device and circuit prices have fallen constantly since their introduction due to the continued improvement in process yields and productivity. During the 1950's the number of units shipped per starting wafer was low and unpredictable (Chapter 3). Today an I.C. manufacturer ships up to 40% of the units started. Yield improvement and improved process productivity have been, and continue to be, two ongoing drivers of semiconductor process research. Yield improvement techniques through the Sixties created continually lower selling prices and the semiconductor industry became a self-fueling one.

These falling prices have made it economical for an increasing
number of industries to switch to solid state circuitry. An
example of this feasibility is the automobile. The $300.00 worth of
solid state electronics in a car in the 1980's would have cost
closer to several thousands of dollars in 1970 (In 1970 a car could
be purchased for $5,000.00). Another example is the simple home
computer which for less than $5,000.00 in 1982 prices has the
power and speed of an IBM million dollar mainframe giant of
fifteen years ago.

The Sixties also saw other trends still characteristic of the
industry:

1. Smaller Image Size
2. Higher Device Count/Circuit
3. Larger Circuit Size

The three are closely related, as the following example illustrates:
A firm is producing a particular device or I.C. and is faced with a
10% drop in selling price. There are two choices to offset the
loss: improve production yields and/or reduce the feature size of
the devices, allowing more chips per wafer leading to an
automatic increase in productivity (more units out for the same
production cost). The circuit designer immediately recognizes
that improved yields and reduced feature size can allow him or
her to design a circuit with many more functions. Such a circuit
is more reliable than the former circuitry because the number of
connections required per function decreases. Every time the
number of connections can be decreased, there is an increase in
reliability.

A third level of improvement is to make the circuit even bigger. In
fact, the number of devices per circuit has steadily increased over
time (see fig. 1.7), resulting in computers that are faster, more
reliable, more compact and less expensive.

To review, the initial trends in device design and production that
still drive the industry are:

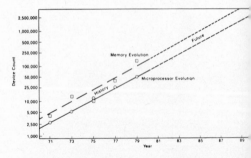

**Fig. 1.7  Device Count vs. Time**

1. Declining prices
2. Improved process and electrical yields
3. Higher device count per circuit
4. Smaller image size
5. Larger circuit size
6. Faster circuits
7. Higher power circuits

The lament of the process engineer continues to be: "As soon as
I get yields up, they densify the design, or reduce the image size,
or increase the die size, or DO ALL THREE!"

## 1.4 THE PRODUCTION DECADE (1971–1980)

By the early 1970's, most of the current fabrication processes were identified, if only in the laboratory. Plasma etching and stripping machines were being offered. The first spin/bake, develop/bake systems were in operation. Synthetic, uniform negative resist formulas were available, as were projection alignment, automatic alignment machines, ion implantation, E-beam and X-ray. A host of automatic handling and control systems were also developed, waiting in the wings for device density, image size and process control to require their services. Wafer processing moved to batch processing and automatic wafer handling via inline processing. Material suppliers felt the pressure to supply more consistent, ever cleaner chemicals, and high resolution, quality photo resists and photo plates.

During the 70's the circuits moved to higher levels of integration. Each increase in integration required more sophisticated materials, processes and equipment. The industry also adopted a scale to indicate device density in an integrated circuit. From S.S.I. (Small Scale Integration) to V.L.S.I. (Very Large Scale Integration). The approximate device count per circuit is indicated below:

**Table 1.1    Integration Levels**

| Level | Abbreviation | # Components per Chip |
| --- | --- | --- |
| Small Scale Integration | SSI | 2 - 50 |
| Medium Scale Integration | MSI | 50 - 5000 |
| Large Scale Integration | LSI | 5000 - 100,000 |
| Very Large Scale Integration | VLSI | Over 100,000 - 1,000,000 |
| Ultra Large Scale Integration | ULSI | > 1,000,000 |

The geographical trend of the 70's was a move away from Silicon Valley. Firms headquartered there found that economic pressures made production facilities elsewhere attractive. It is fair to say that the semiconductor industry changed from a three region industry (California, Texas, Boston) to an international one. Plants in Florida, Texas, Arizona, Colorado, Oregon, Idaho, Europe and Japan began pumping "the oil of the 80's."

The decade also saw the growth of the captive semiconductor producer. As more industries included solid state circuitry in their products they started up their own wafer shops. The 1970 decade opened with an MSI Technology and handed into the 1980's a VLSI industry.

## 1.5 THE AUTOMATION DECADE (1981–1990)

All the pressures and trends in semiconductor fabrication lead to automatic fab processing. By the beginning of the eighties, most individual processes had become self-automated. Today the operator's role is to load the system, check or select the process and push the start button.

To fully appreciate technological improvement in this industry, one has to understand that new processes, materials or machines are developed to produce the current "state of the art" device. But the current "S.O.T.A." device takes time to replace the "old" device. A new device and process breakthrough does not immediately obsolete an old process. For example, diode and transistor devices do not have the performance requirements of LSI devices, therefor their processes do not require LSI process sophistication. Economically, it would not be cost effective to convert a diode line (ASP $0.05 or less) to processes capable of producing VLSI devices (ASP = $5.00).

In short, a semiconductor process follows the life cycle of the device it produces. As long as the device (or one at a similar level of integration) is needed the processes producing it will prevail. This fact is often obscured by the focus of R&D and published papers on the advanced techniques.

## 1.6 SEMICONDUCTOR PRODUCTS

It is interesting that the semiconductor products developed in the 1960's are still produced today. They are:
Discrete devices
Integrated circuits

## 1.7 DISCRETE DEVICES

Discrete devices are single function devices fabricated in semiconductor materials. They are resistors, capacitors, diodes and transistors. They are produced by the same basic techniques used in I.C. manufacturing. Generally, discrete devices have less demanding operating parameters than I.C.'s and, therefore, can be produced with less than state-of-the-art processes. The dollar volume of discrete device sales has tracked the semiconductor's industry growth at a constant 30–40% level.

## 1.8 INTEGRATED CIRCUITS

I.C.'s are the primary product of the semiconductor industry and the main focus of this book. They come in an endless variety of forms, functions and sizes. By definition, an I.C. is a circuit containing two or more components (devices) fabricated in and on a single piece of semiconducting material.

The way in which a particular I.C. is built is dictated by its final use. Resurrecting our automobile analogy, we know that offroad vehicles and golf carts have similar parts and functions, but the choice of materials and construction techniques is dictated by their use. Similarly, different I.C.'s are built using either bipolar or MOS techniques. Within these two broad categories there are numerous variations. Chapter 20 explores the technologies in more detail. Table 1.2 is a guide to the major product categories produced by the semiconductor industry.

Chapters 2 through 17 cover the process techniques of microchip fabrication. Chapters 18 through 20 detail the types of devices made with this technology, examine bipolar and MOS building techniques and survey the major circuits produced by this amazing industry.

Table 1.2 lists the major structure variations used by the industry to fabricate semiconductor devices.

## 1.9 PACKAGING OF SEMICONDUCTOR DEVICES

At the conclusion of the fabrication process, the semiconductor device is in the form of a "chip." In this form it is vulnerable to contamination and devoid of electrical connections.

Before inclusion in a computer or other electrical circuit, the chip must be put in a package and connected to the outside world via the package connections. The usual packages are metal "cans" designated for from three to five for simpler chips, and dual in-line (DIP) packages for larger chips.

Firms that manufacture the chips package them in an operation called "assembly".

While the fabrication process is technology-intensive, the assembly process is labor intensive. Consequently the majority of assembly operations are located "off-shore" in low labor rate areas. However, the rising economies of third world nations are erasing the previous wage differential. This trend is fueling the development of automated assembly factories in the U.S.A.

## 1.10 HYBRID CIRCUITS

Hybrid circuites, sometimes called monolithic chips, provide an alternative to the individual packaging of chips. These monolithic circuits are ceramic substrates with screened resistors and conductors on which chips, resistor arrays and capacitors are cemented. The conductors are connected to pins around the periphery of the substrate.

## 1.11 PRINTED CIRCUIT BOARDS

The printed circuit board is another method for building a larger circuit. Packaged semiconductor devices and a host of other electrical components (resistors, capacitors, inductors, etc.) are soldered onto a "plastic" board whose surface is covered with copper conductive paths. Printed circuit board technology includes many different materials and processing techniques. A recent version features unpackaged chips attached directly onto the board.

**TO3 or TO5**
**"Cans"**

**Dual-in-Line DIP**

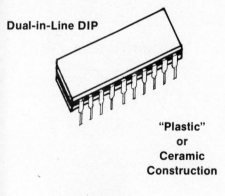

**"Plastic"**
**or**
**Ceramic**
**Construction**

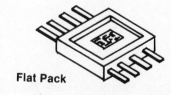

**Flat Pack**

**Fig. 1.8   Semiconductor Packages**

Hybrid and printed circuits are assembled by both merchant and captive facilities. Their technologies are different from microchip manufacturing and constitute different industries.

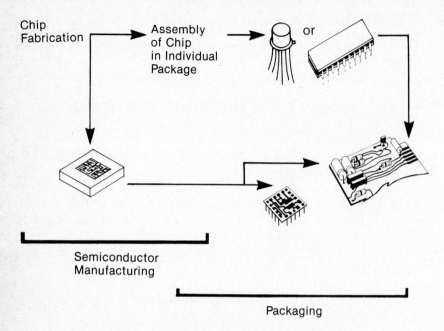

**Fig. 1.9    Relationship of Semiconductor
Hybrid and Printed Circuit Board Industries**

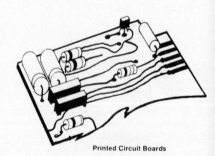

Printed Circuit Boards

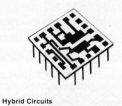

Hybrid Circuits

**Fig. 1.10
Hybrid and Printed Circuit Board**

**Table 1.2    Overview of
the Semiconductor Industry**

| | Discrete Devices | Circuits | | | | |
|---|---|---|---|---|---|---|
| | | Hybrid | | Integrated | | |
| Level of Integration | 0 | Low | SSI | MSI | LSI | VLSI |
| Device Count | 1 | 10–100 | 2–50 | 50–50,000 | 5,000–100,000 | 100,000 |
| Technologies | Mesa Planar VMOS | Single Level Double Level Thin Film Thick Film | **Bipolar** Junction Isolated Dielectric Isolated Silicon of Sapphire $I^2L$ | | **MOS** Metal Gate Silicon Gate CMOS FET J FET V MOS | |

## 1.12 USES OF SEMICONDUCTOR PRODUCTS

In 1947 it became obvious that the newly discovered transistor would replace vacuum tubes in computers. What was not obvious was that the tiny devices and their offspring – the integrated circuit – would allow the design of circuits and equipment that at that time seemed like science fiction.

A vast number of chips still end up in computers but other uses are growing rapidly, especially in the consumer market. Table 1.3 lists the uses of chips since 1950. Based on the history of the last twenty years, we can assume that the 1990 list will include uses just now being conceived.

### Table 1.3: Semiconductor Uses Since 1950

**50's**
   Radio
   Military Navigation and Communication
   Mainframe Computers

**60's**
   TV
   Minicomputers

**70's**
   TV Games
   Calculators
   Watches
   Automotive Engine Control
   Personal Computers
   Telecommunications
   Computer Peripherals

**80's**
   Artificial Intelligence
   Automobiles
   Systems Integration
   Home Electronics
   Defense

**90's**
   Computerized Manufacturing
   Electronic Banking System
   Worldwide TV/Information Networks
   Computerized Homes
   ??
   ??

# Overview of Semiconductor Manufacturing

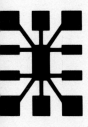

Chapter 2.

## INTRODUCTION

In Chapter 1 we introduced the various products produced by the Semiconductor Industry. This chapter overviews the entire manufacturing process from raw material to shipped device. Since silicon accounts for ninety percent of the devices produced, the majority of the process steps illustrated will be those used in silicon technology.

The reader should complete this chapter with an understanding of the "What" and "Why" of each of the various process stages, a familiarity with the terminology of each stage, and an understanding of how semiconductor lines are organized to accomplish the high tech birth of microchips.

## 2.1 SILICON MANUFACTURING PROCESS SAND TO CIRCUIT

Silicon is one of the most plentiful elements on the earth. We stumble through tons of it in the form of silicon dioxide every time we go to a beach. The silicon in that sand can eventually end up as a semiconductor device or circuit. During the transformation, the silicon passes through four distinct manufacturing stages. Each of the stages encompasses a separate set of process steps and technology. The four stages are:

1. Materials Preparation
2. Wafer Preparation
3. Wafer Fabrication
4. Assembly

TABLE 2.5 at the end of this chapter illustrates their relationship and the "unit of processing" for each area.

## 2.2 MATERIALS PREPARATION

The first step in the production of a silicon semiconductor device is the extraction of the silicon from its natural form, silicon dioxide.

Mere extraction is not sufficient, however. It is imperative that the silicon finally obtained be extremely pure. Purified silicon in which the impurity level has been reduced to a level of no more than several parts per million is termed electronic or semiconductor grade. Two methods are used to produce this high grade silicon: hydrogen-reduction and thermal decomposition of silicon-containing gases. The chemical reactions start with Silicon Tetrachloride or Trichlorosilane. They are:

Silicon Tetrachloride: $SiCl_4 + 2H_2 \longrightarrow 4HCl + Si$

Trichlorosilane:  $2SiHCl_3 + 2H_2 \longrightarrow 6HCl + 2Si$

After the silicon is extracted it is cast into rods that have a polycrystalline structure. The silicon in this form is referred to as polysilicon or simply, poly. The production of polysilicon is a multibillion dollar international business involving twenty suppliers.

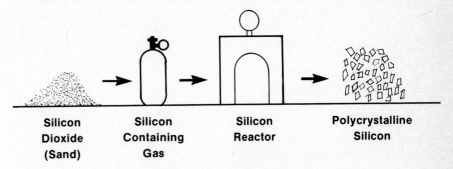

| Silicon | Silicon | Silicon | Polycrystalline |
| Dioxide | Containing | Reactor | Silicon |
| (Sand) | Gas | | |

**Fig. 2.1   Conversion of Silicon Dioxide to Semiconductor Grade Silicon**

## 2.3 CRYSTAL GROWTH AND WAFER PREPARATION

Discrete devices and I.C.'s are formed in and on the surface of wafers of semiconducting material. Silicon wafers are cut from crystals that have been formed from the chunks of polysilicon. During formation of the crystals, dopants are added to the silicon to create the required electrical characteristics and the silicon structure is rearranged to a single crystal form. The resultant crystal is ground to the required diameter, and individual wafers are sawed from the crystal. Each raw wafer is polished to optical flatness and the required thickness before electrical measurements and clean room packaging occur.

Companies supplying wafers generally specialize in both crystal growth and wafer preparation. A few also produce polysilicon, and several of the large semiconductor device manufacturers have in-house wafer preparation facilities. For the majority of device producers, however, wafers are a purchased material.

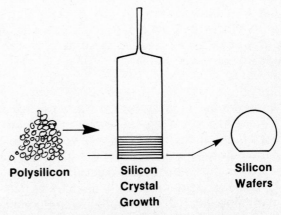

**Polysilicon**          **Silicon Crystal Growth**          **Silicon Wafers**

**Fig. 2.2   Poly Silicon to Wafers**

## 2.4 WAFER FABRICATION

Wafer fabrication encompasses the manufacturing processes that create the semiconductor device or I.C. in and on the wafer surface. The manufacturing area and the collective processes are called both *fabrication* and the abbreviated *Fab*. The blank wafer enters fab and emerges four to eight weeks later containing up to hundreds of identical patterns, each containing a separate discrete device or I.C.

### 2.4.1  Wafer Terminology

A typical semiconductor wafer is depicted in fig. 2.3 above. The wafer diameter may vary as may the size of the individual patterns. The common parts are:

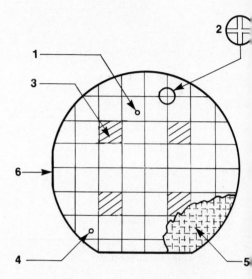

**Fig. 2.3  Wafer Terminology**

1. Chip, Die, Device, Circuit, Microchip, or Bar:
   Upon completion the wafer surface is covered with identical patterns. Each pattern may contain a single discrete semiconductor device or an integrated circuit. The terms listed above are all used to refer to the individual units.

2. Scribe Lines:
   The die are separated from each other by regions that contain no units or circuitry. These areas will eventually be sawed through to separate the wafer into individual chips.

3. Engineering Test Die:
   Each wafer contains a number of chips or die that appear to have a different pattern. Upon closer inspection, usually by microscope, it is evident that they indeed are different. These die contain special test devices created by the same processes as the "regular" die. Their difference is in their size. The individual transistors, diodes, resistors and capacitors of an integrated circuit are too tiny to be tested during the processing. The special test die are designed on a larger scale to allow in-process quality control.

   A second use of the test die enhances yield. The patterns on the finished wafer are the result of multiple applications of the patterning operation when the patterns are "stacked."

   There are yield advantages to "stacking" the same die coordinates at each patterning step. In other words, die number 3A is created from die 3A location on each of the masks. The engineering test die serve to allow the required "stacking" of patterns.

4. Edge Die
   Every wafer contains die located at the wafer edge that are incomplete. Because of this incompleteness these partial die cannot function and are therefore "lost" wafer real estate. The percentage of "lost" real estate is a function of the relative die and wafer size. Larger die on smaller wafers will have a higher percentage of unusable die. This mathematical reality has contributed to the pressure to produce larger diameter wafers.

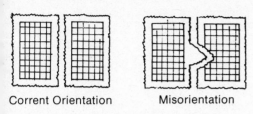

Corrent Orientation    Misorientation

**Fig. 2.4  Effects of Die Orientation
on Die Separation**

5. Crystal Planes:
The cutaway section of fig. 2.4 illustrates the crystal structure of the wafer. It is important that the die be located on the wafer surface in a specific alignment to the wafer crystal structure. The orientation is required to prevent "ragged" die edges when the wafer is separated into individual die.

6. Wafer Flats:
The wafer crystal structure is not evident to the naked eye. A "major" flat is ground on the crystal to indicate the orientation of the wafer structure. Patterns are oriented on the wafer with one of the scribe lines perpendicular to the major flat.

A shorter or "minor" flat is ground onto some of the crystals to indicate the particular crystal structure and electrical type (N or P). The exact code is explained in the section on crystal growth.

### 2.4.2 Basic Wafer Fabrication Operations

In wafer fabrication, circuit formation in and on the wafer requires many sophisticated processes. The actual number of steps the wafer goes through will vary with the type and complexity of the circuit being built. The total number may reach up to thirty major steps, and each major step may involve up to fifteen substeps. Despite the many steps, only three basic operations are performed on the wafer:

1. Layering
Thin layers of different materials are grown on, or added to, the wafer surface.

2. Patterning
Portions of the thin layers are selectively removed from the wafer.

3. Doping
The resistivity and conductivity type of selected regions in the wafer are changed by the addition of dopants.

### 2.4.3 Layering

The first step in fabricating silicon microchips is to grow a thin layer of silicon dioxide on the silicon wafer surface. During fabrication, additional layers of silicon dioxide are grown on the wafer and other layer materials deposited on the surface. The layers function in the circuit as insulators (dielectrics), semiconductors or conductors.

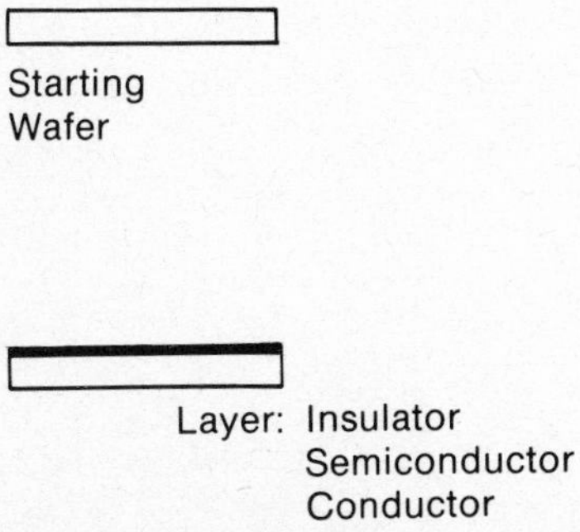

Starting Wafer

Layer: Insulator
Semiconductor
Conductor

**Fig. 2.5  Layering**

Fig. 2.5 does not accurately represent the thickness relationship of the layer to the wafer. A typical layer is 0.75 microns thick and a 100mm diameter wafer is 20 mills thick. That represents a ratio of 1:700!

Table 2.1 lists the layers used in silicon technology, their function in a circuit and the techniques used to put them on the wafer surface. The exact role(s) of each layer and the four techniques are explained in subsequent chapters.

**Table 2.1   Semiconductor Layers and Layering Techniques**

| Layers | Thermal Oxidation | Chemical Vapor Deposition | Evaporation | Sputtering |
|---|---|---|---|---|
| Insulators | Silicon Dioxide | Silicon Dioxide Silicon Nitrides | | Silicon Dioxide Silicon Monoxide |
| Semiconductors | | Epitaxial Silicon Poly Silicon | | |
| Conductors | | | Aluminum Aluminum/Silicon Aluminum/Copper Nichrome Gold | Tungston Titanium Molybdenum |

## 2.4.4 Patterning

After the layers are put on the wafer, selected portions of it are removed, leaving only a "pattern" remaining on the wafer (the major exception is epitaxially deposited silicon). The patterning process is called by various names including *photomasking, masking* and *photolithography.*

The pattern is first formed on a glass plate through a photoresist process similar to photography. The pattern on the glass mask is transferred onto the wafer surface layer.

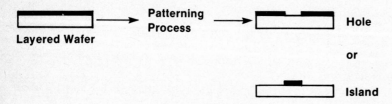

**Fig. 2.6   Patterning**

The hole formed in the layer or island of material left exposes the layer below for subsequent doping or metalization processes.

Patterning is the most critical of the three basic operations influencing yields. The majority of the contamination on a wafer occurs during patterning. Also, poor process control can result in a distortion or size change of the patterned holes or islands. These distortions result in a physical dimension change in the electrical components (e.g., resistors) which in turn causes a shift in electrical performance. Much of process development is focused on minimizing these problems.

Improvements in miniaturization are limited by the size opening (feature size) that is possible in photomasking.

## 2.4.5 Doping

The operating parts of an I.C. are the transistors, diodes and resistors formed in the silicon wafer. These components are formed as local regions in the wafer surface where added dopants have changed the conductivity type and resistivity.

Doping takes place to the wafer through the holes patterned in the surface layer. The two techniques used are:

1. Thermal Diffusion
2. Ion Implantation

Thermal diffusion is performed by heating the wafer to the vicinity of 1000°C and exposing it to vapors containing the desired dopant. The dopant atoms diffuse into the wafer surface, creating a localized region filled with the dopant atoms.

Ion implantation is a technique in which dopant atoms are accelerated to a high speed and "shot" into the wafer surface. Ion implantation takes place at a much lower temperature (2000°C – 4000°C) than thermal diffusion.

The fabrication of the finished circuit can require up to eleven doping steps.

Table 2.2 is a summary of the three basic wafer fabrication processes, and shows the major techniques used to accomplish them. Each of the techniques is explained in the following chapters.

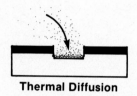

**Thermal Diffusion**

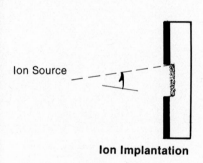

Ion Source

**Ion Implantation**

**Fig. 2.7  Doping**

## Table 2.2   Wafer Fabrication Process

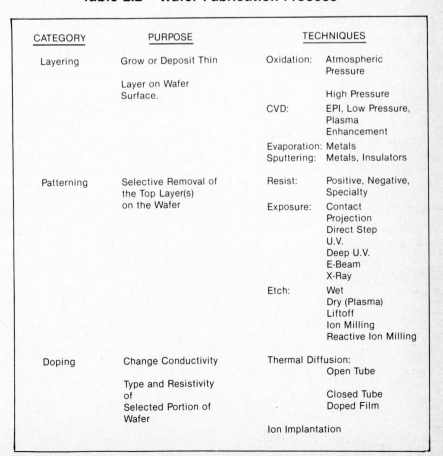

| CATEGORY | PURPOSE | TECHNIQUES | |
|---|---|---|---|
| Layering | Grow or Deposit Thin Layer on Wafer Surface. | Oxidation: | Atmospheric Pressure |
| | | | High Pressure |
| | | CVD: | EPI, Low Pressure, Plasma Enhancement |
| | | Evaporation: | Metals |
| | | Sputtering: | Metals, Insulators |
| Patterning | Selective Removal of the Top Layer(s) on the Wafer | Resist: | Positive, Negative, Specialty |
| | | Exposure: | Contact Projection Direct Step U.V. Deep U.V. E-Beam X-Ray |
| | | Etch: | Wet Dry (Plasma) Liftoff Ion Milling Reactive Ion Milling |
| Doping | Change Conductivity Type and Resistivity of Selected Portion of Wafer | Thermal Diffusion: | Open Tube |
| | | | Closed Tube Doped Film |
| | | Ion Implantation | |

## 2.5 FABRICATION SEQUENCES

The production of a semiconductor circuit is similar in flow to the production of a vehicle. An auto manufacturing plant uses basic techniques such as welding, painting, and metal bending to produce a car. The type of vehicle being produced dictates the sequence and number of techniques used. A compact car follows a different production path than a bus.

The same principle applies to semiconductor fabrication. Each wafer goes through a different sequence and number of processes. The flow varies with the building technology used (MOS, Bipolar, etc.) and the complexity of the device or circuit. A simple metal gate MOS wafer requires five masking steps and one diffusion while a basic bipolar wafer receives seven masking steps and four diffusions. Fig. 2.8 illustrates a bipolar process flow from the perspective of basic fab operations.

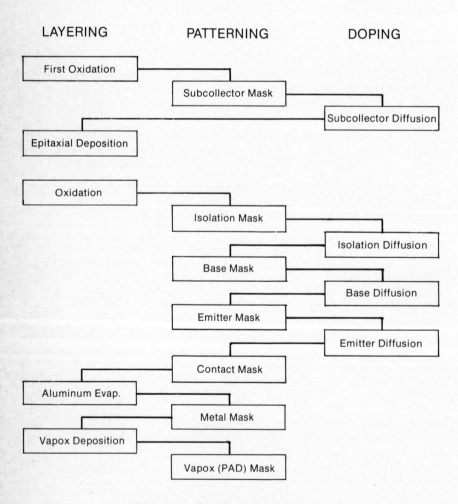

Fig. 2.8   Bipolar Process Flow

The operations can be grouped into three basic sequences:

1. Doping Sequence
2. Metalization Sequence
3. Passivation Sequence

### 2.5.1 Doping Sequence

This three-step sequence results in the formation of the localized N or P-type regions in the wafer surface. The basic sequence of operations is:

> Layering
> Patterning
> Doping

This is the most frequently used sequence in the fabrication of semiconductor devices. When a second doping sequence is required, the starting layer is usually grown as part of the preceeding diffusion process. If a doping sequence follows an ion implantation, a separate oxidation step is required.

### 2.5.2 Metalization Sequence

After the electrically active regions are created through the doping sequences in the wafer surface, the regions or components have to be "wired" together. In semiconductor technology the "wiring" is a thin layer of aluminum that is deposited on the wafer surface, on top of the insulating layer of silicon dioxide or silicon nitride. A masking operation precedes deposition to create holes in the insulating layer for the aluminum to pass through, in order to contact the regions in the wafer surface below. The name of this masking step is *Contact Mask.* This sequence is completed with a masking step that patterns the metal into lines connecting (wiring) the various components in the wafer surface.

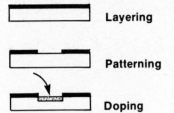

Layering

Patterning

Doping

**Fig. 2.9   Doping Sequence**

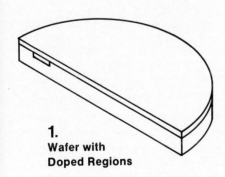

**1.**
**Wafer with Doped Regions**

**2.**
**Patterning: Contact Mask**

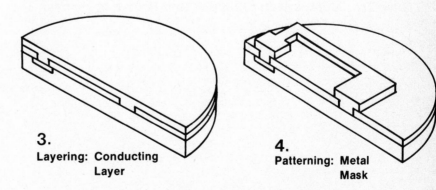

**3.**
**Layering: Conducting Layer**

**4.**
**Patterning: Metal Mask**

**Fig. 2.10   Metalization Sequence**

### 2.5.3 Passivation Sequence

After the required doping sequences and the metalization sequence, the circuit or device is operationally complete. However, two problems must be addressed before the wafer can be transferred to wafer sort:

1. The completed circuit is vulnerable to contamination

2. The thin fragile metalization is susceptible to scratching.

Both problems are solved by covering the wafer with a layer that acts as a contamination barrier and protects the metal.

Unfortunately, covering the wafer also covers the metal contact (bonding) pads. Therefore an additional patterning step to form holes over the bonding pads is necessary to allow "connecting" the chip to the package in the subsequent assembly operation. Table 2.3 shows the bipolar process flow compared to an MOS metal gate flow with the basic sequences identified.

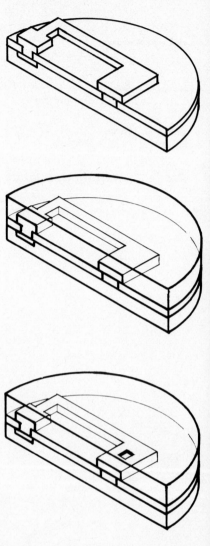

Fig. 2.11    Passivation Sequence

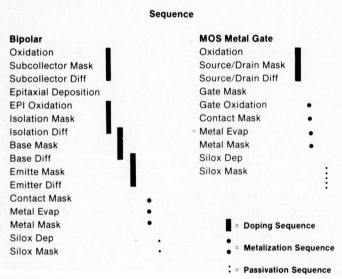

**Sequence**

| Bipolar | MOS Metal Gate |
|---|---|
| Oxidation | Oxidation |
| Subcollector Mask | Source/Drain Mask |
| Subcollector Diff | Source/Drain Diff |
| Epitaxial Deposition | Gate Mask |
| EPI Oxidation | Gate Oxidation |
| Isolation Mask | Contact Mask |
| Isolation Diff | Metal Evap |
| Base Mask | Metal Mask |
| Base Diff | Silox Dep |
| Emitte Mask | Silox Mask |
| Emitter Diff | |
| Contact Mask | |
| Metal Evap | |
| Metal Mask | |
| Silox Dep | |
| Silox Mask | |

▮ = Doping Sequence

• = Metalization Sequence

⋮ = Passivation Sequence

**Table 2.2    Comparison of Bipolar and MOS Sequences**

### 2.5.4 Semiconductor Building Technologies

The three basic fab operations and three basic sequences can be used to build different transistor structures. The two major structures are Bipolar and MOS. They vary from each other in many ways including power handling capabilities, speed of operation, and integration density. The two are compared more deeply in Chapter 19.

Bipolar was the first technology developed. MOS devices, with several major variations have continually gained popularity and are now the dominant technology. However, Bipolar devices will continue to share the market due to their unique capabilities. Bipolar circuits (circuits based on Bipolar transistors) are capable of handling higher power levels and faster speed, and are less sensitive to contamination. Their principle use is in logic circuits. MOS circuits cost less to produce because fewer steps are involved, are denser and are used principally in computer memories and consumer applications. Within each of these two circuit building technologies there are several variations. Each variation has specific device characteristics and applications in the end product.

### 2.5.5 Wafer Fab Costs

Wafer fab costs are influenced by material specifications and equipment sophistication, which are in turn influenced by the level of integration and the number of steps in the process.

The number of wafers scrapped during fab also influences the final cost. Labor, overhead, facility requirements and inventory are all dictated by the three factors. I.C. wafer costs, from start to wafer sort, vary between $100 and $500. That cost continues to rise with the continuously increasing integration level and decreasing feature size.

## 2.6 WAFER SORT

Chapter 3 addresses a major reality of semiconductor circuit manufacturing – namely that the circuit yield of each wafer is less than 100%. In the fab area the circuits are processed in wafer form. This "batch" processing is relatively efficient, with wafer production costs, as noted varying between $100 and $500 per wafer.

After fab the wafer will be separated into individual chips and mounted and connected to a package. This series of operations is called *assembly*. The mounting and connecting (bonding) steps are labor intensive processes and the package materals are expensive. In fact, the material and labor cost of assembling one chip is approximately the same as its fabrication cost.

Since a sizeable percentage of the chips will be nonfunctioning, it is wasteful to assemble them. Identifying the functioning chips is done at *Wafer Sort* (also called *Die Sort* or *Electrical Test*).

For this test, the wafer is mounted on a flat vacuum chuck and each bonding pad on the die is contacted by a series of metal

**Bipolar**

Junction Isolated
Dielectric Isolated
Silicon on Saphire
I²L

**MOS**

Metal Gate
Silicon Gate
CMOS
FET
JFET
VMOS

**Table 2.3**
**Bipolar and MOS Device Schemes**

probes. After contact, the die is electrically tested for D.C. parameters and functionality. The actual test is computer directed and may take from one second to several minutes. Non-functioning or out-of-spec circuits are autimatically marked by the testor with a drop of ink.

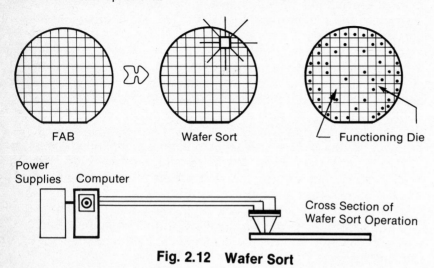

FAB          Wafer Sort          Functioning Die

Power
Supplies    Computer

Cross Section of
Wafer Sort Operation

**Fig. 2.12    Wafer Sort**

## 2.6.1 Chip Terminology

Fig. 2.13 is a photomicrograph of an M.S.I. circuit.

1. Metalization interconnections (usually aluminum) are visible as being lighter in shade and having a "grainy" appearance.

2. Circuit Designation. The circuit number designation occurs in the upper left-hand corner. Quite often the number assigned to the circuit for fab is different than the number under which the circuit is sold.

3. Bonding Pads. The circuit input and output terminals are located on the periphery of the chip for ease in connecting it to the package (*bonding*).

4. Contamination. The piece of contamination identified is much smaller than the size of ordinary room dirt.

5. Bipolar Transistor. A typical bipolar transistor is noted. Please refer to chapter 18 on semiconductor devices, other bipolar devices to identify the other bipolar devices present in the circuit.

6. Scribe Lines. The circuit area is bounded by the surrounding line. The area outside the line is unused real estate whose function is to separate the chips.

7. Unconnected Devices. Many circuit designs include individual devices to construct several different circuits. A finished circuit may contain devices not used.

8. Alignment Marks. The alignment of all of the patterns is accomplished with the aid of alignment marks, or aids, located on the outside edge of the chip.

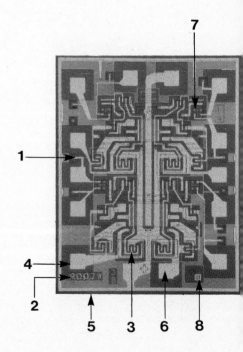

**Fig. 2.13    Chip Terminology**

## 2.7 WAFER FABRICATION LINE ORGANIZATION

Most of the early semiconductor producers started with one fabrication area. As business grew and new circuits were required, they were added to those already being processed through the fab area. This led to a bewildering array of device types in fab, with the production areas expanding to the size of airplane hangars.

This approach created new problems, including lower yields. Each device or circuit has its own alignment and doping sensitivities. For example, linear circuits require greater resistor control than digital circuits, and MOS devices are far more contamination sensitive than bipolar devices. Processing them through common stations resulted in lower yields due to less operator attention, lack of dedicated equipment, and higher levels of contamination.

Another major liability of this production approach was the potential of major plant shutdowns. Periodically, every process step "goes south" (very low or no yield). The result in a fab line with common processing was to stop all wafer flow.

Successful semiconductor companies found that expansion resulted in very large fab areas, with high inventories and long wafer throughput times. All three of these factors have an adverse affect on yield and productivity.

A product line approach was soon adopted to overcome these problems. This approach groups circuits with similar process steps and circuit requirements in the same fab area. The benefits of this organization are:

1. Focused Training of Staff
2. Operators with Higher Specific Skills
3. Faster Wafer Throughput
4. Higher Yields
5. Lower Shut-down Probability

The product line organization itself is self-contained, and each has its own production and engineering staff. The equipment maintenance staff typically reports to the product line manager, as does the circuit design staff. In smaller companies, equipment maintenance and circuit design are service organizations to all of the fab lines. Quality Control is almost always a corporate function.

Within Fab there is physical separation of the Doping, Photomasking, CVD and Evaporation areas, each having its own supervisor and engineering specialists. Wafers are moved from area to area to receive the required processing.

Table 2.3 illustrates a typical product line table of organization. The engineering staff defines the processes and materials used in manufacturing, while the manufacturing staff is responsible for execution of those processes, and cost control. In practice, the process areas are attended by a "team" consisting of

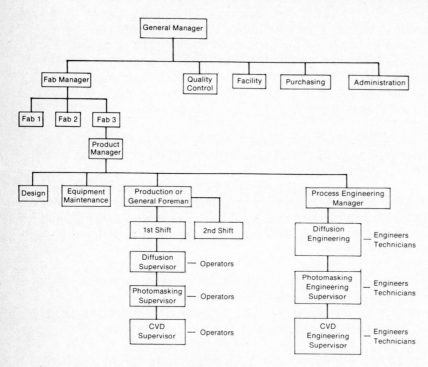

**Table 2.5**
**Typical Semiconductor Product Line Table of Organization**

Engineering, Manufacturing, and Equipment Maintenance personnel. These groups generally specialize in a specific process. The nature of semiconductor processing makes it ideally suited for a quality circle approach.

## 2.8 CAPTIVE AND MERCHANT SEMICONDUCTOR PRODUCERS

The widespread use of semiconductor devices in many diverse industries has led to the inevitable decision to produce chips "in-house." At some level of semiconductor use, both economics and a guaranteed source of chips dictate a captive in-house fab line. During the past twenty years, there has been a steady rise in the percentage of captive producers. In fact, the largest semiconductor producer in the world, IBM, is a captive supplier.

The advantages of an in-house supply of chips to the system or product producer are obvious:

1. Verification of Performance
2. Quick Turnaround
3. Guaranteed Supply
4. Control of Deliveries

Due to the cost involved in setting up a fabrication area, captive producers are usually larger electronics firms. The choice of equipment and processes is made with the same criteria used by merchant suppliers – namely the level of technology, efficiency and yield.

Captive suppliers have the same goals as merchant suppliers but different priorities. The merchant supplier is looking for yield and production efficiency to maintain a competitive stance in the marketplace. The captive supplier doesn't realize payback on the chip cost until the final product is sold. A captive fab line must produce a steady supply of chips at a known reliability. In order for either type of chip manufacturer to be successful, all four factors are required.

## 2.9 SILICON FOUNDRIES

The high cost of chip manufacturing has led to the rise of custom circúit (or silicon foundry) shops. A circuit or systems designer has a choice of designing with standard circuits or creating a custom circuit. The high cost of circuit design, mask design and chip manufacture make low volume runs and experimental chip design costs prohibitive. Silicon foundries have come into existence to supply chips to the small or experimental user.

Silicon foundries offer two services. First, they produce chips from outside supplied designs and masks. Second, they produce master chips that contain standard device functions. The customer specifies the required input/output functions and the foundry "wires in" the functions at the metalization step. Another variation is master wafers that may contain different circuits fabricated on the same wafer. This approach is geared to the production of low volumes. The yield of master chips is usually lower due to the extra size of the chips and the extra process steps required.

## 2.10 ASSEMBLY

After wafer sort, the wafer is transferred to the assembly area to be packaged. Since the assembly operation is labor intensive, it is often located "off shore" in lower labor cost areas.

However, the trend of higher labor costs in the Third World has led to the development of more automated processes. Like Fab, Assembly is served by its own production and engineering organization.

### 2.10.1 Assembly Process Flow

The major steps that the wafer goes through after leaving Wafer Sort are listed below.

1. Backside Preparation
   The wafer is mechanically thinned to fit in the package and/or the backside is evaporated with a thin metal to allow attachment of the die to the package.

2. Die Separate
   The wafer is separated into die by scribing or sawing.

3. Pick
   The noninked die (electrically functioning) are selected and sent into the assembly operation.

4. Die Attached
   The die is soldered or glued in or on the package.

5. Wire Bonding
   Thin gold or aluminum wires are attached between the die
   bonding pads and the lead connections in the package.

6. Lid Sealing
   A lid is sealed over the package to hermetically protect the
   die.

7. Environmental and Mechanical Testing
   The circuit and package is tested for resistance to high
   temperature and humidity conditions and mechanical shock.
   Highreliability (Hi Rel) circuits receive more stringent
   testing.

8. Final Test
   The die is given a final electrical test similar to the wafer
   sort test.

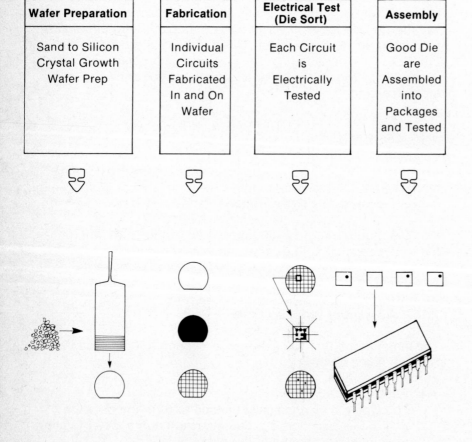

| Wafer Preparation | Fabrication | Electrical Test (Die Sort) | Assembly |
|---|---|---|---|
| Sand to Silicon Crystal Growth Wafer Prep | Individual Circuits Fabricated In and On Wafer | Each Circuit is Electrically Tested | Good Die are Assembled into Packages and Tested |

Table 2.5   Integrated Circuit Manufacturing Sequence

# Semiconductor
# Process
# Yields

Chapter 3.

# INTRODUCTION

The term *yield* is probably referred to more in the semiconductor industry than any other single concept or goal. Any product, service or process improvement that promises higher yields gets an immediate hearing by the fab engineers. Likewise, engineers and departments that cannot maintain "yields" quickly lose credibility, if not careers. The reason for this emphasis on yields is simple although not obvious to those not familiar with the technology. The fact of semiconductor manufacturing is that most of the mistakes or problems encountered in the manufacturing process are fatal, i.e., not reparable.

Referring back to our comparison of semiconductor manufacturing with car manufacturing, we know that if an automobile arrives at the final inspection station and a radio is defective, the radio will be repaired or replaced before the car leaves the plant. The same is true of any of the other parts of the automobile. In no case is the automobile scrapped. Unfortunately, semiconductor parts that are defective cannot be replaced or repaired in the same manner. In fact, due to defects and process problems a typical integrated circuit manufacturing facility ships only 25%–30% of the product that is started.

Yield is calculated at three points in the process:

1. After Fab
2. Wafer Sort
3. After Assembly

# 3.1 FABRICATION YIELD

Fabrication (or wafer) yield is the percent of wafers arriving at wafer sort compared with the number started into the process.

There are several major reasons that this yield falls below 100%. They are:

1. Wafer Breakage
2. Process Variation
3. Process Defects

### 3.1.1 Wafer Breakage

All of the yield limiting factors listed above are heightened or aggravated by the sheer number of steps that the wafer has to go through before final test. A typical bipolar manufacturing line involves seven masking steps, five diffusion and three CVD operations, plus wafer sort and assembly. And each one of those steps involves five to ten individual handlings. For example, let us just examine one simple process step, *oxidation.* Listed in table 3.1 is the flow for the operations.

**Table 3.1    Oxidation Flow Diagram**

| | # Handlings |
|---|---|
| Wafers are removed from carrier and placed in cleaning boat. | 1 |
| Wafers are processed through the clean operation, including a spin rinse dry. | 1 |
| Wafers are removed from cleaning boat, inspected for cleanliness and loaded on a quartz boat for oxidation. | 1 |
| The oxidation process. | |
| Boat removed from the furnace. | |
| Wafers are removed from the boat and placed back in the carrier. | 1 |
| Test wafers are removed from the carrier and tested for oxide thickness and cleanliness. | 1 |
| Wafers are transferred to the log station where they are quite often again counted. | |
| | TOTAL = 5 |

Every time the wafers are handled, there is an opportunity to scratch or break the wafer or abrade the edge of the wafer. The move toward automated equipment has been driven by the effort to reduce wafer breakage.

### 3.1.2 Process Variation

By the time a completed wafer arrives at Wafer Sort it has received a number of layers, patternings and dopings. Each of the processes must produce a closely controlled physical parameter, whether it be a thickness, pattern size or resistivity. The electrical performance of the circuit is dependent on the process parameters being "in spec." However, each of them exhibits some variations due in part to the inability of even the most sophisticated equipment to produce the exact same product day after day. The industry's interests in automation are to minimize process variation and increase productivity.

### 3.1.3 Process Defects

Defects are the largest cause of non-performing devices. The causes and sources of defects from the environment and handling processes are covered in the chapter on contamination control. Every time a wafer is handled, exposed to a chemical, dried, or loaded into a machine, there is an occasion to induce a defect.

Of all the defect-producing processes, photomasking is the most destructive. The wafer is handled more and is exposed to more chemicals than during any other process. The primary problem is the vulnerability of the resist to defect causing damage. The photoresist layer is soft and any holes or tears in it will be permanently transferred to the wafer. Photomasking process defects also originate from the photomask. Unwanted chrome spots, holes in the chrome, glass damage and contamination all show up on the wafer as a defect.

The development of non-contact alignment systems (projection, direct wafer step) and positive resist processes (thicker resist layers) are two of the approaches created for reducing masking defects. Throughout this text the many other defect-reducing techniques will be illustrated.

Process defects are discovered primarily by optical inspection. When the amount exceeds a certain level the wafer is rejected.

## 3.2 CALCULATION OF ACCUMULATIVE FABRICATION YIELD

Table 3.2 illustrates the calculation of an accumulative fab yield, for a five step process. Notice that each individual yield step is relatively high. Yet, when we start with 1,000 wafers at the first step, we now only have 980 available to go into the second step. Accumulating the effect through all the steps results in a 78% yield out of a process of just five steps.

Keep in mind that in fab the wafers go through between 10 to 20 major yield steps. The effect of one step having a very low yield can be devastating. A typical integrated circuit line will maintain a 70%–80% yield up to sort. Automation is expected to raise the accumulative wafer yields to the 90% range.

**Table 3.2**
**Accumulative Yield Calculation for Five Step Process**

| STEP | # WAFERS IN | STEP YIELD | # WAFERS OUT |
|------|-------------|------------|--------------|
| 1 | 1000 | 0.98 | 980 |
| 2 | 980 | 0.96 | 941 |
| 3 | 941 | 0.97 | 913 |
| 4 | 913 | 0.95 | 867 |
| 5 | 867 | 0.90 | 780 |

$$\text{Accumulative Yield} = \frac{\text{\# Wafers Out}}{\text{\# Wafers Started}} = \frac{780}{1000} = 78\%$$

## 3.3 WAFER SORT (ELECTRICAL TEST) YIELD

After fab each circuit on each wafer is electrically tested for functionality and D.C. electrical parameters. Wafer sort yield (# good die/total die) is typically the lowest of the major yield points ranging from 1% to 50% for I.C.'s. Sort yields on discrete and S.S.I. circuits can reach above 90%.

Wafer Sort Yield is influenced by many factors, including:

1. Wafer Diameter
2. Die Area
3. Number of Processing Steps
4. Circuit Density
5. Defect Density
6. Crystal Defect Density

### 3.3.1 Wafer Diameter

As the wafer diameter increases two yield enhancers are realized. First, the percentage of edge die lost from dislocations decreases. Second, the percentage of partial edge die decreases.

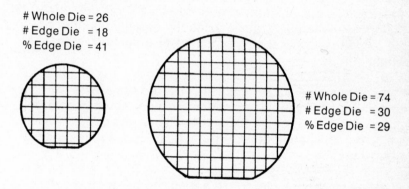

# Whole Die = 26
# Edge Die = 18
% Edge Die = 41

# Whole Die = 74
# Edge Die = 30
% Edge Die = 29

**Fig. 3.1    Effect of Larger Wafer Diameter of % of Partial Die**

### 3.3.2 Die Area

A given defect density will influence sort yield differently for different die sizes.

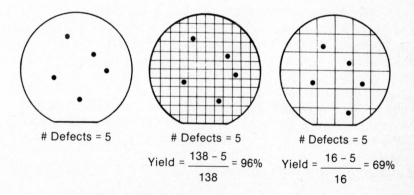

# Defects = 5

# Defects = 5
$$Yield = \frac{138 - 5}{138} = 96\%$$

# Defects = 5
$$Yield = \frac{16 - 5}{16} = 69\%$$

**Fig. 3.2    Effect on Die Size on Sort Yield**

Every increase in die size requires a compensating reduction in defect density to maintain the same yields.

### 3.3.3 Number of Processing Steps

Obviously, the greater number of processing steps (particularly masking steps), the greater the exposure of the wafer to defect inducement. Processes like metal gate MOS yield higher than the CMOS wafers that require many more process steps.

### 3.3.4 Circuit Die Density

As the industry increases its ability to produce smaller patterns on the wafer surface there will be a corresponding decrease in yield. This yield decrease is due to the higher probability that an active part of the circuit will encounter a masking, process or crystal defect. The yield formulas in 3.4 assume a constant die area.

### 3.3.5 Defect Density

While the wafer is being processed it is exposed to particulate contamination from the air, process chemicals, etc. These contaminants cause disruption of the surface films and distortion of the circuit patterns. In some cases the defects result in holes in the oxide that allow doping of the wafer in an unwanted location.

Defects of this type are sometimes called *point defects* to distinguish them from defects caused by poor process control, such as an out-of-spec film thickness. The defect density yield factor refers to all point defects from all sources in the process and environment.

The visual inspections performed during the process to detect defects use a sample plan and many defects go undetected. Each fab line or process produces a basic defect density which is the result of the process equipment use, cleanliness levels and mask quality. The inspections serve to detect variations above the basic level.

### 3.3.6 Crystal Defects

Silicon, germanium and the III-V compounds are crystal substances. It is impossible to produce a "perfect" crystal or wafer from any of them. Throughout the crystal there are various types of defects which influence the electrical performance of the circuit. One particular defect, called a *vacancy*, is a position in the crystal for an atom which is not there. Every crystal has a number of vacancies after crystal growth. The number increases with heat treatments (diffusion, etc.), from both the temperatures and the rates of heating and cooling. Another type of point defect is a dislocation, which is a discontinuity in the crystal lattice. (See Chapter 5 on crystal growth.)

Dislocations also increase in number with heat treatments. A large problem is dislocations induced by edge damage. A chip on the wafer edge results in crystal dislocations that move into the wafer center, contributing to the lower yield at the edge.

One of the yield advantages of larger diameter wafers is that the dislocation lines affect a smaller percentage of the die than in smaller diameter wafers.

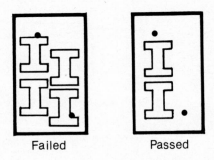

Failed          Passed

**Fig. 3.3
Relation of Die to Density Defects**

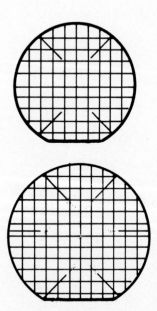

**Fig. 3.4   Effect of Dislocations on
Wafer Sort Yield for
Different Wafer Diameters**

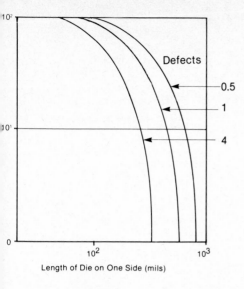

Length of Die on One Side (mils)

**Fig. 3.5**
**Graphical Solution(s) of Yield Formula**

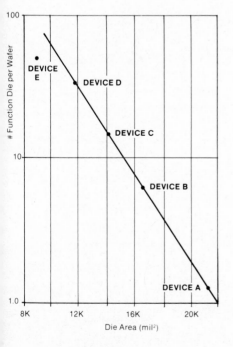

**Fig. 3.6**
**Yield vs. Die Size**

## 3.4 WAFER SORT YIELD FORMULAS

There are two relationships of wafer sort yield to the factors discussed above. On wafers where the die size/diameter relationship results in over 300 die the yield formula is:

$$Y = 1/( e^{ADn} )$$

Where: A = Die Area (Sq. In.)
D = Defects per Square Inch
n = # of Masking Steps
r = Radius of Wafer (In.)
Y = Ratio of Good to Bad Die

This formula is an empirical relationship. The number of total process steps is represented by the number of masking steps since the largest share of defects is contributed by masking.

The exponential nature of the relationship results in a rapid yield fall-off with both increasing die size and defect density

When the die size increases to the level where the number of edge die is significant a better approximation is:

$$Y = 1/(1 + DA)^n \times [(r - A)/A]^2$$

In actual practice, the parameters (Y, n, A, r) are plugged into the formula and overall defect density calculated. The calculated D consists of the actual "Die Killing" defects which include both process and crystal defects.

The base level defect density influence on wafer sort yield relative to die size is illustrated in fig. 3.7. On the graph three of the four devices fall on the same defect density curve. The fourth falls below the expected yield. Two possible causes for this are a faulty design or a higher circuit density.

A typical I.C. has active devices in and on 60% of its area. A higher device density would cause a high vulnerability to the defect density and therefore a lower sort yield.

## 3.5 VARIATION OF WAFER SORT YIELDS

A typical sort yield plot is illustrated below. The wafer-to-wafer and day-to-day variation comes about from the fluctuations. A gross process mistake, such as a very deep diffusion or out-of-spec gate oxide thickness will plunge the wafer sort yield out of the normal range (wafer #3).

In general the majority of "good" die are grouped in the center of the wafers. The reasons are:

1. No partial die.
2. Resist and wafer damage occurs on the edge.
3. Exposure uniformity is greater across the center.
4. Temperature variation during diffusion and CVD processes is less across the center.
5. Dislocation lines that cause edge die failure.

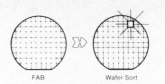

**Table 3.8   Wafer Sort**

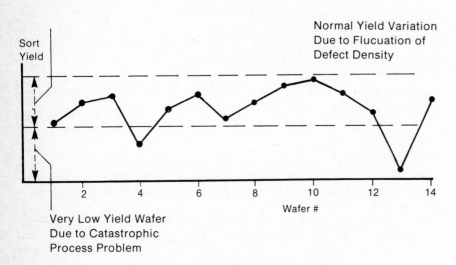

**Fig. 3.7   Plot of Wafer Sort Yields**

## 3.6 ASSEMBLY YIELDS

The functioning die that leave wafer sort are assembled in packages and final tested. Assembly is a well established process with yields typically 98%. Final test yields, assuming wafer sorting is accurate, also should be in the high nineties. High reliability (high rel) devices will have a somewhat lower yield. The product of the two yield points is typically between 85% – 95%.

## 3.7 OVERALL YIELD FORMULA

The overall yield result is the mathematical product of the three major yield points.

> (Fab Yield) × (Sort Yield) × (Assembly & Test Yield) = Overall Yield

Given the continuing trends to larger die, larger wafers, smaller dimensions and increased performance (process control), the focus on yield and yield improvement will be a continuing pressure on fab and assembly processes.

The true measure of yields is the number of die out of fab or shipped out of assembly per started wafer! It is possible to increase sort yields and final test yields by tightening the process inspection criteria in fab. However, unless real process improvements are made the overall yield will stay the same. In some situations forcing a higher sort yield this way may be less cost effective if a substantial amount of money becomes invested in the wafer before it is rejected.

The table below illustrates typical overall yield results for products at various positions in the product cycle.

### Table 3.3  Typical Yields for Various Products

| Product | Level of Integration | Position in Product Cycle | Feb Yield % | Sort Yield % | Assembly and Final Test Yield % | Overall Yield % |
|---|---|---|---|---|---|---|
| IC | VLSI | Introduction | 60 | 2 | 85 | 1 |
| IC | LSI | Mature | 80 | 50 | 95 | 38 |
| IC | MSI | Mature | 85 | 60 | 97 | 49 |
| Discrete | — | Mature | 95 | 80 | 98 | 74 |

# Semiconducting Materials

Chapter 4.

# INTRODUCTION

The unique functions of semiconductor devices and circuits are the direct result of the electrical and physical properties of semiconducting materials. These materials possess properties different from conductors and dielectrics (insulators). For use as semiconductor substrates the materials must be changed electrically (*doped*) both in the starting wafer and during wafer fabrication. In this chapter the electrical properties of intrinsic and doped semiconductors are examined. The physical properties required of these materials for semiconductor use are explored in chapter five.

## 4.1 ATOMIC STRUCTURE

The understanding of semiconductor materials requires a basic knowledge of the composition of elements and atoms.

Atoms are composed of three parts called *atomic particles*: electrons, protons and neutrons. The electrons are negatively charged particles moving in orbital paths around the nucleus of the atom. The nucleus contains two particles; a positively charged proton and an electrically neutral neutron.

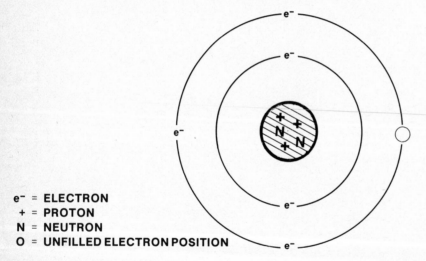

e⁻ = ELECTRON
 + = PROTON
 N = NEUTRON
 O = UNFILLED ELECTRON POSITION

### Fig. 4.1  Atomic Particles and the Bohr Atom Model

First postulated by Niels Bohr, the Bohr Atom Model adequately explains the most common electrical, mechanical, chemical and physical properties of elements.

Everything in the physical universe is composed of ninety-six stable elements and twelve unstable ones. Each element is composed of different combinations of the three atomic particles.

Fortunately, nature combined the atomic particles in an orderly manner. Two of the atom building laws are:

1.  There are equal numbers of protons and electrons in every atom.

2. Electrons move in specific orbits which can contain a maximum number of electrons.

A numerical number is assigned to each element equal to the number of protons (and therefore the number of electrons) in the atom. It is called the atomic number. We know immediately that the element with atomic number 20 (Calcium) has 20 protons and 20 electrons. Fig. 4.2 shows the structure of elements #1 – 3, with just the protons and electrons.

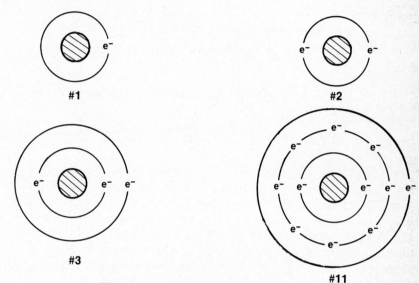

**Fig. 4.2  Elements 1, 2, 3, and 11**

The circles represent the maximum number of electrons assigned to each orbit. Note that the first orbit is filled at two electrons, whereas the second can hold eight. Also note that the outer ring of #1 has one electron and that the outer ring of #3 also has one electron.

At element #11 the outer ring again has only one electron. We now can state three additional general laws of atom structure:

3. Elements with the same number of outer ring electrons have similar properties.

4. Elements tend to be stable with eight electrons in the outer ring (the first orbit is an exception).

5. Atoms tend to combine with other atoms to create eight electrons in the outer ring.

Law #3 is the basis of the periodic table of the elements. The table was created after observing element properties. Elements with the same number of outer ring electrons fall in the same column. For example, all of the elements in Column IV (called a "group") have five electrons in their outer ring and have similar properties.

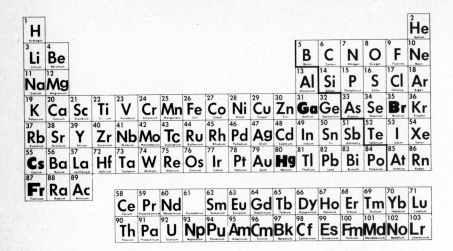

Fig. 4.3   Periodic Table of the Elements

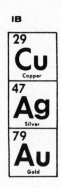

Fig. 4.4   Conductors

## 4.2 ELECTRICAL CONDUCTION

Semiconducting materials, as the name implies, conduct electricity. An electrical current is simply the flow of electrons. In some atoms the attraction between the outermost electrons and the protons in the nucleus is weak, allowing the electrons to move with relative ease. This condition exists in metals. In fact, the three best conductors are copper, silver, and gold. Not surprisingly, they are in the same group in the periodic table.

The ability of all materials to conduct electricity is measured as its *conductivity*. Gold, being the best conductor, has the highest conductivity. Another way to rate conductivity is to measure the material's resistance to current flow, its *resistivity*. Conductivity and resistivity are reciprocals of each other.

Electrical resistivity is a function of the attraction between the outer electrons and the protons. In some atoms the attraction is weak and the electrons are easily freed into the material to conduct electricity. In others the electrons are tightly bound to the nucleus. The former materials are termed *conductors* (low resistivity) and the former are *insulators* (high resistivity).

Semiconductors, as the name implies, are poor conductors, or in terms of resistivity, fall between conductors and insulators.

## 4.3 INTRINSIC SEMICONDUCTORS

The metals that are semiconductors are elements that have four electrons in their outer ring (Group IV), or are compounds of metals from the III and V groups.

The single elements used are silicon and germanium. The most common compound semiconductors are gallium-arsenide and gallium-arsenide-phosphide. In their intrinsic (pure) states the semiconducting materials are of no use in semiconductor devices.

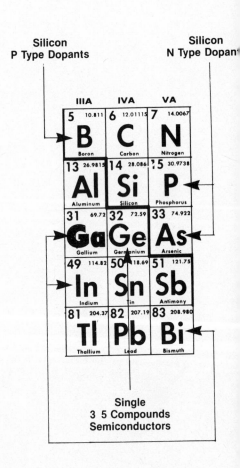

Fig. 4.5   Semiconductor Materials and Silicon Dopants

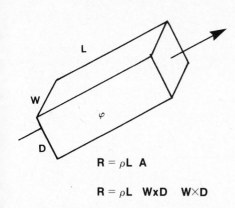

$$R = \rho L \ A$$

$$R = \rho L \ \ WxD \ \ \ W\times D$$

**Fig. 4.6 Relationship of Resistance to Resistivity and Dimensions**

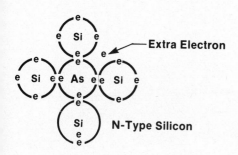

**Fig. 4.7 N-Type Doping of Silicon**

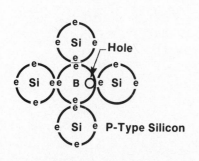

**Fig. 4.8 P-Type Doping of Silicon**

## 4.4 DOPED SEMICONDUCTORS

The usefulness of semiconducting materials in electrical devices is determined by two unique properties:

1. Precise Resistivity Control.
2. Electron and hole current.

In semiconductor materials the resistivity can be precisely and controllably changed by the introduction of small amounts of specified elements, known as *dopants*. While metals have a conductivity range limited to $10^4 + 10^6$/ohm-cm, semiconductor conductivities can range from $10^{-3}$ to $10^3$/ohm-cm, depending on the doping level.

The advantage of precise resistivity control is illustrated with resistor values. The resistance of a resistor is related to its dimensions and material resistivity by:

$$R = \rho \frac{L}{A}$$

R = Resistance  L = Length
$\rho$ = Resistivity  A = X Sectional Area

Different resistor values are obtained by varying any of the parameters. A resistor formed from a metal has a fixed resistivity. The resistivity of a semiconductor device can be changed by varying the resistivity (through doping) and the physical dimensions.

A metal conducts electricity only by electrons. Semiconductor materials can conduct by electrons or holes. The electrons and holes are created in the semiconductor materials because only a small amount of dopant is required to achieve the resistivity. Only 0.1% to 0.000001% dopant will create the required conductivity. This means that each dopant atom will be surrounded by semiconductor atoms.

Referring back to law #5 -- atoms attempt to satisfy the eight electron requirement by borrowing or sharing electrons from neighboring atoms. When we add a group V element (such as As) to silicon, note that an extra electron (the ninth) is available.

This "extra" electron, in conjunction with other "extra" electrons in the material, are easily moved, creating *conduction*. Since an electron carries a negative charge, a semiconductor so doped is called *N-type*. A dopant that results in an extra electron in the silicon is called a *donor*.

Now consider the effect of adding a group III element like boron to silicon:

The silicon atoms surrounding the boron contribute four electrons, leaving a position unfilled. The unfilled position is called a *hole*.

Within the semiconductor material there are tens of thousands of holes. Electrons from neighboring atoms have a tendency to leave their positions and fill a hole. However, the position abandoned

44

by an electron is left empty, leaving the "new" hole to be filled. This filling of holes by electrons is random in the material. However, when the doped material is part of an operating semiconductor device and voltage is applied to it, the voltage gives a direction to the electron flow. From an electrical perspective it appears that the holes are flowing, but in the opposite direction of the electrons.

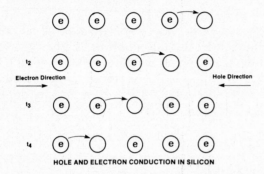

HOLE AND ELECTRON CONDUCTION IN SILICON

## Fig. 4.9 Hole Flow in Semiconductors

Since the hole acts like a positively charged particle, the semiconductor material is called *P-type* and the dopant referred to as an *acceptor*.

The dopants used to dope silicon are listed in Table 4.2 below.

## Table 4.1: Electrical Classification

| Classification | Electrons | Examples | Conductivity |
|---|---|---|---|
| 1. Conductor | Free to Move | Gold<br>Copper<br>Silver | $10^4 - 10^6$<br>/ohm-cm |
| 2. Insulator<br>(Dielectric) | Bound | Glass<br>Plastic | $10^{-22} - 10^{-10}$<br>/ohm-cm |
| 3. Semiconductor<br>a. Intrinsic | Some Available | Germanium<br>Silicon<br>III-IV | $10^{-9} - 10^3$<br>/ohm-cm |
| b. Doped | Controlled Amount Available | N-type Semiconductor<br>P-type Semiconductor | |

## Table 4.2: Characteristics of Doped Semiconductors

| | Deposition | Drive-in |
|---|---|---|
| Goals | Introduction of Dopant | 1. Redistribution of Dopant<br>2. Reoxidation |
| Variables | | 1. Surface Concentration<br>2. Junction Depth<br>3. Time<br>4. Diffusivity<br>5. Temperature<br>6. Quantity of Atoms |

# 4.5 USES OF SEMICONDUCTOR MATERIALS

In summary, semiconductor circuits are made in semiconducting materials. These materials are poor conductors in the pure state. Through doping processes the conductivity can be controllably and precisely changed. Semiconductors are capable of both negative (electron) and positive (hole) current flow.

The semiconducting materials most commonly used are germanium, silicon, gallium arsenide and gallium-arsenide-phosphide. Early solid state device development was accomplished using germanium. Some devices, primarily discretes, are still produced in germanium. However, the discovery of the natural oxide of silicon and its advantageous properties swung the industry over to silicon.

Silicon, with its oxide, offers several process and device structure benefits. The discovery that silicon dioxide is capable of being patterned gave rise to Planar Technology. Silicon has a higher melting point than germanium, allowing higher temperature processing and hence less time in diffusion. In addition, the silicon dioxide protects the silicon surface from contamination, and in a circuit minimizes surface current leakage. And silicon dioxide "blocks" all of the silicon dopants, thus allowing the precise selective doping of the silicon surface. For the future, semiconductors will be almost synonymous with silicon.

In 1952, it was noted that combinations of elements from Groups III and V exhibited semiconductor properties. Not having a natural oxide like silicon and not offering significant electrical device operation advantages, the III-V compounds have found specialized use in acoustic wave and optical devices.

The table below compares some of the physical and electrical properties of the three most commonly used materials, and silicon dioxide.

## Table 4.3   Comparison of Semiconductor Materials

| | Ge | Si | GaAs | $SiO_2$ |
|---|---|---|---|---|
| Atomic Weight | 72.6 | 28.09 | 144.63 | 60.08 |
| Atoms/cm$^3$ 2.3 × 10$^{22}$ or Molecules | $4.42 \times 10^{22}$ | $5.00 \times 10^{22}$ | $2.21 \times 10^{22}$ | |
| Crystal Structure | Diamond | Diamond | Zinc–Blends | Amorphous |
| Atoms/Unit Cell | 8 | 8 | 8 | — |
| Density | 5.32 | 2.33 | 5.65 | 2.27 |
| Energy Gap | 0.67 | 1.11 | 1.40 | 8 (approx.) |
| Dielectric Constant | 16.3 | 11.7 | 12.0 | 3.9 |
| Melting Point (°C) | 937° | 1415° | 1238° | 1700° (approx.) |
| Breakdown Field (V/ ) | 8 (approx.) | 30 (approx.) | 35 (approx.) | 600 (approx.) |
| Linear Coefficient of Thermal Expansion | $5.8 \times 10^{-6}$ | $2.5 \times 10^{-6}$ | $5.9 \times 10^{-6}$ | |

AL    1
0.5 × 10⁻⁶
LT    C

# Crystal Growth and Wafer Preparation

Chapter 5.

# INTRODUCTION

*Crystal growth* and *wafer preparation* are the processes used to convert chunks of polysilicon into wafers. During crystal growth the polysilicon is converted to a single crystal containing the proper dopant. Wafer preparation consists of the steps required to slice the wafers from the crystal and polish their surfaces. Two methods of silicon crystal growth are used: *Czochralski* (CZ) and *Float Zone*. Gallium arsenide and the other III-V compound crystals are grown by similar methods.

## 5.1 CRYSTAL ORIENTATION

In certain materials, the atoms collect themselves into structured groups called unit cells. Materials with this type of atomic arrangement are called *crystals*. Materials with no definite arrangement of the atoms are termed *amorphous*. Plastics are amorphous materials.

Crystal materials are characterized by their uniformity of physical properties, required for the uniform processing and operation of semiconductor devices. All of the semiconductor materials are crystal materials.

Crystalline materials can have two possible internal arrangements of cells to one another. Unit cells collected together in a random manner form a *polycrystalline* material, such as that formed by a disorderly pile of blocks. *Single crystalline* substances have all the unit cells "arranged" in a definite and repeated fashion, much like an orderly stack of blocks. A common term used to describe single crystals is *lattice*. Silicon has a diamond shaped unit cell. Thus silicon has a diamond lattice.

Within a single crystal, natural planes exist between the unit cells. Each of these planes or interfaces contains different numbers of atoms. This variation in atom count and the binding energies associated with them results in different physical, chemical and electrical properties for each plane. Semiconductor wafers are cut from single crystals along specific predetermined crystal planes.

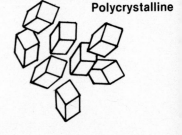

Polycrystalline

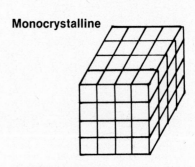

Monocrystalline

**Fig. 5.1**
**Poly and Single Crystal Structure**

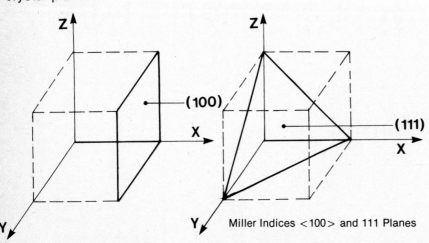

Miller Indices <100> and 111 Planes

**Fig. 5.2   Crystal Planes**

The two most commonly used planes are illustrated in fig. 5.2. A series of three numbers, called the *Miller indices*, are used to designate each plane. The triangular plane in fig. 5.2 has a Miller indice of {111}. Generally {111} oriented wafers are used to make bipolar wafers while the {100} oriented wafers are used in MOS technology.

## 5.2 CZOCHRALSKI (CZ) METHOD

In the CZ method of crystal growth, chunks of polysilicon and dopant are melted in a graphite crucible. *Radio Frequency* (R.F.) heating is required to achieve the 1,425° C melting temperature. A seed crystal of either {111} or {100} orientation is touched to the molten surface and slowly raised. The surface tension between the seed and molten silicon causes a small amount of the liquid to rise with the seed and cool. Upon cooling, the atoms in the melt orient themselves to the structure of the seed, repeating the seed orientation in the growing crystal.

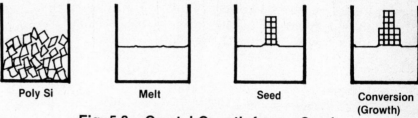

| Poly Si | Melt | Seed | Conversion (Growth) |

**Fig. 5.3  Crystal Growth from a Seed**

To achieve doping uniformity and diameter control, the seed and crucible are rotated in opposite directions. This method is capable of producing crystals up to four feet long and six inches or more in diameter. The CZ method accounts for the majority of silicon crystals grown for semiconductor use.

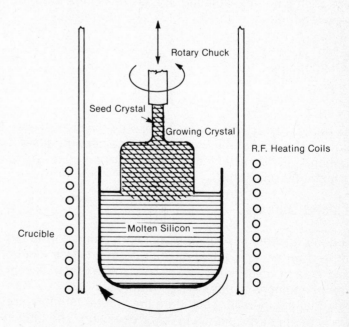

**Fig. 5.4
Czochralski Crystal Growing System**

## 5.3 FLOAT ZONE

During crystal growth small amounts of oxygen are invariably included in the crystal. Some semiconductor devices require wafers with a lower level of oxygen than can be provided by the CZ method. To meet these low oxygen requirements, crystal growth is done by the *Float Zone* technique. This process starts with a cast bar of polycrystal material with a seed attached to the end. An R.F. coil is moved slowly along the axis of the bar, melting a small portion of the bar to a molten state. As in the CZ method, the atoms in the melt solidify in the same orientation as the seed. When the R.F. coil moves on, the section cools, freezing the atoms permanently in their newly oriented positions.

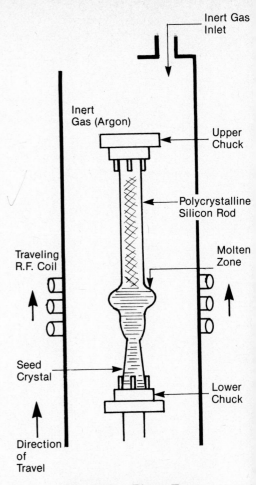

**Fig. 5.5   Float Zone Crystal Growing System**

**Table 5.1   Comparison of CZ and Float Crystal Growing Methods**

| PARAMETER | CZ | FLOAT ZONE |
|---|---|---|
| Large Crystal | Yes | Difficult |
| Cost | Lower | |
| Dislocations | $0 - 10^4/cm^2$ | $10^3 - 10^5/cm^2$ |
| Resistivity | Up to 100 ohm-cm | 2000 ohm-cm Max. |
| Radial Resistivity | 5 – 10% | 5 – 10% |
| Oxygen Content | $10^{16} - 10^{18}$ atoms/$cm^3$ | 0 – Very Low |

## 5.4 CRYSTAL QUALITY

Semiconductor devices require a high degree of crystal perfection. But with even the most sophisticated techniques a perfect crystal is unobtainable. Crystal defects fall into three major categories:

1. Point Defects
2. Dislocations
3. Growth Defects

These defects affect the process steps by causing uneven oxide growth, poor epitaxial film quality and uneven diffusions. Device performance is also affected in the form of soft (leaky) junctions and premature breakdown.

### 5.4.1 Point Defects

Point defects come in two varieties: extra atoms in the lattice due to contamination, and atoms missing from a lattice location. The second type of point defect is known as a *vacancy*. Vacancies are natural phenomena in any crystal. Unfortunately, they increase exponentially in number each time the crystal temperature is raised, a frequent occurence in fab processing. The prevention of vacancy formation is one of the benefits of low temperature processing.

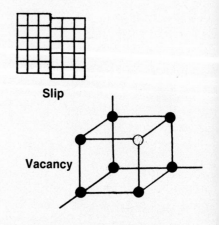

**Fig. 5.6    Crystal Defects**

### 5.4.2 Dislocations

As a crystal grows, the atoms form themselves into unit cells and the unit cells orient themselves in a single crystal structure. Sometimes the unit cells are not exactly lined up, causing a "dislocation" of the lattice. To understand what this looks like, picture a pile of blocks askew.

Dislocations result from growth conditions and lattice strain in the crystal. They also result from physical abuse of a wafer during processing. A chip or abrasion of the wafer serves as a lattice strain site and a line of the dislocations progresses into the wafer interior with each high temperature processing. Dislocations are revealed by preferentially etching a wafer and counting the defects. A "good" wafer still has approximately 400 – 1000 dislocations per $cm^2$.

### 5.4.3 Growth Defects

During the crystal growth process certain conditions can result in gross structural defects. One is *slip*, when the crystal groups of atoms slip or shift along crystal planes. Another is *twining*, where the crystal starts growing in two directions.

## 5.5 WAFER PREPARATION

After crystal growth, a series of operations takes place to produce the finished wafers.

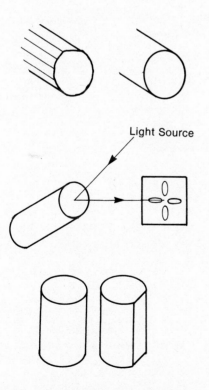

Light Source

Inside Diameter
Diamond Saw

| STEP | PROCESS OR METHOD |
|---|---|
| 5.5.1 Crystal Grinding | Centerless Grinder |
| Grind crystal to diameter. Precise diameter control is required to process the wafers in automated handling equipment. | |
| 5.5.2 Crystal Orientation | X-Ray Diffraction, Colimated Light Refraction |
| Crystal is mounted on a block at the proper position to allow wafers to be cut to the required orientation. | |
| 5.5.3 Flat Grinding | Grinder |
| The flats are ground on the crystal to denote conductivity type and resistivity. | |
| 5.5.4 Wafer Slicing | Inside Diameter Diamond Saw |
| Crystal is sliced into individual wafers. | |

5.5.5 Rough Polish
(Lapping) Saw damage is
removed from the top
surface.

Abrasive (Slurry) Grinding

5.5.6 Chem/Mech Polishing

Chemical/Mechanical
Polishing

The top surface is polished
by a combination of
chemical etching and
mechanical polishing.

5.5.7 Edge Grinding
The edges of the wafer are
rounded to minimize edge
damage and abrasion during
processing.

Edge Grinder

5.5.8 Back Side Damage
For some uses, back side
damage is left on or
purposely caused on the
water. This crystal damage
extends into the wafer where
it acts as a trap or getterer
for mobil ionic
contamination in the wafer.

5.5.9 Wafer Evaluation:
Resistivity
Orientation
Cleanliness
Crystal Quality
Diameter
Thickness
Flatness

<100>   <111>

90°   60°

Broken

# 5.6 WAFER CODING BY FLATS

Wafer orientation can be revealed by two destructive techniques:
breaking or *selective etching*. Wafers break along their crystal
planes. In selective etching the underlying crystal structure is
revealed as triangles for {111} or squares for {100} oriented
wafers.

Wafer conductivity type (N or P) can be determined by a hot point
probe or noncontact methods directly on the wafer surface.
Unfortunately, during wafer fab the wafer surface is covered with
various layers which prevent checking the conductivity type.

Both orientation and resistivity type must be known to insure that
the right wafers get into the proper process flow. The two
parameters are coded on the wafer by *flat(s)* that is (are) ground
onto the crystal. SEMI (Semiconductor Equipment and Materials
Institute) has standardized the industry with the code shown in
fig. 5.7.

Etched to
Reveal Crystal
Defects

**Fig. 5.7
Wafer Orientation Indicators**

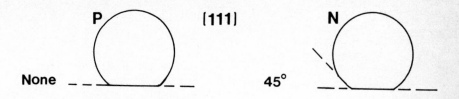

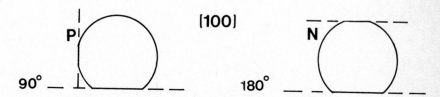

**Fig. 5.8   Wafer Flat Locations**

## 5.7 RESISTIVITY VS. DOPING LEVEL

The resistivity of a wafer varies with the dopant level
(concentration). However, the same N or P concentration level will
not result in equal resistivity levels. this is because an electron
can be moved within the silicon crystal structure with less energy
than a hole can. For the same dopant concentration level, N-type
silicon will exhibit a lower resistivity than P-type silicon. The
relationship is shown in fig. 5.9.

**Fig. 5.9   Silicon Carrier
Concentration vs. Resistivity**

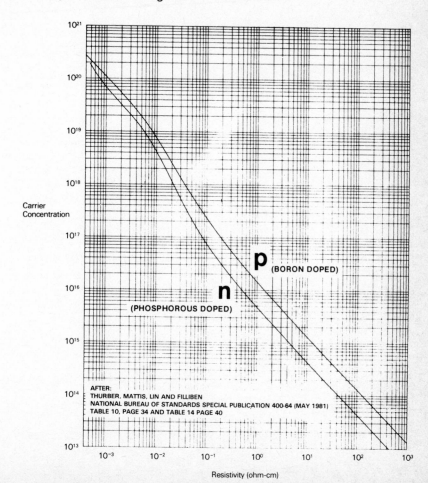

# N/P Junctions

Chapter 6.

## INTRODUCTION

In chapter four we noted that semiconducting materials are differentiated from conductors by their ability to conduct electricity by either electrons or holes. In a semiconductor device the electrically active components are formed from different N and P-type regions in the wafer. During device operation, the current is either confined in an N or P-region or crosses from one to another. The dividing line between an N-region and a P-region is called a *junction*. In this chapter we will explore the basic concept of junctions and some aspects of their properties.

## 6.1 DEFINITION OF A JUNCTION

Fig. 6.1 illustrates a bar of semiconducting material with one side featuring excess electrons (N-type) and the other having an excess of holes (P-type).

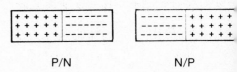

P/N               N/P

**Fig. 6.1   Junctions**

The separation line between the two regions is defined as the junction. The junction itself is neither N nor P-type but is electrically neutral. Junctions come in two varieties, N/P or P/N. The first letter designates the type that has the highest concentration.

## 6.2 FORMATION OF A DIFFUSED JUNCTION

The third step in the doping sequence is putting the dopant into the wafer. The purpose of doping is to create a junction in the wafer. A junction is understood by examining its formation by the diffusion process.

The wafer shown in cross section in fig. 6.2 has been through oxidation and patterning and is ready for diffusion. The "P's" represent P-type dopants mixed in the crystal during growth, and are uniformly distributed throughout the wafer.

In the diffusion tube, the wafer is exposed to vapors containing an N-type dopant. Assuming the conditions in the tube have been properly set, the N-type atoms will diffuse into the exposed silicon. The nature of diffusion results in more dopant atoms residing closer to the surface, rather than further down in the wafer.

An accounting of the relative concentrations is shown to the right of fig. 6.3. Since there are more "N" atoms than "P" atoms in layer #1, layer #1 is "N"–type. The diffusion continues down into the wafer with the concentration of "N" atoms diminishing at each layer. At layer #4 the concentration of the "N's" equals that of the "P's". This is the location of the N/P junction. This location in the wafer is neither N or P-type but electrically neutral.

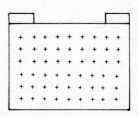

**Fig. 6.2    P-Type Wafer Ready for Diffusion**

The diffusing dopant atoms do not stop at the junction level. On the "other" side of the junction there exist diffused dopant atoms, but they are outnumbered by the "host" dopant atoms. In our illustration the layers below the junction are still P-type.

| Layer | # N's (−) | # P's (+) | Net (N − P) | Layer Type |
|---|---|---|---|---|
| 1 | 12 | 5 | 7 | N |
| 2 | | 5 | | |
| 3 | | 5 | | |
| 4 | | 5 | | |
| 5 | | 5 | | |
| 6 | | 6 | | |

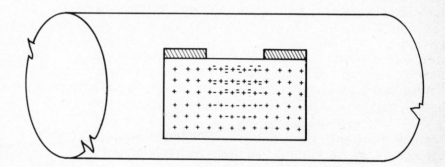

− = N Type Dopants Atoms

**Fig. 6.3   Start of Diffusion Process**

Junctions can also be formed by ion implantation. The distribution of the dopant atoms is different than in diffusion but the condition at the junction is the same.

| Layer | # N's (−) | # P's (+) | Net (N − P) | Layer |
|---|---|---|---|---|
| 1 | 12 | 5 | 7 | N |
| 2 | 10 | 5 | 5 | N |
| 3 | 8 | 5 | 3 | N |
| 4 | 5 | 5 | 0 | 1 ct |
| 5 | 3 | 5 | −1 | P |
| 6 | 0 | 5−5 | | P |

**Fig. 6.4   Cross-section of Wafer
at Conclusion of Diffusion**

## 6.3 GRAPHIC REPRESENTATION OF JUNCTIONS

### 6.3.1 Cross-sections

As indicated in fig. 6.3, a junction is usually represented in a cross section of a semiconductor device as a rectangular area. In the case of a diffused junction the junction shape is actually curved at the sides. Note also that the junction, due to side diffusion, extends underneath the oxide mask.

There is no convention in cross sectional drawings to indicate the conductivity type of each region, other than labelling them.

**Fig. 6.5
Cross Sectional Representation of Diffused Junctions**

## 6.3.2 Concentration vs. Depth Graphs

The cross-sectional representation gives little information about the junction location or the concentration of the dopants. Due to the extreme shallowness of most junctions the cross-sectional drawing does not even come close to being to scale.

A two (2) micron deep junction diffused into a 20 millimeter (20 mil) thick wafer occupies only about 0.4% of the thickness of the wafer. If the wafer thickness was represented by an eight foot high wall, the junction would occupy only the top four tenths (0.4″) of an inch!

The device engineer is interested in the junction depth and dopant concentration in the wafer. (S)he is also interested in knowing the *steepness (slope)* of the change in concentration near the junction. This information is normally presented in a *concentration vs. depth curve*.

To illustrate the principle, let's construct a curve from the data in fig. 6.4. The graph is constructed with the depth represented by the X-axis (horizontal) and the concentration by the Y-axis (vertical).

Note that there are two types of dopant in the wafer: the uniformly distributed P-type and the nonuniform N-type. On a concentration vs. depth graph, all of the dopants are represented as they exist at a cross-section through the diffused junction.

Starting with the P-type dopants we note that at every layer there are exactly five (5). Plotting that data the graph looks like:

Now the number of N-type dopants is plotted on the same axis.

Examining the graph of the two dopants we note a crossing of the two curves at layer number 4. This is the location of the junction. Above the junction (layer 4) there are more N-type atoms. Below it there are more P-type atoms.

The actual concentration vs. depth curve shape is governed by the physical laws of diffusion. Fig. 6.9 represents a typical graph with the depth in microns and the concentration (Y-axis) on a logarithm scale (see appendix).

It is also possible to diffuse a second layer of dopants into the first diffused layer. When that situation occurs such as in a bipolar transistor, three regions and two junctions are indicated on the graph. An important factor in device operation is the concentration of the dopant at the surface, which is indicated in fig. 6.9.

Some devices require doping a section of the wafer with the same type of dopant that is already in the wafer. When this situation occurs there is a change in resistivity in the diffused region, but no change in type and no junction formed.

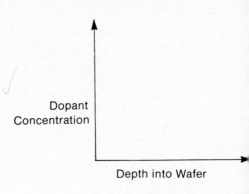

Fig. 6.6   Axis of Concentration vs. Depth Graphs

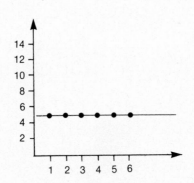

Fig. 6.7 Concentrations of P-Type Atoms

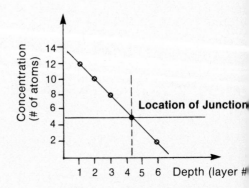

Fig. 6.8   Concentrations of P and N-Type Atoms

Dopant Concentration
(Atoms/cc)

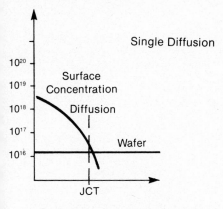

Depth into Wafer (microns)

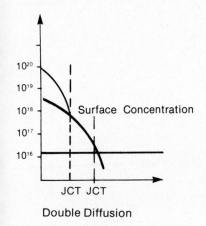

Double Diffusion

**Fig. 6.9   Single and Double
Diffused Concentrations
vs. Depth Graphs**

## 6.4 ELECTRICAL PROPERTIES OF JUNCTIONS

Junctions possess unique electrical properties. They have the ability to allow the passage of electrical current in one direction, but not the other. This property is known as *diode action*, and, in fact, every N/P junction is a semiconductor diode.

The miniature doped regions in the wafer are really islands of either N or P-type separated by the junction. The devices fabricated from the doped regions and junctions are described in chapter 20.

# Contamination Control

Chapter 7.

# INTRODUCTION

Semiconductor electrical performance and yields are the result of our ability to introduce only the desired impurities into the wafer and our ability to precisely reproduce the mask dimensions on the wafer surface. Unfortunately, semiconductors are sensitive to unwanted contamination, even from amounts as small as several parts per million. Pattern dimensions, too, are altered by dirt as small as a few microns in diameter.

At this level of sensitivity almost everything in a normal production environment would be judged "too dirty" to make semiconductors. A considerable amount of technology and money must be invested in maintaining a "clean" semiconductor production line environment. The cleanliness requirement is particularly stringent in the photomasking area. Not only are all of the critical dimensions produced here, but the frequent chemical operations present many opportunities for accidental contamination.

The problem of contamination affects three areas:

1. Device processing
2. Device performance
3. Device reliability

Device processing in a contaminated environment can cause wafers to fail in-process quality checks. Dirty air or chemicals can contaminate the wafers in process. Microscopic size dirt can cause holes in the sensitive photoresist layer. These failures result in lower fabrication yields and higher production costs due to reworking the wafers.

Device performance problems are those contamination-related electrical failures such as soft or leaky junctions and premature breakdown.

Device reliability is the most insidious of the contamination failures. Low levels of contamination can be introduced during wafer fab and not be detected during normal circuit testing. However, in time the contamination will migrate to the active devices and reach a level high enough to cause a circuit failure. Device reliability is a primary concern of the space and defense industries.

## 7.1 CONTAMINATION SOURCES

Literally everything the wafer comes in contact with is a potential source of contamination. The categories of contamination are:

1. Air
2. Production Facility
3. People
4. Water
5. Chemicals
6. Gases
7. Static Charge

Each category represents a unique contamination source and each is rendered clean with special techniques. *Contamination* is defined as anything that results in the failure modes defined in the introduction. An element or compound desired in one step may be a contaminant at another.

The following sections will examine the nature of the contaminants from each source, their detection, the control methods, and the cleanliness specifications each source must meet to permit successful wafer fabrication. Table #1 at the end of this chapter lists the contamination sources and their control. Table #2 lists the contamination sources and the clean specifications they must meet.

## 7.2 CLEAN ROOM STRATEGIES

### 7.2.1 Airborne Contaminants

The major contamination source which must be controlled is the air in the fabrication facility. Plain everyday air (even non-smoggy air) is dirty. The atmosphere contains copious amounts of particulates and water vapor as well as photochemical smog. The small dimensions involved in photomasking are smaller than the diameter of the most common particulates in air. Table 7.1 shows typical particulate sizes and fig. 7.1 compares relative sizes.

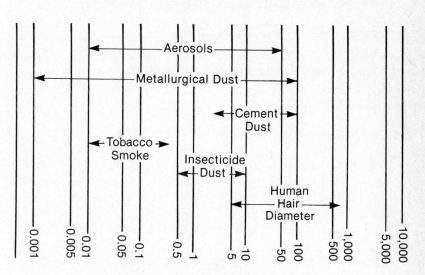

**Table 7.1    Relative Size of Airborne Particulates (Microns)**

It's not hard to visualize the effect of a 2 micron diameter particle on a wafer with 1 micron of photoresist.

### 7.2.2 Air Class Number

Air cleanliness levels are defined in Federal Standard 209a, paragraph 5.1. Two factors must be specified to rate air cleanliness:

1. The maximum size particulate allowed
2. The maximum quantity allowed

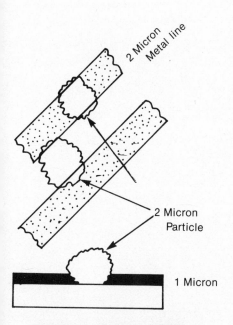

**Fig. 7.1    Relative Size of Airborne Particulates to Wafer Dimensions**

LSI semiconductor stations must filter the air to a 0.5 micron level. Particulate quantity levels are measured in the air stream in the process stations. The number of particulates per cubic foot per minute is expressed as the *class number* of the environment. VLF hoods must meet a specification of class 100 conditions. Table 7.2 lists the class numbers of various environments. VLSI processing requires levels down to class 10 at a maximum particle size size of 0.3 microns.

### 7.2.3 Mobile Ionic Contamination

Semiconductor devices are particularly sensitive to the ions of certain metals introduced into (or on) the wafer during processing. Many references have been made to them in this chapter. The metals in question are many. However, they are destructive to devices in proportion to their mobility (diffusion) in silicon, with sodium having the highest mobility. As sodium is generally present in chemicals, materials and on people in greater quantity than the other metals, the issue of control focuses on sodium, and consequently the whole family of metal ion contaminants is lumped under the banner *sodium control.*

Once in the wafer (surface metal ions are diffused in during high temperature steps) the ions can migrate to the active junction regions, causing a variety of device performance problems. Circuit leakage and high threshold voltages (MOS) are two problems. They represent a device reliability problem because they can also migrate throughout the wafer due to the fields generated by an operating circuit.

Since their destructive powers are large and their sources many, control of this contaminant rivals that of particulate control in necessity and concern.

### 7.2.4 Early Clean Room Design

The need for air filtered to high levels of purity first became a requirement in the space industry. Spacebound satellites needed to be assembled in clean environments. Small rooms were constructed with filters in the ceilings and walls and designed to assemble only a few units at a time with few personnel.

In conjunction with other *clean room* procedures, these rooms are capable of achieving high levels of cleanliness.

### Table 7.2   Class Numbers

| Environment | Class # | Particle Size Micron |
|---|---|---|
| VLSI Area | 10 | 0.3 |
| VLF Hood | 100 | 0.5 |
| Typical Fab Area | 10,000 | — |
| House Room | 100,000 | — |
| Outdoors | >100,000 | — |

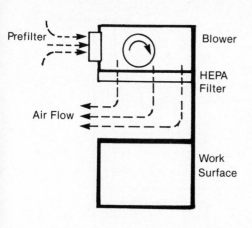

**Fig. 7.2
Cross-section of VLF Hood**

**Fig. 7.3   Hepa Filter Design**

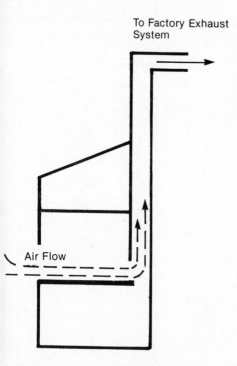

**Fig. 7.4   Cross-section
of a Fume Exhaust Hood**

When semiconductor firms first set up their clean rooms to manufacture semiconductors, the rooms had to be scaled up in size to accommodate the larger number of personnel and equipment required for a production line. While the space industry relied on elaborate entrance and exit procedures to keep contamination levels low, the semiconductor industry had to allow the many exits and entrances required during a normal shift. Another change was the increased number of work surfaces, which collected any contamination that was in the air. The result of expanding clean rooms to production line size was contamination far above any acceptable level.

### 7.2.5 Clean Work Station Strategy

To reduce the contamination level of large rooms the industry developed the clean station concept. It is easier to maintain the required cleanliness levels in a smaller volume individual station as compared to an entire room. The wafers are only exposed (and processed) in the process stations. Successful maintenance of the air cleanliness levels in the individual stations requires additional special clean room techniques, which are discussed in this chapter.

### 7.2.6 Vertical Laminar Flow Stations

The work horse of the *clean work station* approach is the *vertical laminar flow station*. These units, known as *V.L.F. hoods* are a miniature version of a clean room.

Room air is pulled into the hood top through a prefilter by a blower unit. The air passes through a special filter and on down to the work surface. The arrows in fig. 7.4 indicate the laminar nature of the air flow. A V.L.F. hood is effective for two reasons. Wafers in the hood are exposed only to clean air. And any contamination from the room or personnel is prevented from entering the hood by the slight positive pressure of the air flow. The final filter used in V.L.F. hoods is called a *high efficiency particulate air (hepa) filter.* Constructed of fragile fibers, the filter has an accordian-folded design, allowing a large filtering area at an air velocity low enough for operator comfort.

The unique design of the hepa filter permits a filtering efficiency of 99.99%.

A particular problem arises in maintaining wafer cleanliness during the many chemical or "wet" operations. The fumes from the various chemicals have to be exhausted from the room for safety reasons. The classic fume exhaust hood used in chemical labs solves the safety problem, but the dirtier room air is drawn across the wafers.

This problem is solved by setting a V.L.F. unit on top of a fume hood. With this addition, both safety and cleanliness can be achieved. The hoods have to be designed so that the acid fumes are exhausted out the back with clean laminar flow air covering the front portion of the work surfaces.

### 7.2.7 Tunnel Concept

The *tunnel* approach to clean room design is to control particulate contamination that comes from the Fab personnel. The operators, technicians, supervisors and engineers necessary to run a fab area are themselves a major source of particulates. Also, their movement about the area stirs up particulates that may end up in a process hood or on the wafers.

The purpose of the tunnel concept is to isolate a portion of the Fab line in its "own" tunnel. Only the personnel required to operate that portion of the line are near the wafers and the tunnel walls protect the wafers from dirt "stirred up" in another portion of the Fab area.

The tunnel is fitted with ceiling hepa filters and V.L.F. work stations to insure a clean environment.

### 7.2.8 Ultra Clean Rooms

The development in clean room and air filtering technology has allowed a return to the open "clean room" fabrication line.

The rooms are constructed with hepa filters in the ceiling and grated floors to allow the downward flow of clean air. The flowing air carries any particulates from personnel or equipment down below the working surfaces. Table tops in ultra clean rooms are perforated to allow air flow.

The rooms must be operated with meticulous procedures to eliminate outside contamination from entering. (The procedures are explained in the next sections.) When all the procedures are followed, an ultra clean room is capable of a class 10 condition.

## 7.3 CLEAN ROOM PROCEDURES

The successful operation of a clean room requires control of every possible source of contamination. Each source represents a different danger and requires special procedures to control the contamination. The sources and control methods are identified below.

### 7.3.1 Facility Construction

Construction of a clean room is a trade-off of cleanliness vs. cost. However, every facility is built upon basic principles. All floor, wall and ceiling materials are non-shedding and smooth surfaced. Where accoustical type ceiling panels are used they are covered with a non-porous material such as mylar. Piping-holes through walls and ceilings must be caulked and sealed. Vacuum and mechanical pumps should be located outside the area. Flat surfaces not under laminar flow should be minimized to prevent the collection of dust.

Light fixtures should have solid covers to prevent dust buildup on the bulbs. The area should be supplied with non-shedding towels and cleaning solutions should be as metal ion-free as possible.

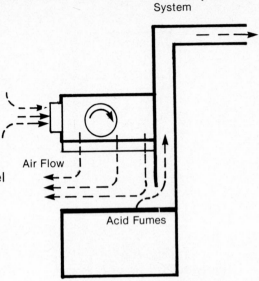

Air Flow

To Factory Exhaust System

Acid Fumes

**Fig. 7.5   Cross-section of a VLF/Fume Exhaust Hood**

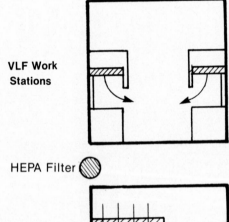

VLF Work Stations

HEPA Filter

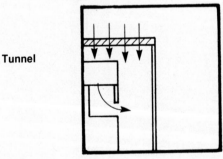

Tunnel

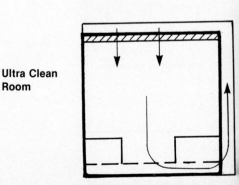

Ultra Clean Room

**Fig. 7.6   Clean Room Strategies**

V.L.F. hoods should not contain large bulky equipment that interrupts the laminar air flow. Pencils are also banned from use in fab areas. All production forms should be printed on non-shedding paper, or polymer paper substitutes.

Isolation of the fab area from contamination brought in from the outside is accomplished by several techniques:

1. Air Pressure Balancing
2. Double Door Entrances
3. Air Showers
4. Tacky Floor Mats

An air filter has a lifetime proportional to the amount of work it has to do. A dirty room will shorten the filter lifetime and increase the chance for accidental contamination of the wafer or the V.L.F. hood interior. The production room air can be reduced to a class 10,000 condition or better by proper balancing and maintenance of the room pressure.

At class 10,000 level or below, the V.L.F. stations perform more efficiently and longer than they do in a "dirty" room. By raising the room pressure above that of the rest of the factory, any dirt in the air is prevented from entering the area. A further refinement is to utilize a double door entrance area, with tacky mats to collect dirt from shoe bottoms. By balancing the pressures such that $P_1 > P_2 > P_3$ the production area is protected from the factory. With no outside dirt entering the area, the V.L.F. hood filters only recirculate clean room air.

An additional refinement is an air shower at the fab entrance to dislodge loose particulates carried in by personnel entering the area.

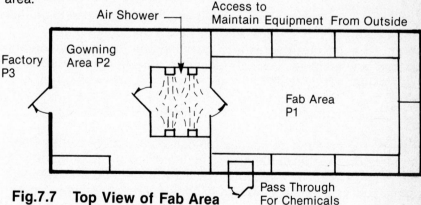

**Fig.7.7   Top View of Fab Area**

### 7.3.2 Temperature, Humidity and Smog

Most of the photomasking operations are temperature sensitive. It is imperative that the temperature be controlled to 72° C ± 2° C for process control as well as personnel comfort. Humidity is also a parameter that requires control. High humidity causes adhesion problems of the photoresist to the wafer surface. Low humidity can lead to the generation of static charge. Static control is considered in section 7.7. A typical specified humidity range is 15%-50%.

Projection aligners are particularly sensitive to temperature and humidity variations. Special stations with temperature control to ± 1° C are required to house the aligners.

Unfortunately, few semiconductor companies are located in smog free areas. It has been established that smog causes unwanted and unpredictable results in photoresist development. The problem is minimized by using charcoal filters in the house air conditioning system.

### 7.3.3 Fab Personnel

People, the largest source of contamination in a clean area, continually give off a variety of vapors and particulates. The problem is compounded by the use of cosmetics, facial hair, and the shedding nature of clothing. A person can never be rendered "clean" for more than a few minutes at a time. The only solution available is to eliminate as much surface dirt as possible and cover up the remaining dirt.

A typical facility will utilize a double door entrance as a dressing area. Entering personnel will don various garments stored in the partially clean area. The basic dress is a lab smock made from a non-shedding, non-static producing material. Some companies require just a lab smock. Additional gear would be a hat or hood and shoe coverings. Gloves are typically used for particular operations only. Facial hair may be required to be covered with special hoods or surgical masks.

Before moving into the photomasking area, the personnel may be required to pass through an air shower to knock off particulates. At the entrance door, there may be a tacky mat to pull off any dirt on the shoes or shoe coverings.

The degree of personnel garmenting and cleaning depends on the type of devices being made and the yield experience of a particular company. The range of gowning practice is from street clothes (low tech) to extremely elaborate procedures, requiring head-to-foot suits (VLSI).

### 7.3.4 Wafer Handling

Perhaps the greatest contamination danger to wafers comes from an operator's hands and fingers, which are not acceptable for handling wafers. The salt and oils always present on skin can render the devices inoperable from sodium contamination. To solve this problem, the semiconductor industry originally used stainless steel tweezers commonly found in chemical and medical laboratories. However, the tool's design allowed gripping the wafer in the center, causing torn photoresist and contamination. *Limited grasp tweezers* specifically designed for handling wafers have become the standard design. The design limits wafer contact, except at the very edge. Unfortunately, the physical contact of the tweezer with the wafer edge still results in some chipping and torn resist. The chipped region can serve as a starting point for crystal damage. During processing the damage can spread from the edge to the wafer interior.

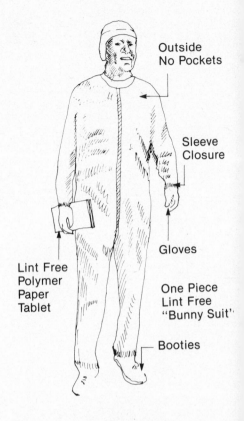

Outside
No Pockets

Sleeve
Closure

Gloves

One Piece
Lint Free
"Bunny Suit"

Lint Free
Polymer
Paper
Tablet

Booties

**Fig. 7.8**
**Personnel Clean Room Garb**

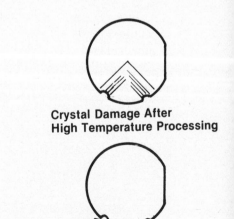

**Crystal Damage After**
**High Temperature Processing**

**Wafer Edge Damage**

**Fig. 7.9**
**Tweezer Induced Crystal Damage**

**Vacuum Pickup Tweezer**

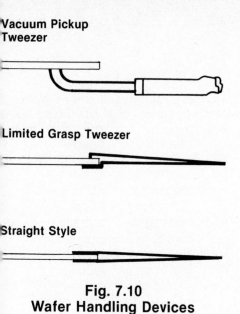

**Limited Grasp Tweezer**

**Straight Style**

**Fig. 7.10
Wafer Handling Devices**

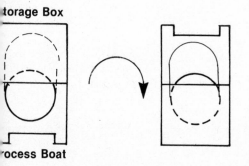

**Storage Box**

**Process Boat**

**Fig. 7.11    Flip Transfer**

Vacuum wands resolve both the wafer surface and edge damage problems. The wafer is held on the back by vacuum from a small wand. Another advantage of vacuum wands is their permanent location. Unlike tweezers, they are not convenient for use as screwdrivers or fingernail cleaners and do not get stored in lint-infested pockets.

In some situations wafers must be placed or picked up from a horizontal flat surface. *Bernouli pickups* are convenient for this use. A flow of filtered nitrogen flows out of the apparatus, creating a negative pressure. The principle is the same as a breeze creating a negative pressure in a chimney. The wafer is drawn into the negative pressure region. When using a Bernouli pickup, the wafer "floats" in the nitrogen making no physical contact with the pickup. Care must be exercised to insure that the nitrogen flow does not blow contamination on nearby wafers.

### 7.3.5 Wafer Storage and Transporation

During processing the wafers are transferred between clean stations. To protect them from contamination they are transported and stored in sealed containers. Various designs and materials are available. Generally, plastic boxes intended for home use should be avoided as they often give off contaminating vapors. Flip load polypropylene boxes also must by used with care. The hard plastic material can chip wafers as they are flipped into the boxes. The resultant silicon dust can further contaminate the wafers. (Automatic "flip" machines reduce this problem.) Wafer boxes should be inspected and cleaned regularly. A good practice is to blow out each box with filtered nitrogen immediately prior to loading the wafers.

Contamination is further reduced by the use of antistatic materials for box and carrier construction.

## 7.4 HIGH PURITY WATER

In the course of the fab operation, a wafer spends a total of several hours being rinsed in water. This is the highest level of exposure to any one environment, other than the room air. And like air, water can contain high levels of contaminants. Listed in order of potential hazard the contaminant categories are:

1. Dissolved Minerals
2. Particulates
3. Bacteria

Each contaminant is removed from the water with a special technique.

The water in a city system contains significant amounts of dissolved mineral salts. These salts exist in the water as ions ($NaCl$ becomes $Na^+$ and $Cl^-$) and can be electrically active in semiconductors. The ions are removed by two techniques: first, through a reverse osmosis process; second, through deionization by ion exchange. In-line measurements are made of the water purity before the water is released into the fab area.

*Demineralization (deionization)* of water changes it from a conductive medium to a resistive one. In fact, pure water exhibits a resistivity in excess of 18,000,000 ohm-cm at room temperature. This fact allows us to measure the degree of deionization by a resistivity measurement of the water.

Semiconductor facilities strive to produce 18 meg ohm-cm water but often allow a lower limit of 15 meg ohm-cm.

Solid particles are removed from the water, down to the sub-micron range, by various methods. Techniques include sand filtration, diatomaceous earth filtration and membranes with 0.1 micron pores.

Bacteria and fungi find water a favorable host, and if allowed to exist they act as a contaminant on a wafer. They are removed from the water by filtration, after being killed by ultraviolet light sterilizers.

Due to the cost of purifying water, it is normally cheaper to reclean used water than to clean up a new supply. Most fabs use a recirculating system, where water that tests above a certain resistivity is reclaimed. Excessively dirty water is directed to the drain. For ecological considerations, all waste water is treated to a neutral condition (pH = 7) before discharge.

Fig. 7.11 depicts a typical system showing the stages of cleanup, reclaim and neutralization. Note that the water in the storage tank is protected from $CO_2$ absorption by a layer of nitrogen.

**Table 7.3   Resistivity of Water vs. Concentration of Dissolved Solids**

| Resistivity Ohms–cm C25°C | Dissolved Solids (ppm) |
|---|---|
| 18,000,000 | 0.0277 |
| 15,000,000 | 0.0333 |
| 10,000,000 | 0.0500 |
| 1,000,000 | 0.500 |
| 100,000 | 5.00 |
| 10,000 | 50.00 |

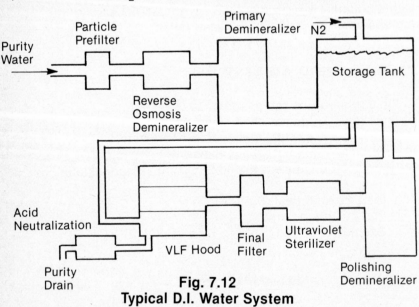

**Fig. 7.12**
**Typical D.I. Water System**

## 7.5 CHEMICALS

Throughout the process, the wafers are cleaned in various acids and solvents. Like water, these chemicals contain other elements that function as contaminants to semiconductors. Unlike water, the chemicals are used as purchased, and cleanliness levels must be specified to the vendor. The majority of commodity acids and solvents available do not meet the cleanliness level requirements of semiconductor manufacturing. These chemicals are titled *commercial grade.* The cleaner grades are titled *reagent, electronic* or *semiconductor grade.* There are presently few standards of cleanliness for chemicals in the semiconductor industry. Although SEMI (the trade organization) is establishing cleanliness specifications for all fab materials, it is not uncommon to find one manufacturer's semiconductor grade to be dirtier than another's electronic grade. The only reliable way to determine chemical cleanliness is to read and/or test the chemical analysis of the product for impurities. The semiconductor industry is particularly concerned about sodium and other metallics that are mobile in silicon. Maximum amounts are 1 part per million (1 ppm) of each individual metallic ion.

**Table 7.4    Material Analysis of Burmar 712D Photoresist Stripper**

| IMPURITY | PARTS PER MILLION |
|---|---|
| Na | 0.20 |
| Pb | 0.20 |
| Zn | 2.00 |
| Cr | 0.20 |
| Ni | 0.25 |
| Na | 0.10 |
| Si | 0.07 |
| Ca | 0.12 |
| Al | 0.05 |
| Mo | 0.03 |
| Cu | 0.02 |
| Mn | 0.015 |

Chemical purity also requires filtering the chemicals to a submicron level. VLSI requirements are 0.2 microns.

The chemical purity (*assay*) of the product must be very high to prevent unwanted reactions to the wafer from unknown chemical impurities. Clean room packaging is also necessary to insure contamination-free wafers. Steps include bottle washing, lint-free labels and bagging of the bottles during shipment.

In the interest of economy, many firms purchase clean chemicals in bulk quantities. Special care must be maintained to ensure the continued cleanliness of the chemicals. Where possible, the bulk containers should be stored in clean areas and transfer containers should be cleaned on a regular schedule. Of particular concern is *cross contamination.* Each container should be reserved for one chemical only. Additional employee training and discipline are required if a bulk chemical system is used.

## 7.6 GASES

Semiconductor wafers are exposed to industrial and specialty gases at every process step. The gas suppliers, like the chemical suppliers, have developed lines of extremely pure gases for semiconductor manufacture. Gas purity is measured in four categories:

1. Purity
2. Water Vapor Content
3. Particulates
4. Metallic Ions

High purity is required of the reactant gases used in oxidation, diffusion, plasma etch, CVD, reactive ion etch and others (see the process section for the exact processes). If the gases are contaminated with other gases or hydrocarbons, unwanted reactions will take place, or the rate of reaction will be changed. For example, contaminants in argon used in sputtering can end up in the sputtered films.

Gas purity is specified by the assay number with typical values being 99.99% – 99.9999%, depending on the gas and application.

Dry gases (no water vapor) are essential in semiconductor processing due to the ease of oxidizing silicon. At all process temperatures even trace amounts of $H_2O$ can cause the growth of $SiO_2$, which can block diffusions or cause uneven epitaxial growth. Water vapor limits are 5 ppm.

Like the chemicals, supplied gases must be particulate free down to the 0.2 micron level. Ion implantation is a particularly sensitive process because any particulates will be implanted in the wafer along with the dopant. One source of gas particulate contamination is the facility piping system. Great care must be exercised in installing and maintaining the house system. A major portion of epitaxial system preventive maintenance is system cleaning, to guarantee particulate-free gases.

All of the considerations and specifications concerning metallic ion contamination in water and chemicals also apply to gas

## 7.7 STATIC CHARGE

As the industry moves to smaller feature size and higher density, the class 100 conditions are not sufficient to process wafers at high yields. To reach class 10 conditions requires the reduction of static charge in the process hoods and equipment. When the wafers pick up a static charge they attract unacceptable levels of particulates from the air and work surfaces.

Static charge can reach 50,000 volts, and comes from many sources. Plastic shipping containers and plastic storage boxes generate high static levels. A particular problem is the charge generated by moving air or nitrogen, such as in V.L.F. hoods and

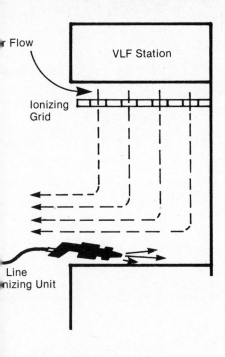

Flow

VLF Station

Ionizing
Grid

Line
Ionizing Unit

**Fig. 7.13    Static Charge Ionizers**

the rapid return of the charge after it is drained off. Static control falls into two approaches:

1. Prevent Static Buildup
2. Static Discharge Methods

The prevention of static buildup is accomplished primarily by the use of antistatic wafer carriers and garments, and topical antistatic solutions. Topical antistatic solutions are applied to walls and work surfaces and prevent static buildup by continuously neutralizing any charge buildup. The film left on the surface solution can be effective up to one year, if it is not physically disturbed.

The moving air in V.L.F. hoods and in Nitrogen blow-offs are two primary sources of static. The method for preventing static charge buildup is to place ionizers in the path of the moving air or nitrogen. The ionizers neutralize the charge built up in the gas. Since the ionizers are an integral part of the system, the problem of charge return is eliminated. Figure 7.12, which follows, shows a V.L.F. hood with ionizers in the hood and on a nitrogen gun.

**Table 7.5    Semiconductor Cleanliness Requirements**

| SOURCE | | SPECIFICATION |
|---|---|---|
| **Air** | | |
| Particulates | LSI | Class 100 @ 0.5 micron |
| | VLSI | Class 10 @ 0.3 micron |
| Humidity | | 15–50% |
| Temperature | | 68–74°F |
| Photochemical Smog | | 2 pphm (parts per hundred million) |
| **Deionized Water** | | |
| Resistivity | | 15–18 meg 52 cm |
| Particulate | | Less than 100 particulates per centiliter after 0.5 micron filtration |
| Bacteria | | Less than 100 colonies per ml sample after 0.5 micron filtration |
| **Chemicals** | | |
| Metallic Impurities | | Less than 1 ppm |
| Filtration | | To 0.2 micron |
| **Gases** | | |
| Purity | | Greater than 99.9% |
| Water Vapor | | Less than 5 ppm |
| Filtration | | To 0.3 micron |
| **Static Charge** | | Less than 50 volts |

**Table 7.6  Overview of Fabrication "Contaminants"
and Contamination Control**

| Source | Type | Detection | Control |
|---|---|---|---|
| Atmosphere | Particulates | Particle Counter | Laminar Flow Hoods<br>Clean Rooms<br>Air Locks<br>Positive Pressure Rms.<br>$N_2$ Dry Boxes |
| | Gasses (Pollution) | Ozone Detector | Airconditioning<br>Charcoal Filters |
| | Water Vapor (humidity) | Humidity Meters | Airconditioning |
| | Heat | Thermometers | Airconditioning |
| Water | Other Liquids | Resistivity Meters | Deionized Water |
| | Heavy Metals | Resistivity Meters | Deionized Water |
| | Bacteria | Culture Counts | Ultraviolet Light |
| | Electrolytes | Resistivity Meter | Deionized Water |
| People | Particulates<br>-Lint, Dandruff, etc.<br>-Makeup, Hairspray | Particle Counter &<br>Visual Inspection | L.F. Hoods, Clean<br>Rooms, Smocks,<br>Hoods, Booties |
| | Chemicals (sweat) | — | Gloves, Hoods,<br>and Tweezers |
| Chemicals | Particulates | Visual | Filtering (Vendor<br>& Point of Use) |
| | Metals and Sodium | Chemical<br>Analysis | Electronic Grade<br>Chemicals |
| Room/Work<br>Stations | Particulates | Particle Counter | Clean Room<br>V.L.F. Hoods |
| | | Visual | Sealed Surfaces |
| Gasses | Particulates | Visual | Line Filters |
| | Other Gasses | Gas Analysis | Construction of Facility |

# Oxidation

Chapter 8.

## INTRODUCTION

One of the advantages of silicon as a semiconductor material is its natural oxide, silicon dioxide ($SiO_2$). The oxide layer serves three primary functions as part of a semiconductor device. They are:

1. Surface Passivation
2. Diffusion Barrier
3. Surface Dielectric

## 8.1 SILICON DIOXIDE USES

### 8.1.1 Surface Passivation

Recall from Chapter 4 that the resistivity and conductivity type of silicon can be altered by as little as 0.001% of added dopant. Unfortunately, processing-added contamination and chemical contamination can also alter the resistivity and conductivity type, and subsequent device operation.

A layer of silicon dioxide reduces the susceptibility of the wafer surface to those contaminates in two ways. First, it physically prevents the contamination from reaching the silicon. Second, the layer grows "down" into the silicon wafer, continually creating a new "surface." Contaminants that may be present on the "old" surface are drawn up into the oxide where they are less dangerous.

### 8.1.2 Diffusion Barrier

Step three in the basic doping sequence is the diffusion or implantation of the dopant through a hole patterned in an oxide. During the doping process, the dopants actually *diffuse* (penetrate) into the oxide surface. However, they move more slowly in the oxide than in the silicon. By properly selecting the oxide thickness, the dopant is prevented from reaching the wafer surface. The rate of movement (*diffusivity*) of the common dopants in silicon is listed in the chapter on diffusion.

### 8.1.3 Surface Dielectric

At the end of the fabrication sequence the active regions in the wafer are connected by strips of aluminum running along the top of the oxide. The insulating property of the oxide prevents the metalization layer from electrically shorting to the silicon wafer. Shorting can occur if the oxide is too thin or the voltage present in the metal strip causes (induces) a charge in the wafer surface. The structure is actually that of a *capacitor*, with the oxide serving as the *dielectric*. The region on the device where the oxide serves this function is called the *field oxide*.

In MOS transistors the oxide in the gate region is purposely grown thin enough to cause the induction of a charge, which creates the channel between the source and drain regions. The oxide is called the *gate oxide, or gate ox*.

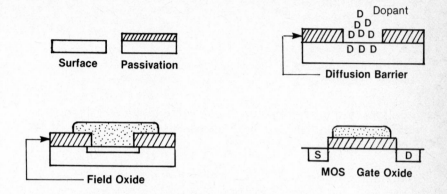

**Fig. 8.1   Uses of Silicon Dioxide**

## 8.2 THEORY OF OXIDATION

Silicon will readily grow an oxide if exposed to oxygen in the air or in chemicals. This natural oxide will grow to between 50 and 100 angstroms. The range of useful oxide thicknesses in semiconductor structures, however, is from about 1000 angstroms for MOS gates to 15,000 angstroms for MOS field oxides. Most bipolar oxides grown are in the 5000 – 8000 angstrom range. Achieving these thicknesses in a reasonable time requires an oxidation temperature of 900° C to 1200° C. Oxidation and process temperatures are selected out of compromise. The temperature has to be high enough to cause the desired result in an efficient amount of time. Of course, the temperature should be as low as is practical to minimize the inducement of crystal defects. At the upper end, 1200° C is the maximum temperature. At 1200° C, wafer warpage becomes excessive and the quartzware starts to sag and has a limited lifetime.

The chemical formula for thermal oxidation is straightforward:

$$Si + O_2 \dashrightarrow SiO_2$$

900° C – 1200° C

It states that whenever silicon is exposed to oxygen, silicon dioxide is formed. The formula does not reveal the growth mechanism. To understand the mechanism of silicon oxide growth, consider a silicon wafer immediately after exposure to oxygen (fig. 8.2):

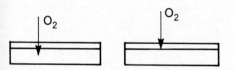

**Fig. 8.2
Mechanism of Silicon Oxidation**

The silicon and oxygen are now separated by the newly formed oxide. For more oxide to grow, either the silicon has to move to the oxygen or vice-versa. Actually, the oxygen moves to the silicon by diffusing through the existing oxide.

As the oxide gets progressively thicker it takes longer for the oxygen to move (diffuse) through the oxide, resulting in a slower rate of oxidation. The growth rate of silicon dioxide is thus not linear but, after the initial growth, conforms to a parabolic rate:

R = Growth Rate
x = Oxide Thickness
t = Time of Oxidation

$$R = \frac{x}{t}$$

The effect of this relationship is a slowing down of the added thickness of oxide as time progresses. As with most chemical reactions, R increases with temperature.

Examination of the oxidation curves at the end of this chapter reveals that the achievement of a 7000 angstrom oxide in oxygen at 1,200°C requires 10 hours of time. This time is excessive from a production consideration.

If silicon is exposed to water vapor ($H_2O$) rather than oxygen at 900° C to 1200° C, a curious phenomenon takes place. The water molecule breaks up into hydrogen (H) and the hydroxyl ion (OH–). The OH– ion diffuses through silicon dioxide at a much faster rate than does oxygen. Silicon dioxide thus grows to the required thickness in much less time.

$$Si + 2H_2O \ \text{-------}\blacktriangleright\ SiO_2 + 2H_2$$

In water vapor, a 7000 angstrom layer only requires 0.65 hours at 1,200°C.

In production, most oxides are grown in a water vapor or steam ($H_2O$ over 100° C = Steam) atmosphere by the methods illustrated in section 8.3. formed from water vapor oxidation is less dense than oxygen-grown oxide, due to the inclusion of hydrogen in the film (as predicted by the formula above). However, subsequent heating steps, such as in diffusion, drive off the hydrogen, causing a densification of the oxide.

## 8.3 THERMAL OXIDATION METHODS

The oxidation of silicon can take place by several different methods. It can take place in a tube open to atmospheric pressure, or in a closed tube at an elevated pressure. Each method offers different advantages and disadvantages. The majority of oxidations are performed at atmospheric pressure.

### 8.3.1 Atmospheric Oxidation

The equipment used for the thermal atmospheric oxidation of silicon is the same as that used in thermal diffusion. The system is composed of four subassemblies:

1. Reactant(s) Source Cabinet
2. Reaction Chamber
3. Heating Method
4. Wafer Holder

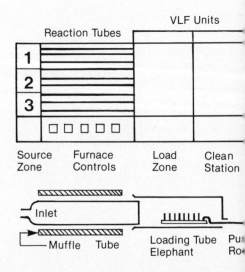

**Fig. 8.3**
**Oxidation/Diffusion Equipment**

### 8.3.2 Reactants Source Cabinet

The source cabinet at the back end of the oxidation furnace contains a gas flow controller and oxidant source. Process gases such as oxygen and nitrogen are piped to the cabinet from the facility supply.

All semiconductor processes involve more than one cycle and/or gas. Oxidation requires three cycles, whereas epitaxial growth requires up to ten. The sequence of gases and the time of each cycle is under the control of the gas flow controller. In its simplest version this consists of manual valves and timers. The operator sets the time for each cycle and opens and closes the required valves. Obviously this system is subject to errors, as well as inconsistencies from run to run.

Fully automated gas flow controllers feature solenoids with mass flow controllers metering the gas flow. The systems are timed and controlled by microprocessors. The operator selects the correct program and the microprocessor directs the required gases into the tube, at the required flow rate and for the required time.

The gas flow controller connects to the quartz tube reaction chamber. Resistance heating coils surround the quartz tube, raising the wafers to the required temperature. The wafers are placed in a slotted quartz holder called a boat which is placed in the center of the quartz tube. The oxidant-bearing gases flow into the reaction chamber and oxidize the wafers.

### 8.3.3 Reaction Chamber

Quartz tubing is the usual material for an oxidation reaction chamber, due to its thermal resistance and purity. Silicon carbide tubes are used in place of quartz for their strength and long life but cost more. High pressure oxidation processes require a stainless steel chamber.

### 8.3.4 Heating Method

The oxidation tube sits inside three separate resistance coils. An electrical current heats the coils, which in turn heats the quartz tube by conduction, and the wafers by radiation. Separate coils are necessary to maintain the stringent temperature requirement of ±2° C the entire length of the wafer boat.

Each zone is controlled by its own proportional band controller, a sophisticated device designed to proportion power to the coil in response to the amount of variation of the actual temperature from a fixed "set point". The three controllers are wired to "communicate" with each other a change in either end zone has a minimal effect on the center zone. This highly temperature controlled region that the oxidation takes place in is known as the *flat zone*.

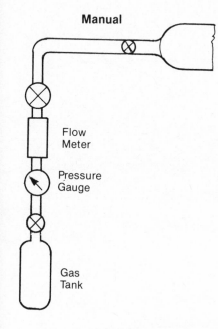

**Manual**

Flow Meter

Pressure Gauge

Gas Tank

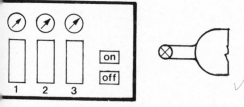

**Automatic**

1  2  3

on
off

**Fig. 8.4**
**Typical Gas Flow Systems**

### 8.3.5 Wafer Holders

Like the reaction tubes, the preferred material for wafer boats is quartz. Generally the wafers are held vertically in slots either parallel or perpendicular to the flow. Parallel loading results in a more uniform reaction and is favored for diffusion steps.

Perpendicular loading is generally adequate for uniform oxidation and has the benefit of allowing more wafers per inch of flat zone. Up to 300 wafers can be oxidized at once by using this method.

The slots in the boat must be narrow enough to hold the wafers upright without pinching them too tightly, which could cause edge dislocations during the temperature cycles.

Unfortunately, HF cleaning of the boats will eventually widen the slots until they allow the wafers to touch each other during oxidation.

Use of silicon carbide boats solves both of these problems. Silicon carbide expands and contracts at the same rate as the wafers, minimizing the dislocation problem. And silicon carbide is resistant to HF so the slots maintain their dimensions during boat cleaning.

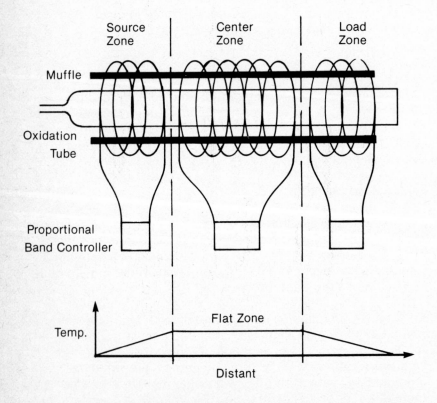

**Fig. 8.5   3 Zone Heating and Temperature Profile**

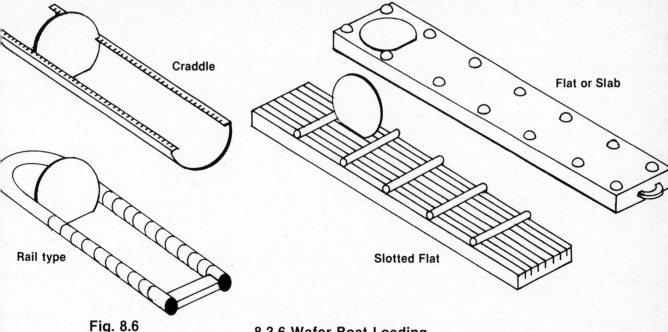

Craddle

Flat or Slab

Rail type

Slotted Flat

**Fig. 8.6**

**Oxidation/Diffusion Boats**

### 8.3.6 Wafer Boat Loading

The wafer boat must be loaded slowly into the furnace to minimize the formation of crystal dislocations. The higher the oxidation temperature and/or the more wafers on the boat (higher thermal mass), the slower the wafers must be introduced into the flat zone. A typical entrance/exit rate is 1″ per minute.

In the interest of uniformity and better use of operators this task is often performed by an automatic boat push/puller.

### 8.3.7 The Oxidation Station

Since thermal oxidation involves several steps, the station is designed so that each of them can take place without the wafer leaving a class 100 condition. The oxidation furnace opens into a VLF topped load station which in turn is located next to a wet sink for wafer cleaning.

The wafers are inspected and loaded into a boat. The boat is placed in a quartz holder which mates to the quartz oxidation tube. This unit has come to be referred to as an *elephant* or *white elephant*. An outlet near the opening of the elephant allows the hot gases to be directed into the exhaust system.

### 8.3.8 Oxygen Source

When oxygen is used as the oxidant it is supplied to the source cabinet from either the house system or from a tank of compressed oxygen.

### 8.3.9 Water Vapor Sources

#### 8.3.9.1 Bubblers

There are several methods used to supply water vapor (steam) into the oxidation tube. The most commonly used method is to heat deionized water in a quartz flask to approximately 98-99° C.

A carrier gas ($O_2$ or $N_2$) is "bubbled" through the heated water on its way into the oxidation tube. This "carrier" gas picks up water vapor and carries it to the wafers.

### 8.3.9.2 Flash System

In a flash system drops of water are dropped on a hot plate inside a small quartz tube. The droplets immediately "flash" to vapor and are carried into the tube by a carrier gas.

### 8.3.9.3 Dry Ox or Dry Steam

At oxidation process temperatures, oxygen and hydrogen will form water vapor. The resultant oxidation is the same as any water vapor system but with some improvements. Using gases as a source eliminates any contamination likely to be picked up from the D.I. (deionized) water or from the quartzware. Second, the flow of reactants can be more precisely controlled, resulting in more consistent oxide growths.

A drawback to this system is the explosion potential of hydrogen. The danger is minimized by mixing the gases only in the heated tube, and in the presence of excess oxygen, to guarantee that all of the hydrogen will mate with oxygen to form the water. A flame or heated element at the exhaust end of the tube used to burn off excess hydrogen, and hydrogen detectors are additional safety precautions.

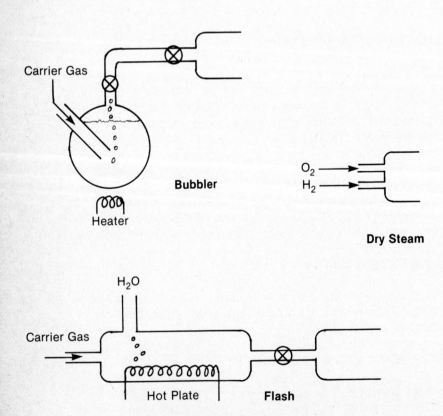

**Fig. 8.7   Water Vapor Sources**

## 8.4 HIGH PRESSURE OXIDATION

The process engineer would like to minimize the temperature of each process. That option is available by performing the oxidation above atmospheric pressure. Every increase of one atmosphere allows a 30° C reduction in temperature. Another option is to maintain the same temperature and reduce the time of oxidation.

A typical pressure level is ten atmospheres. The reaction chamber is (and has to be) constructed of stainless steel to safely contain the pressure. The oxidant source(s) are the same as those used for atmospheric oxidation.

## 8.5 OXIDATION PROCESS STEPS

Incoming
Wafers
↓
Preclean
↓
Oxidation
↓
Surface Inspection
↓
Oxide Evaluation
↓
To
Masking

**Fig. 8.8    Oxidation Flow Diagram**

### 8.5.1 Preclean

It is absolutely essential that the wafers contain no surface contamination prior to the high temperature oxidation step. The contamination can cause uneven oxide growth, stained or etched wafer surfaces or device reliability problems if metallic ions are introduced into the wafer.

The preclean process can include a number of different cleaning agents depending on the condition of the wafers or the sensitivity of the device to contamination. For instance, an MOS wafer prior to a gate oxidation must be extremely clean. Four types of contamination may be on the wafer:

1. Particulates
2. Organic Residues (oils, finger prints, etc.)
3. Inorganic Contaminants
4. Oxide Layer

Particulates are removed by mechanical scrubbers or acid cleaning. The acid clean is normally hot sulfuric acid plus an oxidant. This cleaner is the same one used for resist stripping.

Organic residue can be removed either by solvents (such as TCA or alcohol) or in the hot sulfuric acid/oxidant cleaning step previously mentioned. Solvent cleaning is avoided whenever possible because it is difficult to rinse the chemicals from the wafer. Organic contamination can also be removed in baths of ammonium hydroxide, water and hydrogen peroxide.

Inorganic contaminants will come off during the hot sulfuric acid cleaning step or may require removal in baths of hydrochloric acid, hydrogen peroxide and water.

In the cleaning baths, the silicon grows a thin (100–200 angstroms) film of silicon dioxide which can interfere with the subsequent oxidation. Uniformity and thickness control requires the removal of this thin oxide in hydroflouric acid/water mixtures. Table 8.1 lists the steps used. The procedures range from a two-step process (Process A) to a many-step process (Process B).

Process B is referred to as the *RCA Clean,* after RCA Laboratories, the firm that developed this "cadillac" of cleaning processes. The cleaning procedures used prior to oxidation are also required prior to thermal diffusion steps.

TABLE 8.1:  PREOXIDATION (Diffusion Cleaning Processes)

| SURFACE PROBLEM | PROCESS A | PROCESS B |
|---|---|---|
| Particulates | Hot Sulfuric + Oxidant Acid | Mechanic Scrubbing |
| Organic Residues | | Ammonium Hydroxide |
| Mixtures | | |
| Inorganic Contaminates Mixtures | | Hydrochloric Acid |
| Oxide Layer | HF/Water | HF/Water |

## 8.5.2 Oxidation Cycles

The actual oxidation of the wafer in the furnace occurs in three separate cycles. To understand the need for a three cycle process, consider the effect on thickness uniformity if only one cycle is used. As the wafers are introduced into the furnace, the front wafers reach temperature first, thus starting the oxidation process. At the conclusion of the process the reverse situation takes place. The last wafer on the boat exits first, leaving the front wafer hotter, longer. The net result is that the front wafers have a thicker oxide.

The solution to the problem is to load and unload the boat in an inert gas atmosphere such as nitrogen. The boat is pushed into the flat zone and the temperature allowed to stabilize before the gas controller switches the system over to the oxidant. At the conclusion of the "oxidation" cycle the system is switched back to nitrogen for the exit cycle. Thickness control to within several hundred angstroms is possible with this process.

Actually, the entrance and exit cycles may be performed in oxygen if the oxide thickness grown is relatively thick (5000 angstroms). The amount of oxide grown in dry oxygen during the cycle would be a small percentage of the total, due to the large difference in the oxidation rate of silicon in oxygen and water vapor.

## 8.5.3 Surface Inspection

A requirement of the oxidation process is a uniform noncontaminated layer of silicon dioxide on the wafer. Any physical anomalies in the layer are easily seen by a wafer surface inspection using a colimated white or U.V. light.

The inspection light is set up in the load station. As the operator unloads the wafers from the oxidation boat (s)he examines each wafer surface in the light. The mated light readily reveals any stains, particulates or irregularities. Experienced operators perform this inspection in one motion as the wafer is transferred from the diffusion boat to the wafer carrier.

## 8.5.4 Oxide Evaluation

### 8.5.4.1 SiO$_2$ Thickness

SiO$_2$ thickness is measured on a sampling of the wafers. The techniques are detailed in chapter 17.

The total oxide thickness on the wafer increases with each additional oxidation process. The process engineer is interested in knowing the oxide thickness grown at the latest new step, rather than the total amount on the wafer. Test (bare) wafers are added to each boat, at specific locations for the purpose of measuring oxide thicknesses.

### 8.5.4.2 Dielectric Strength

Since the oxide has to function as an insulator in the circuit its *dielectric strength* is of importance. Fortunately the dielectric strength changes only with the addition of impurities, a rare occurrance during oxidation. The dielectric strength measurement is made periodically, rather than run by run.

The dielectric strength test is made by measuring the *rupture voltage* of the oxide, which is a *destructive test*. This test is performed on a test wafer.

### 8.5.4.3 Index of Refraction

Changes in oxide density and composition will also alter the *index of refraction*, which can introduce an error into some of the thickness measuring techniques.

Like the dielectric strength, the index of refraction is measured on a sample basis on test wafers.

86

### 8.5.4.4 Oxide Cleanliness

Mobile ionic contamination that may be present in the oxidation system (quartz, wafer, gas) will locate in the oxide. A capacitance/voltage plot on test wafers will measure the amount present. The technique is used both to detect wafer contamination and to certify the system itself as "clean" for use.

## 8.6 SUMMARY OF THERMAL OXIDATION

1. Oxidant Sources — Oxygen / Water Vapor
2. Reaction Chamber — Quartz or Silicon Carbide Tube
3. Wafer Holder — Quartz or Silicon Carbide Slotted Boat
4. Loading Orientation — Perpendicular to Flow
5. Temperature Range — 900° – 1200° C
6. Temperature Uniformity — ± 2° C
7. Thickness Range — 250A – 15,000A
8. Oxidation Process:

| Thickness | Cycle | Ambient | Purpose |
|---|---|---|---|
| 5000A–15000A | 1 | $N_2$ or $O_2$ | Temp. Stabilization |
| | 2 | Oxidant | Grow Oxide |
| | 3 | $N_2$ or $O_2$ | Exit Cycle |
| under 5000A | 1 | $N_2$ | Temp. Stabilization No Oxide Growth |
| | 2 | $O_2$ or $H_2$ Oxidant | Grow Oxide |
| | 3 | $N_2$ | Exit Cycle – No Oxide Growth |

9. Evaluation:

| Parameter | Method | On | Frequency Wafer | Runs |
|---|---|---|---|---|
| a. Thickness | Color Interference Ellipseometry | Test Wafer | Sample | 100% |
| b. Dielectric Strength | Oxide Rupture | Test or Device Wafer | | Sample |
| c. Index of Refraction | Interference | Test or Device Wafer | | Sample |
| d. Cleanliness | Visual CVC Plot | Test Device | Sample | 100% Sample |

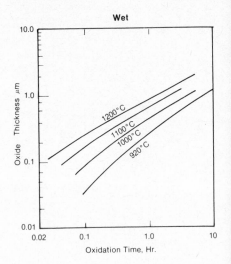

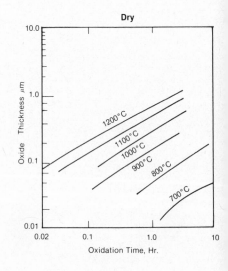

**Fig. 8.9 Oxide Growth in Wet and Dry Oxygen**

# Introduction to Photomasking

Chapter 9.

## INTRODUCTION

The *photomasking process* is the technique by which the top layer (or layers) of the wafer is selectively removed or patterned. The process can involve many steps. This chapter illustrates the basic ten-step process and several standard variations.

The pattern that ends up on the wafer surface is transferred during the photomasking process from a photomask. The design and creation of the photomask is an important subsegment of semiconductor processing.

## 9.1 CIRCUIT DESIGN TO PHOTOMASK

Photomask production starts with *circuit design*. The major steps required to produce the photomask are illustrated in figure 9.1 below.

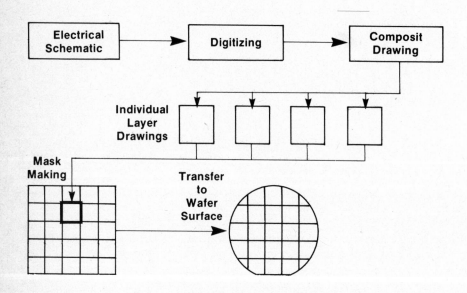

**Fig. 9.1  Pattern Design Sequence**

## 9.2 FUNCTIONAL DIAGRAM AND CIRCUIT DESIGN

Circuit design starts with a functional block diagram of the circuit function. This diagram shows the operation of the circuit without any of the design specifics. The circuit designer is concerned with the electrical functions of the finished device or circuit. Working backwards, the designer will first establish the circuit parameters and then design the individual semiconductor components required to produce the required circuit function.

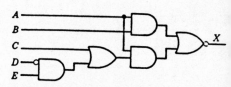

**Fig. 9.2    Example Circuit Functional Diagram**

The circuit design is called a *schematic diagram*, as illustrated in figure 9.2. It consists of symbols of the devices and will include electrical specifications.

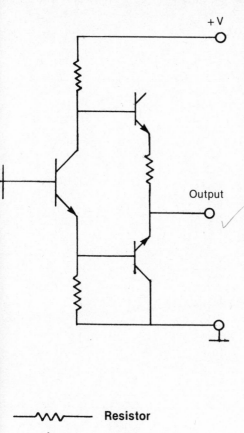

+V

Output

Resistor

Capacitor

Diode

NPN Transistor PNP

MOS

**Fig. 9.3   Schematic Diagram and Component Symbols**

## 9.3 MASK MAKING

Mask making starts by translating the required electrical parameters to physical dimensions. Next the pattern is transferred into the surface of a glass plate. The photomask surface may be an emulsion, chrome, iron oxide or silicon monoxide.

Most masks are fabricated from chrome on glass. A discussion of mask materials is included in chapter 12.

Two different techniques are used to produce the photomask: *reticle* and *E-beam* technology. Reticle technology produces photomasks that are of sufficient quality for 2–3 micron geometries. E-beam technology is required to produce photomasks used for 1–micron (and smaller) geometries. The process steps are shown in fig. 9.4.

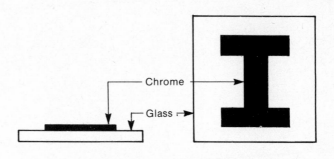

Chrome

Glass

**Fig. 9.4 Photo Mask**

### 9.3.1 Circuit Layout

The first step in circuit layout is the calculation of the physical device dimensions required to produce the required electrical parameters. The vertical dimensions determine CVD and doping thickness specifications. The horizontal dimensions determine the wafer pattern dimensions and are the basis for a scaled drawing of the finished circuit, called a *composite drawing*. Complicated circuit composite drawings are laid out and produced with the aid of a computer (CAD).

Since the circuit is built one layer at a time, the next step in the process is to separate the composite into each of the layers. Figure 9.5 shows a composite of a metal gate MOS transistor and its individual layer drawings.

### 9.3.2 Digitizing

An LSI or VLSI-scaled circuit layer drawing diagram may be as much as 10 feet on a side. Obviously, the drawing must be reduced to the chip's final dimensions. *Digitizing* is the first step in the reduction process.

90

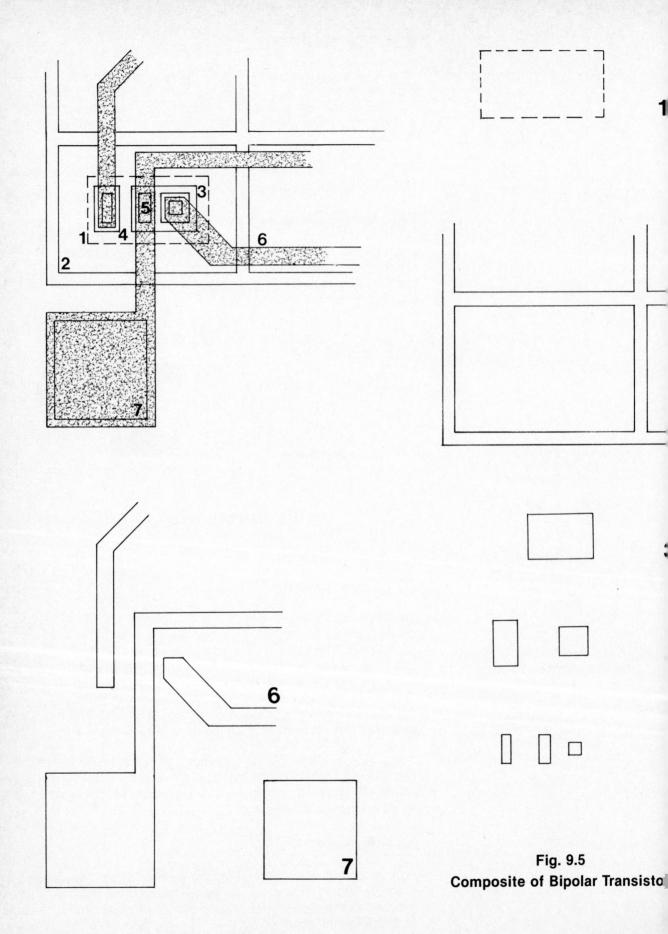

Fig. 9.5
Composite of Bipolar Transistor

The drawing is placed on an X-Y board whose cursor is connected to a computer. The drawing is traced by the cursor, and the size, shape and location of each pattern component is stored in the computer memory. The information is usually stored on tape and is used to either produce the reticle or to drive an E-beam system.

### 9.3.3 Pattern (Reticle) Generation

Step two in the reduction process is to produce an exact copy of the pattern (called a *reticle*). The actual size of the pattern on the reticle is normally ten times the final size (10 ×) of the pattern on the wafer.

A reticle is an emulsion or chrome photo plate that is selectively exposed to light in a pattern generator. The generator is comprised of a light source and computer controlled high speed shutter. The unexposed plate is placed on a stage and is moved under the shutter and light source systems.

The computer tape from the digitizing operation instructs the shutter system to open and close, exposing the reticle in the exact pattern of the original drawing.

The pattern is developed on the reticle surface into transparent and opaque regions using processes similar to those used in photographic developing. Chrome reticles are processed by the same steps used in wafer patterning.

The reticle is a miniaturized reproduction of one layer of the circuit.

### 9.3.4 Step and Repeat

The pattern on the reticle is transferred to the mask in the *step and repeat* operation. The photoresist-coated mask blank (chrome, emulsion, or iron oxide) is placed on an X-Y stage and the reticle positioned over one corner of the mask blank. A light source transfers the pattern on the reticle into the photoresist. The chemistry and mechanism of the photoresist process is detailed in chapter 10. After the first pattern is transferred, the machine "steps" the reticle to the next position and "repeats" the pattern in the next location. This process continues until the entire mask surface is filled with the reticle pattern.

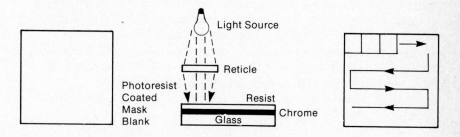

**Fig. 9.6 Step and Repeat of Reticle Pattern onto Mask**

### 9.3.5 Plate Processing

The step and repeat operation transfers the reticle pattern into the photoresist on the plate. In the next operation the plate is developed and etched, thus transferring the pattern into the mask plate surface.

Hard surface plates (such as chrome and iron oxide) go through a series of chemical steps similar to the basic photomasking process described in section 9.4. Emulsion plates go through a series of steps similar to photograph processing.

### 9.3.6 Master Plates to Working Plates

A photomask produced by the sequence outlined above is called a *master plate*. A large number of plates used in photomasking lines are for contact aligners which degrade plate quality. Since the mask-making process is expensive, particularly in producing low defect plates, the initial plate made is reserved as a master. Submasters are printed from the master and working plates printed from the submasters.

The technique used to reproduce the submasters and working plates is *contact printing*. The master (or submaster) is vacuum-clamped to a resist-coated blank mask and the pattern transferred by a light source.

Due to the physical contact of the masks in contact printing there is damage to both of them, resulting in progressively higher defect masks. Obviously the lowest defect mask is the master. High yield imaging techniques such as *projection align* and *direct wafer step* reticles often use master plates as the "working" plate, to produce low defect patterns.

### 9.3.7 E-Beam Mask Making

The generation of a photomask by the reticle, step and repeat process produces two different types of problems. There is some image degeneration (defects, image size) in the transfer from the reticle to the plate. In fact, every time a pattern is transferred there is some loss of quality. Another problem is the *registration* (or alignment) of each pattern to its intended location. The step and repeat machine may misplace the pattern by rotation or in an X-Y direction. Thus there will be alignment errors in using the plate.

*E-beam technology* is a mask making technology that avoids both of the problems above. An E-beam writer is similar to a scanning electron microscope (S.E.M.). The coated mask is placed in a vacuum chamber and an electron beam directed at it. The pattern information stored on tape at the digitizing operation is used to direct the E-beam to the correct locations to expose the photoresist. The pattern is directly written onto the mask without a reticle.

After exposure the plates are processed as described in section 9.3.5. E-beam masks are more expensive to produce but higher in quality. Most masks made by E-beam are used in projection or wafer stepper exposure systems (see ch.11).

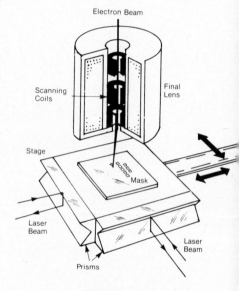

**Fig. 9.7
Electron Beam
Direct Write Apparatus**

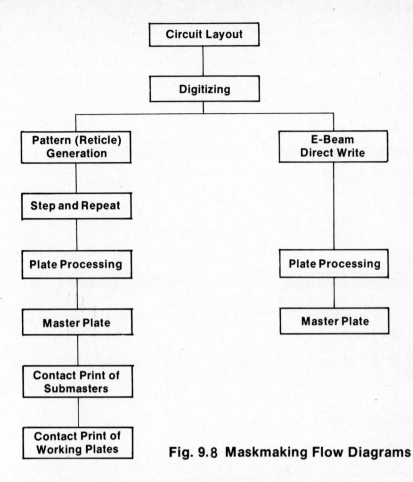

Fig. 9.8 Maskmaking Flow Diagrams

## 9.4 BASIC PHOTOMASKING

*Photomasking* is the transfer of a pattern from a mask to a wafer surface using a photo resist layer. The process involves two pattern transfers. First the mask is transferred to the photoresist layer. The second transfer is from the photoresist layer to the wafer surface. A photograph is an example of a double transfer. In a camera, the image (object) is transferred by the camera to the film. Through processing, the image on the film is transferred to the print paper.

### 9.4.1 Photomasking Results

In semiconductor technology a number of different surface layers can be present on the wafer. The pattern on the mask is transferred into these layers via the photomasking processes, with one of two possible results: A "hole" may be put in the layer or an "island" may be left on the wafer. *Contact mask* is an example where holes are put into the wafer to allow the metal layer to reach down to the silicon. *Metal mask* is an example of an island being left on the wafer surface. Leaving an island is also referred to as *subtractive etch*.

### 9.4.2 Photoresist Polarity

The proper polarity for both the photoresist and the mask is required to produce either the hole or island. Negative photoresist responds to light exposure by forming crosslinked

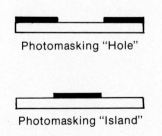

Photomasking "Hole"

Photomasking "Island"

**Fig. 9.9 Photomasking Results**

chains among its molecules, in a process termed *polymerization*. Unexposed positive resist is polymerized and becomes depolymerized during the exposure.

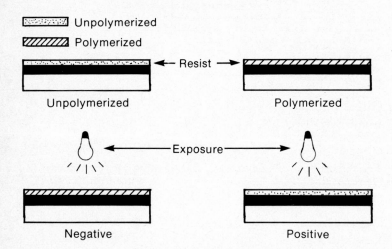

**Fig. 9.10 Negative and Positive Photoresist Reaction to Exposure**

### 9.4.3 Mask Polarity

If the mask pattern is defined on the mask by the opaque areas, the mask is a "light" field mask. If the mask pattern is defined by the clear portion, the mask is a "dark" field mask.

### 9.4.4 The Basic Photomasking Flow, First Transfer

The process of transferring the pattern on the mask to the wafer surface actually requires two transfers. The first is from the mask onto the photoresist layer. This procedure is illustrated using a clear field mask and negative photoresist.

| Process Step | Purpose | Cross Section |
|---|---|---|
| 1. Surface Preparation | Clean and dry wafer surface | 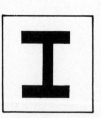 |
| 2. Photoresist Apply | Apply a thin layer of photoresist to the wafer | |
| 3. Softbake | Partial evaporation of photoresist solvents to promote adhesion |  |

**Fig. 9.11**
**Light and Dark Field Masks**

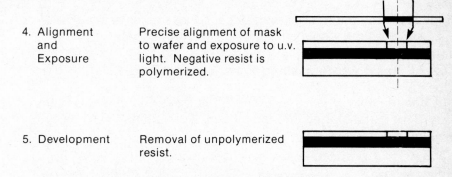

4. Alignment and Exposure — Precise alignment of mask to wafer and exposure to u.v. light. Negative resist is polymerized.

5. Development — Removal of unpolymerized resist.

**Fig. 9.12   First Image Transfer From a Light Field Mask to a Negative Photoresist Layer**

Note that the hard bake operation is shown before the develop inspect operation. Most automatic develop machines are mated to a bake oven. Thus the two steps are accomplished in one operation. If manual equipment is used, the hard bake operation may be performed between develop inspection and etch.

At this point the opaque image on the mask has been transferred to the photoresist layer. The same configuration can be obtained using a dark field mask and positive photoresist.

For brevity, only steps 2, 4, and 5 are illustrated.

| Process Step | Cross Section |
|---|---|

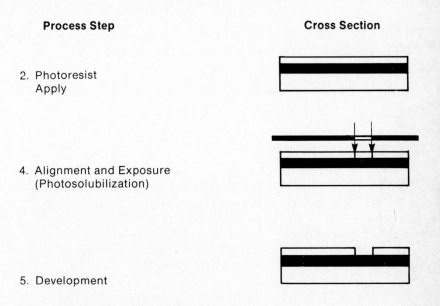

2. Photoresist Apply

4. Alignment and Exposure (Photosolubilization)

5. Development

**Fig. 9.13  First Image Transfer From a Dark Field Mask to a Positive Photoresist Layer**

## 9.4.5 Resist and Mask Polarity Combinations

By choosing the right photoresist and mask polarities, either of the two results – hole or island – can be obtained.

## 9.4.6 Basic Photomasking Flow, Second Transfer

Once the hole or island is produced in the photoresist layer, the pattern is transferred into the surface layer. Steps 8 – 10 below illustrate the process:

| Process Step | Purpose | Cross Section |
|---|---|---|
| 8. Etch | Selective removal of top surface layer | |
| 9. Photoresist Removal | Clean photoresist from the wafer surface | |
| 10. Final Inspection | Inspection of wafer for correctness of image transfer from photoresist to top layer | |

**Fig. 9.14  Second Image Transfer**

The basic ten-step process is used for the majority of photomasking steps. The parameters of each individual step may be different between fab lines. The process parameters and methods are explained in chapters 11, 12 and 13.

In some cases the basic process is not adequate to produce the required pattern in the surface layer. Three variations on the basic process are:

Lift Off Process
Double Masking
Dual Layer Photoresist

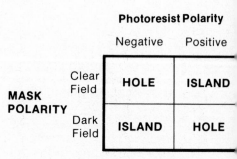

**Fig. 9.15  Mask and Photoresist Polarity Results**

| | | Photoresist Polarity | |
|---|---|---|---|
| | | Negative | Positive |
| MASK POLARITY | Clear Field | HOLE | ISLAND |
| | Dark Field | ISLAND | HOLE |

## 9.5 LIFT OFF PROCESS

In the basic photomasking process there are three steps where the pattern dimensions on the wafer can vary: exposure, development and etch. The lift off process allows patterning of the surface layer with only two of the steps influencing dimension variation, exposure and development. This variation is used to pattern deposited layers such as metals.

This technique follows the basic ten-step process up to the develop step. By varying the exposure and develop cycles, the edge of the resist is created with a "negative" slope. A thin layer of metal is subsequently deposited on the wafer. Where the resist has been developed away, the metal resides directly on the wafer surface.

Due to the reverse taper of the resist island, the metal layer is thinner over the step. When the wafer is immersed in a photoresist stripper (usually with ultrasonic agitation) the metal over the island is "lifted off" the wafer along with the photoresist.

The width of the metal layer remaining on the wafer is exactly the same width as the opening in the photoresist. The dimensional variation added by etch step is eliminated.

| **Process Step** | **Cross Section** |
|---|---|

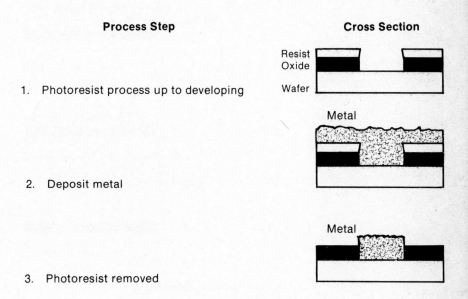

1. Photoresist process up to developing

2. Deposit metal

3. Photoresist removed

**Fig. 9.16 Lift Off**

## 9.6 DOUBLE MASKING

The patterning of small geometries (i.e., contact mask) normally requires thinner resist films and/or shorter expose times. Unfortunately, a thinner film also results in more pinholes, a situation particularly intolerable at contact mask where any etched-through pinhole will result in a direct short from the metal to the substrate.

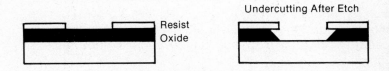

**Fig. 9.17 Undercutting of Thin Resist**

A process which resolves this problem is *double masking.* A thin first layer of resist is applied and processed through develop. This thin layer allows the required dimensional control of the small holes. A second layer is then applied. The exposure of the second layer is achieved with an oversize mask, to allow for alignment errors. The effect of the second layer is to "fill in" any pinholes in the first layer. If there are any pinholes in the second layer, there is a very low probability that they will coincide with the location of a pinhole in the first layer.

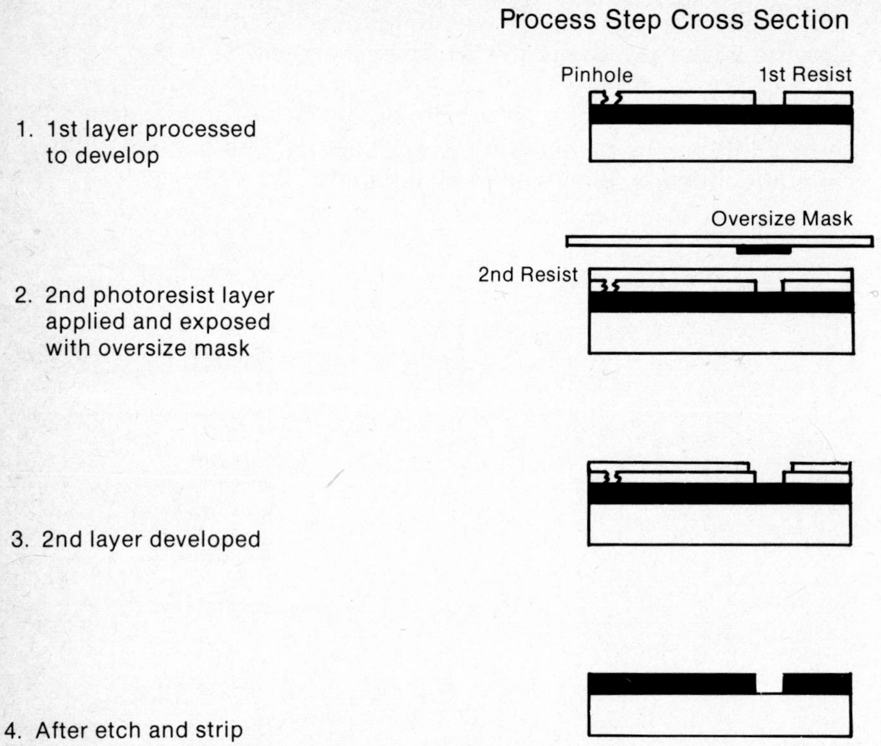

**Process Step Cross Section**

Pinhole                    1st Resist

1. 1st layer processed
   to develop

Oversize Mask

2nd Resist

2. 2nd photoresist layer
   applied and exposed
   with oversize mask

3. 2nd layer developed

4. After etch and strip

## Fig. 9.18    Double Masking

## 9.7 DUAL LAYER PHOTORESIST

Complicated VLSI Circuits require more process steps, resulting
in more layers, which result in turn in an irregular surface
topography. This becomes a problem in photomasking. The
exposure light will diffuse around the mask pattern, changing the
dimension of the pattern on the wafer surface. The patterns that
must be transferred down into a trough will be more affected.

The problem can be solved with a dual photoresist layer of two
different resist polarities. First, a relatively thick first layer is
applied and baked, causing the resist to flow slightly, leveling out
the surface. A second, thinner layer is applied on top and
processed through develop. This top layer acts as a mask to
expose the bottom layer by a flood exposure (no mask). After
development of the bottom layer, the wafer is etched and
stripped. The first layer applied may be either a photoresist or a
polyimide.

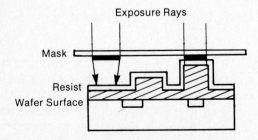

Exposure Rays

Mask

Resist

Wafer Surface

## Fig. 9.19    Effect of Surface Topography
## on Pattern Resolution

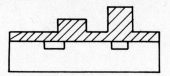

Process Step

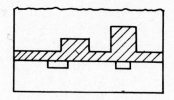

1. Apply 1st layer.

2. Bake 1st layer to cause slight flow.

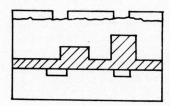

3. Apply 2nd layer and process to develop.

4. Flood expose 1st layer.

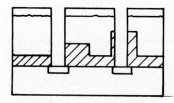

5. Develop 1st layer.

6. Etch and strip.

**Fig. 9.20**
**Dual Layer Photoresist Processing**

# Photoresist Chemistry

Chapter 10.

## INTRODUCTION

In Chapter 9 we discussed the basic photomasking process, focusing on the purpose or result of each step and the results that can be accomplished from the entire process. In this chapter the photoresist itself is examined from a chemical, physical and process point of view.

## 10.1 PHOTORESISTS

The heart of the photomasking process is the *photoresist*. Photoresists are multicomponent chemical mixtures that possess the property of changing their internal structure when exposed to various forms of energy such as light, radiation, or heat. As we explained in Chapter 9, the structural changes of photoresists used in semiconductor applications change them from developable to nondevelopable and vice-versa.

Photoresists have been used in the printing industry for over a century. In the 1920's photoresists found wide application in the printed circuit board industry. The semiconductor industry adapted this technology to wafer fabrication in the 1950's. Development of photoresists specifically designed for semiconductor use was first supplied by the Eastman Kodak Company. In the late 'fifties they introduced their line of KPR and KMER negative resists. At around the same time the Shipley Company introduced a line of positive acting resists. Since then a host of other companies have entered the market to keep pace with ever increasing industry demands to print narrower lines for batch to batch uniformity and decreased sensitivity to process variations. The photoresist practitioner has a range of products designed to match various process requirements.

A resist cannot be selected independent of the image size it must accommodate or the process in use. The selection and qualification of a resist is the result of careful (and often lengthy) testing. The many trade offs of process parameters to resist parameters result in a process that is customized and sometimes delicately balanced. Once established, a resist process is changed only after extensive testing and to achieve major benefits from the change.

## 10.2 PHOTORESIST COMPOSITION

Both negative and positive photoresists are composed of three basic components. The "photo" components of the resist are light sensitive polymers which are suspended in an appropriate solvent. The solvent functions to allow the photoresist to be applied to a semiconductor wafer in ultra thin films (a range of .5 to 1.5 microns). Various sensitizers are added to this solution to control or modify the internal chemistry of the photoresist.

## Table 10.1 Photoresist Components

| Component | Function |
|-----------|----------|
| Polymer | Changes structure in reaction to energy (polymerization or photosolubilization) |
| Solvent | Allow spin application of thin layers |
| Sensitizers | Control or modification chemical reaction when exposed |
| Additives | Specific Needs |

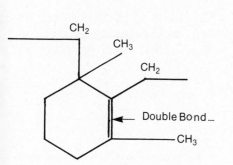

**Fig. 10.1
Polyisoprene Polymer Structure**

## 10.3 NEGATIVE PHOTORESIST CHEMISTRY

As mentioned, the photo portion of a photoresist is the photo sensitive polymer. Polymer chemistry is a fascinating field which has produced our endless variety of plastics. To the nonchemist, polymers are groups of large, heavy molecules formed in a repeated pattern. The polymers in photoresists are organic in nature, i.e., they are composed of the elements carbon, hydrogen and oxygen. Rubber is a naturally occuring polymer known as a polyisopreme. It is this polymer that is the basis of negative photoresist. In fact, the earlier Kodak photoresist used natural rubber as their polymer source. Polymer chemistry has been able to reproduce the rubber structure. Modern negative photoresists are based on synthetic polyisopreme polymers.

### 10.3.1 Sensitizers

Several factors, including the standard chemical system parameters of time, temperature and energy, control how fast and how complete the polymerization proceeds. The reaction is modified by the addition of *sensitizers.* For example, negative resists are sensitized to react primarily to ultra violet light. The polymerization of the polymer occurs in response to only a small portion of the ultraviolet light available in an alignment machine. A sensitizer is added to the photoresist to either increase or decrease the range of wave lengths to which the photoresist responds. This range of wavelengths is termed the *spectral response.*

### 10.3.2 Solvents

The solvent serves as an application vehicle for the photosensitive polymers. The photoresist solvent has the same function as the liquid base of a paint. In fact, the content of a negative photoresist is only about ten percent solids.

Solvents can be divided into two groups: *aromatic* and *aliphatic.* The aromatic solvents are closed chain-ring compounds, such as kerosene. In aliphatic compounds, the carbon atoms are linked in open chains. The usual negative photoresist solvent, xylene, is of the aromatic type.

### 10.3.3 Additives

Various dyes may be added to negative photoresists to improve or control their spectral response.

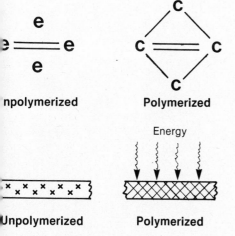

**Fig. 10.2
Polymerization of Negative Resist**

104

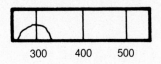

Unsensitized   Photoresist

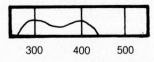

Sensitized   Photoresist

Wavelength (nm)

**Fig. 10.3   Spectral Response of Unsensitized and Sensitized Resist**

### 10.3.4 Oxygenation

Negative photoresist suffers from an oxygenation process during exposure. The carbon in the resist will form $CO_2$ with the $O_2$ in the air, resulting in a thinner film. One solution is to expose only in nitrogen. Projection alignment makes this difficult due to the large exposure cavity. Consequently, resists specially formulated to minimize the oxygenation effect have been developed. Film thickness reduction due to oxygenation during exposure can be up to forty percent (40%) reduction due to oxygenation.

## 10.4 POSITIVE PHOTORESIST CHEMISTRY

### 10.4.1 Polymer

The phenol-formaldehyde polymer is the basis of most positive photoresists. It is also referred to as a *pheno-formaldehyde novalak resin.* Before processing, the polymer is polymerized. Processing the polymer with naphthoquinone diazides increases the light sensitivity of the polymer. Upon exposure to energy (light), the resin changes from an insoluable to a soluable state. The reaction is appropriately termed *photosolubilization.* Actually, the polymer chemistry changes from the phenol-formaldehyde structure to carbolic acid, which is soluable. The polymer is naturally dark in color, giving positive photoresist a self light-filtering action and improved image reduction. Unfortunately, the adhesion property of the resist decreases after exposure.

### 10.4.2 Sensitizers

Sensitizers in positive photoresist do not perform the same functions as the sensitizers in negative photoresist. The positive photoresist sensitizers do not enter into the exposure mechanism of the resist. Photosolubilization produces by-products that are generally soluble only in solvents. The sensitizers change the film from solvent soluble to water soluble. A polymer/sensitizer ratio of about 4:1 is required to accomplish this change. (Negative photoresist contains a polymer/sensitizer ration of approximately 60:1.)

### 10.4.3 Solvents

Like negative photoresist, the solvent is an application vehicle for the polymers and sensitizers. Both ethoxyethyl acetate and 2 methoxyethyl acetate are used as base solvents. Some positive resist systems may have xylene or butyl acetate added to aid the drying and application characteristics.

## 10.5 SPECIAL APPLICATION PHOTORESISTS

As the industry has moved to smaller image size, it has become necessary to develop higher resolution resists and resists that are responsive to different exposure radiations such as E-beam and X-Ray. The development has been both in the improvement of the

Table 10.2   Negative and Positive Photoresist Chemistry

| Parameter | Negative | Positive |
|---|---|---|
| Polymer | Polyisoprenes | Phenol-formaldehyde |
| Reaction to Light | Polymerization | Photosolubilization |
| Sensitizer Role | Controls Spectral Response | Changes Film from Solvent Soluble to Water Soluble |
| Polymer/Sensitizer Ratio | 60:1 | 4:1 |
| Solvent | Xylene | Ethoxyethyl Acetate or 2-methoxyethyl Acetate |
| Additives | Dyes | Drying Solvents |

polyisopreme and novolak polymer based resists and the use of different polymer bases. Table 10.3 lists the resists currently being offered, their polarity, and their intended exposure radiation.

### Table 10.3  Resist Comparison Table

| Resist | Polymer | Polarity | Sensitivity (Coul/cm²) | Exposure Radiation |
|---|---|---|---|---|
| Positive | Novolak (M–Cresol-formaldehyde) | + | $3\text{-}5 \times 10^{-5}$ | UV |
| Negative | Poly Isoprene | – | | UV |
| PMMA | Poly–(Methyl Methacrylate) | + | $5 \times 10^{-5}$ | E-Beam |
| PMIPK | Poly–(Methyl Iso-propenyl Ketone | + | $1 \times 10^{-5}$ | E-Beam/ Deep UV |
| PBS | Poly–(Butene-1-Sulfone) | + | $2 \times 10^{-6}$ | E-Beam |
| TFECA | Poly–(Trifluoroethyl Chloroacrylate | + | $8 \times 10^{-7}$ | E-Beam |
| COP (PCA) | Copolymer–($\alpha$–Cyano Ethyl Acrylate–$\alpha$–Amido Ethyl Acrylate) | – | $5 \times 10^{-7}$ | E-Beam X-Ray |
| PMPS | Poly–(2–Methyl Pentene–1–Sulfone) | + | $2 \times 10^{-7}$ | E-Beam |

## 10.6 PHOTORESIST PERFORMANCE FACTORS

A particular photoresist is selected based on the resolution, adhesion, exposure speed and pinhole count performance of the resist relative to the requirements of design feature size. As we will illustrate, all the processes in the photomasking process are intimately tied to one another. Any of the resist performance parameters can be changed or compromised by a process change elsewhere, or as the result of a poorly selected process.

### 10.6.1 Resolution

The smallest opening or space that can be resolved in a photoresist layer is generally refered to as its *resolution capabilities*. However, the resist layer must be applied to the wafer at a thickness level which insures enough mechanical film strength at etch and, most important, achieves a film thickness which minimizes the formation of holes in the resist. These holes are called *pinholes* and are discussed below.

Thus, resolution capability is the smallest opening and space that can be imaged in the resist in relation to the film thickness. Resolution is expressed as the aspect ratio of the resist and/or process. The aspect ratio is defined as the ratio of the image opening to the resist thickness. One of the most valued properties of positive photoresist is its higher aspect ratio than negative photoresist.

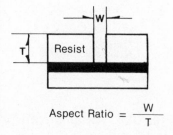

Aspect Ratio = $\dfrac{W}{T}$

**Fig. 10.4   Aspect Ratio**

### 10.6.2 Adhesion

The ability of the photoresist to adhere to the variety of surfaces used in semiconductor processing is a critical parameter. If the resist lifts off the surface during etch, the image size in the layer will be wider or narrower than intended. The natural adhesion ability of a resist is generally insufficient to prevent lifting at etch. Consequently, dehydration and/or a priming process are required to enhance the adhesion of the resist. Negative photoresists generally have better adhesion properties than positive resists.

### 10.6.3 Exposure Speed

The speed with which a particular photoresist reacts to exposure is refered to as its *exposure speed.* A resist process that uses a very fast reacting resist will be more variable due to variation in the timing mechanisms and light intensity of the exposure machine. A resist that requires a long exposure time will increase wafer throughput time

The exposure speed is also a function of the band of radiation the resist is designed to react to. Generally, the narrowed the band the faster the resist. Positive resists are slower in exposure speed than negative resist by a factor 3 to 4.

### 10.6.4 Pinhole Count

The number of pinholes in a photoresist layer is a function of several factors including: the resist itself, the spin conditions and the general cleanliness of the area. Every photoresist layer exhibits pinholes as it thins, which are caused by minute particles in the resist, and the separation of the resist during the spin operation. A photoresist which can be applied thinly enough to allow good image definition and a low pinhole count is desirable. Positive resist with its ability to allow better resolution in thicker films naturally will have fewer pinholes.

### 10.6.5 Process Latitude

During resist processing, there is significant process variation. Since the goal of the photomasking step is to produce a consistent image size, the ability of the resist to be somewhat intolerent to these fluctuations is an important resist parameter. Resolution and process latitude are tradeoffs in selecting a resist and setting the process parameters.

### 10.6.6 Step Coverage

The surface of a wafer becomes more terraced as it proceeds through the various layering and patterning steps. Photoresist layers tend to become thinner as they go over these steps, with a subsequent breakdown at etch. *Step coverage* is a function of the resist, step size and etch time.

## 10.7 COMPARISION OF NEGATIVE AND POSITIVE RESISTS

Photoresist processing was developed in the 1960's primarily with negative resist. Although positive resist which allowed thinner pinhole-free layers offered a better aspect ratio, this quality was not essential because of the device image size (10–15 microns and wider). The higher price of the positive resist, its poorer adhesion properties, and its lower exposure time all limited its

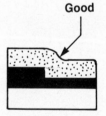
Good

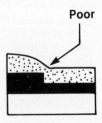
Poor

**Fig. 10.5   Step Coverage**

appeal. However, as the image size shrank to the 2-5 micron range, the earlier objections to the resist were reduced. When smaller image size forces a thinner layer of negative resist, the resist will not maintain its integrity over a step in the surface.

The chemicals required to develop and strip positive resist are another advantage. The developers, which are aqueous-based, are safer to use and easier to dispose of than those used for negative resist. The strippers that effectively remove positive resist are simple solvent combinations which operate at room temperature and, like the developers, are safer to use and dispose of. Table 10.4 summarizes and compares the various attributes of each resist.

**Table 10.4   Comparison of Negative and Positive Resists**

| Parameter | Negative | Positive |
|---|---|---|
| Aspect Ratio (Resolution) | | Higher |
| Adhesion | Better | |
| Exposure Speed | Faster | |
| Pinhole Count | | Lower |
| Process Latitude | Depends On | Process Parameters |
| Step Coverage | | Better |
| Cost | | Higher |
| Developers | Solvents | Aqueous |
| Strippers | | |
|    Oxide Steps | Acid | Acid |
|    Metal Steps | Chlorinated Solvent Compounds | Simple Solvents |

## 10.8 STORAGE AND HANDLING OF PHOTORESISTS

### 10.8.1 Light Sensitivity

Polymerization and photosolubilization of photoresist take place with the application of energy in the form of light or heat. To protect the photoresist from light, the containers are made of dark colored glass. For the same reason, the lighting in photomasking areas is yellow or gold. Photoresists, which are not as sensitive as photographic film, do not require processing in red lights.

### 10.8.2 Heat Sensitivity

Photoresists must be stored under constant temperature conditions. If the storeroom is subject to wide temperature fluctuations, the resists should be stored elsewhere in the building.

### 10.8.3 Viscosity Sensitivity

Viscosity is one of the major determinants of film thickness. A typical specification allows viscosity variations of approximately 10%. The viscosity of a photoresist can change radically if the solvent medium is allowed to evaporate. Care must be exercised to insure that bottle caps are tight. If the photoresist is to be dispensed manually, a glass eye dropper or syringe should be used. (The solvents in the photoresist dissolve many plastic syringes, resulting in viscosity changes.)

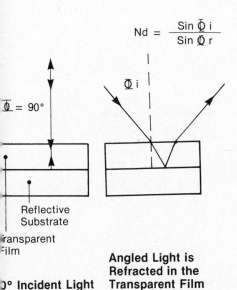

$$N_d = \frac{\sin \Phi_i}{\sin \Phi_r}$$

Reflective Substrate

Transparent Film

0° Incident Light

Angled Light is Refracted in the Transparent Film

**Fig. 10.6   Index of Refraction**

108

### 10.8.4 Contamination

Photoresist dispensers should not be cleaned with trichloroethylene (TCE). TCE is difficult to rinse away, and causes bubbles in the photoresist layer of negative photoresist.

Filtering the resist with a 1 micron filter at the point of use is an effective contamination control method.

### 10.8.5 Shelf Life

All chemical systems contain energy at temperatures above zero degrees Kelvin (absolute zero). The internal energy of a photoresist can lead to polymerization or photosolubilization of the resist with time. This phenomenon limits photoresist shelf life to approximately one year.

**Table 10.5   Handling and Storage of Photoresists**

1. Dark Bottles
2. Yellow Safe Lights (Negative Resist
3. Constant Storage Temperature
4. Tightly Closed Bottles
5. Avoid Cleaning Equipment with TCE
6. Avoid Plastic Dispensers
7. Observe Product Shelf Life
8. Maintain Clean Dispense (Spin) Equipment

## 10.9 PHOTORESIST PHYSICAL PROPERTIES

The internal chemistry of photoresists is not a factor the photoresist practioner can change or specify. If the resist works, it is evidenced in good results. However, the physical properties of the resist directly influence the process results. Poor quality control of viscosity or solids content can result in a high percentage of wafer rejects or poor resolution. The physical properties dictate process parameters. In this section, the various physical parameters are examined. The interaction of the parameters with process parameters is discussed in chapters 11–13.

### 10.9.1 Viscosity

Photoresist, as received, is a suspension of solids in a solvent medium. It is coated onto a wafer by a spinning technique. Photoresist is placed on the wafer and the wafer is coated by spinning at high RPM. The final film thickness will be influenced by the photoresist properties of surface tension, specific gravity, solids content and viscosity. Of the four, the photoresist technologists will be able to select only the viscosity value. The other three parameters are properties of the particular resist and should be constants.

*Viscosity* is the quantitative measure of liquid flow qualities. As a liquid flows, the molecules roll over each other with more or less ease. It is this "internal friction" that we call viscosity. Actually, viscosity measurements are made by measuring the force required to move an object through the liquid.

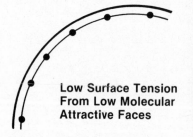

Low Surface Tension From Low Molecular Attractive Faces

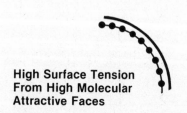

High Surface Tension From High Molecular Attractive Faces

**Fig. 10.7   Surface Tension**

The falling ball viscosimeter is a standard laboratory apparatus for measuring viscosity. Another type known as the Ostwalk-Cannon-Fenske type measures the time for a given volume of liquid to flow through an orifice, or known size. Most commercial viscosimeters are of the torque type. A paddle or spindle of known dimensions rotated in the liquid to a constant RPM is a function of the liquid viscosity. The Synchre-lectric viscometer (Brookfield RVT Model) is a direct reading torque type unit. Extreme care must be exercised to keep any viscosimeter equipment clean. Any dirt or dried resist will cause higher viscosity readings. When reporting a viscosity measurement, it is imperative to record the measuring apparatus and temperature. Different apparatus can give different viscosity values.

As one would expect, liquids change their flow characteristics with temperature. The unit of viscosity is the *poise,* named after the French scientist Poisseulle who investigated the viscous flow of liquids. One poise equals one dyne sec/cm. Photoresist is usually expressed in centipoise (1/100 of a poise) or cps.

Some resist manufacturers report the viscosity in *centistokes.* This value is the absolute viscosity (centipoise) divided by the resist density, and is called the *kinematic viscosity.* (Density is obtained from the specific gravity.) Thus, a 65 cps resist with a specific gravity of 0.8 would have a kinematic viscosity of:

Kinematic viscosity = (cps)/s.g. = (81.25)/0.8 centistokes

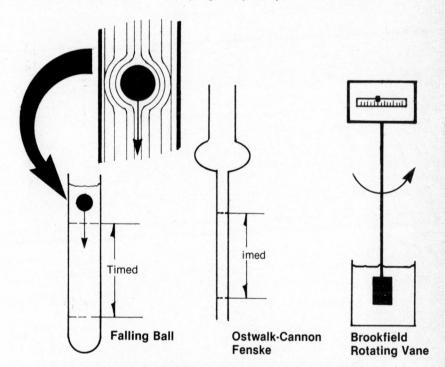

Timed

imed

Falling Ball

Ostwalk-Cannon Fenske

Brookfield Rotating Vane

**Fig. 10.8 Vicosity Measuring Techniques**

## 10.9.2 Flash Point

Photoresists contain flammable solvents which represent a potential fire danger. Above a specific temperature, solvent vapors will ignite in the presence of an open flame. This temperature is the *flash point.* Typical photoresist flash points start at about 30° C 89° F).

### 10.9.3 Contamination

Like other chemicals involved in semiconductors, photoresist must meet various cleanliness levels. The requirements and measurement are the same as those mentioned in chapter 7 on contamination control.

# Photomasking Technology Part 1

Chapter 11.

## INTRODUCTION

In Chapter 9 the basic ten-step photomasking process was explained from a results perspective. In the next three chapters we will examine the techniques and options used to perform these basic steps.

## 11.1 SURFACE CLEANING

### 11.1.1 Introduction

Throughout this chapter, various analogies will be used to aid the reader in understanding photomasking (also called *photolithography*) technology. Let's begin with painting. The application of photoresist to a wafer is similar to the successful application of paint to a surface, beginning with surface preparation. Even the amateur painter quickly learns that the surface must be clean and dry if the paint is going to adhere. Similarly, the wafer must be clean and dry for the photoresist to adhere.

The process problem resulting from poor adhesion is *undercutting at etch*. During the etch process, there are two directions of film removal -- down and to the side. This is called *isotropic etching*. It results in a widening of the etched opening. When this is accompanied by lifting of the photoresist from the surface, the problem can become acute. Etch dimensions become larger, and in extreme cases the pattern is radically altered. This situation becomes intolerable in VLSI devices, where dimensional control and packing density are extremely critical.

A number of things contribute to the problem of undercutting and resist lifting: poor process control, fab environment, wafer surfaces and the type of photoresist used. Positive photoresists typically have more adhesion problems than negative resists. Most semiconductor fab lines include surface preparation processes to insure better photoresist adhesion.

The exact processes utilized and their particular parameters vary from company to company, depending on the level of precision required of the masking process, the facility and the wafer masking step. In general, the processes address three needs: a particulate-free surface, a "dry" surface and a chemically primed surface.

### 11.1.2 Surface Particle Removal

A diffusion, ion implant, CVD or metalization process usually precedes a photomasking step. All of these processes take place in an environment that is clean and dry. In most cases, the wafer surface is in an optimum condition to have a photoresist layer applied. Wafers coming out of a dirty reactor with particulate contamination or wafers that have been through a high phosphorous doping or layering are exceptions to this situation. Unfortunately, the wafers must be unloaded from their previous operation, loaded in a container and transported to the masking area. During journey, there is ample opportunity for contamination

**Normal**

**Excessive**

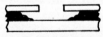

**Catastrophic**

**Fig. 11.1
Illustration of Undercutting**

to occur from the atmosphere, the container and poor handling techniques. The nature of the contamination at this step is ogenerally particulate and not chemical (oil, films, etc.)

If a chemical cleaning is required, hot acid cleaning such as that employed in pre-diffusion cleaning is generally preferred, with hot sulfuric acid with an oxidant added. If the contaminant is primarily particulate, the following methods are usually employed and the acid cleaning step eliminated.

### 11.1.2.1 Filtered Nitrogen Blow-Off

The simplest method of particulate removal is to blow off each wafer with a blast of filtered nitrogen. This operation is best performed immediately prior to applying the photoresist. The blow-off is effective for dust collected from the air, but less effective for particulates held on the wafer by a static charge. The operator must be cautious to direct the nitrogen stream away from wafers already coated with photoresist. Also, blowing a stream of nitrogen carelessly into the hood area can kick up dust, which redeposits on the wafer.

An automatic nitrogen blow-off cycle is incorporated into photoresist spinners. The cycle is automatically activated immediately prior to the photoresist application. Care must be taken not to rely on an automatic blow-off cyle to remove highlevels of particles or statically attached particles. These blow-offs are either too low-pressure and/or too far away from the wafer to be effective for all situations.

### 11.1.3 WAFER SCRUBBERS

The stringent wafer cleanliness requirements for epitaxial growth led to the development of mechanical scrubbers. These machines have been adapted into other fab cleaning processes, including prespin. The machine holds the wafer on a rotating chuck with a vacuum. A rotating fiber roller brush is brought in contact with the rotating wafer. The result is a high speed cleaning action due to the motions of the wafer and brush.

During the cleaning cycle the wafer is flooded with D.I. water and/or detergents. After scrubbing, the wafer is rinsed with D.I. water and spun dry at high RPM. Process control parameters include brush pressure against the wafer and brush cleanliness. Whenever the wafer is physically contacted, the opportunity for added contamination is increased. A well-controlled scrubbing process is very effective in reducing contamination.

Scrubbers used for pre-spin cleaning can be standalone units or integrated into the spinner.

### 11.1.3.1 High Pressure Water Cleaning

The high pressure water cleaning process was originally developed to clean photomasks. A high pressure stream of water (2000 – 4000 lbs./in$^2$) is swept across the wafer, dislodging any particulates. The process is effective and not prone to secondary contamination. Only clear water touches the wafer. Drying is

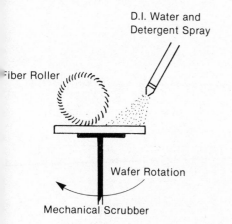

D.I. Water and
Detergent Spray

Fiber Roller

Wafer Rotation

Mechanical Scrubber

### Fig. 11.2   Mechanical Scrubber

accomplished by high speed rotation. Often an anti-static agent must be added to the water to prevent buildup of a static charge on the wafers.

Both the mechanical scrubbers and high pressure water systems are available as standalone units or integrated with a photoresist spinner. With this arrangement, the wafers are automatically cleaned prior to spinning.

## 11.2 DEHYDRATION

A more subtle and serious wafer surface problem is moisture. Again, using the paint analogy, we know that paint does not readily adhere to wet surfaces. Similarly, photoresist does not adhere to wafer surfaces. The terms "wet" and "dry" are qualitative descriptions of wafer surface conditions. The more technical terms are *hydrophilic* and *hydrophobic* surfaces. A hydrophilic surface is one that will allow water to spread across it in large puddles. Another term for a hydrophilic surface is "wetted."

Hydrophobic surfaces, on the other hand, will not support a large pool of water. The water is pulled into droplets on the surface. These surfaces often are termed "dewetted." Applying wax to an old car finish changes its surface from hydrophilic to hydrophobic. The purpose of a dehydration process is to create a hydrophobic condition on the wafer.

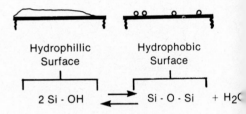

Fig. 11.3    Hydrophilic vs. Hydrophobic Surfaces

### 11.2.1 Prevention of Water Absorption

Most wafers arrive in masking from a high temperature or vacuum process. The wafer surface condition coming out of one of these processes is strongly hydrophobic. During the storage time before spin, moisture is absorbed from the atmosphere into the surface, creating a hydrophilic condition. A number of methods are employed to minimize the absorption of water on the wafer surface. The hydrophilic condition can be minimized by maintaining a low humidity room, typically with less than 50% relative humidity. A second solution is to spin up the wafers as quickly as possible after they arrive in masking. Many studies have shown that the faster the wafers are coated with photoresist, the better the adhesion. It is not uncommon for photomasking process specifications to require resist coating within a certain time. Wafers coming from a phosphorus doping or deposition step are particularly vulnerable to adhesion problems. These wafers are often coated within an hour of their entry into masking. A third method to minimize surface conversion to hydrophilic conditions is storage in nitrogen-purged dessicators.

Regardless of the precautions taken to prevent "wetted" surfaces, a dry wafer surface cannot be guaranteed. The vast majority of photomasking processes include a separate dehydration (or bake) step. Before examining the various methods of dehydration baking, we will review the basics of heat transfer. There are three methods of transferring heat: conduction, convection, and radiation.

### 11.2.2 Conduction

Heat transfer by conduction requires physical contact between the source and the object to be heated. The vibrations of the atoms of the hotter object cause vibrations in the cooler object, resulting in a temperature increase in that object. Examples of conduction heating are electric burners, hot plates and immersion heaters.

### 11.2.3 Convection

Convection heating is the transfer of heated gas. The gas is heated in one location and transferred to the object to be heated. Home forced-air heating systems and hair dryers are examples of convection heating.

### 11.2.4 Radiation

Radiation is another term for electromagnetic waves that can travel through the air as well as through a vacuum. Electromagnetic waves carry energy which is transferred directly to the solid objects they impinge upon. The degree of heating will depend upon the wavelength of the radiation (infrared, microwave, X-ray) and the material being heated. Heat lamps and our own sun heat by radiation.

### 11.2.5 Low Temperature Dehydration Baking

Wafer surfaces can be restored to a hydrophobic condition by baking. The surface water is evaporated from the surface at elevated temperatures. Typical dehydration bake temperatures are greater than 100° C. The rate of evaporation is a time-temperature dependent process; the effectiveness is increased by higher temperatures and longer times. A typical process is 150° C for 30 minutes in a convection oven or 150° C for 5 – 10 minutes in an IR oven. The process requires an inert (nitrogen or argon) atmosphere in each type of oven. (Baking technology is detailed in the section on soft bake.) To realize the benefits of the bake, wafers should be coated with photoresist as soon as possible or water will be reabsorbed onto the surface.

Depending on the severity of the humidity problem and the wafer surfaces, the wafers may need a re-dehydration bake anywhere from 30 minutes to several days after arriving in the photomasking area.

### 11.2.6 High Temperature Baking

Water vapor on the wafer surface layer is usually chemically bonded with the surface atoms. With silicon dioxide surfaces the bond is with the silicon. At temperatures in excess of 850° C, this silicon-water bond is broken and the surface restored to a strong hydrophobic condition. Unfortunately, at 850° C, junction movement also takes place and contaminants on the surface can diffuse into the wafer. Consequently, wafers are rarely baked at this temperature.

There is also a chemical change that takes place on the surface at approximately 450° C. While oconsiderable less junction movement would take place at this temperature, the wafer is still vulnerable to surface contamination. Another factor that has steered process engineers away from higher temperature dehydration bakes is the length of time required to bring the wafers up to temperature.

### 11.2.7 Vacuum Baking

Vacuum baking is another method of wafer dehydration. The reduced pressure in the chamber allows a higher degree of dehydration compared to the same time and temperature of a convection bake. Dehydrating the wafers in a vacuum oven (20 – 30 torrs) at 100 – 150° C results in a dehydrated surface equivalent to an 800° C convection baking. The advantages of vacuum baking are obvious: the lower temperature results in no junction movement, no contamination diffusion into the wafer and no exposure of the wafer to the possibility of contamination by the gas. And the absence of a gas atmosphere eliminates the possibility of contamination from the gas or the piping system.

Drawbacks to vacuum baking include the length of time needed to heat the wafers to the dehydration temperature, and wafer temperature variation in the chamber (see section 11.4 on soft baking).

## 11.3 PRIMER PROCESSES

### 11.3.1 Primer Chemicals

Paint adhesion to adverse surface conditions can often be enhanced by first applying a primer coat. The same procedure can be used in photoresist technology. In its simplest form, a solvent wash of the wafer -- such as xylene -- dehydrates the surface and promotes better adhesion. The chemical dichlorosilane is superior to xylene in promoting adhesion. It actually bonds to both the wafer surface and photoresist layer. However, dichlorosilane is very hydroscopic (attracts water). The pick-up of water by the chemical eventually compromises its effectivness. Also, dichlorosilane is difficult to obtain ultra-clean, and photoresist films coated on its surface exhibit high pinhole counts. In addition, it is very toxic and corrosive.

The preferred primer is hexamethyldisilizane -- usually referred to as HMDS. HMDS is mixed with xylene in solutions that vary according to the surface being primed and the experience (or fears) of the process engineer. Priming with 100% HMDS is also a common practice. HMDS is particularly effective on aluminum surfaces.

### 11.3.2 Spin Priming

The primers can be applied by a number of techniques. Spinning and vapor are the most commonly used methods. Spin application of the primer is effective for most applications and has the advantage of efficiency. Since the photoresist is applied to the wafer by spinning, it is efficient to prime the wafer just prior to the photoresist spin. Most automatic production photoresist spinners include a priming dispense system.

The wafer is positioned on the chuck and secured by a vacuum. A quantity of primer sufficient to cover the wafer is dispensed on the wafer. After a brief wait, the wafer is accelerated to a high speed and the access primer flung from the wafer. The priming layer is created by a film of HMDS a few angstroms thick.

### 11.3.3 Vapor Priming

A new technique is the application of the primer from the vapor state. The wafers are bathed in the HMDS vapors, resulting in the required monolayer(s) on the surface. Thus the wafer never comes in contact with any possible contamination in the liquid or, in the case of HMDS, any particles of hydrolyzed HMDS. This technique has the major advantage of using less primer, since a small amount of liquid yields a large amount of vapor.

There are a number of techniques available to bathe the wafers in the priming vapor. The vapor can be applied in a chamber filled with HMDS vapors carried by nitrogen. Another method is to use a vapor degreaser filled with HMDS. In this system, the wafers are suspended in the vapors. This method must be used with caution, as HMDS is explosive at the temperatures used.

### 11.3.4 Vacuum Baking Vapor Priming

The most effective application method combines the advantages of vacuum dehydration baking with vapor priming. The dehydration part of the system is accomplished in vacuum. Vacuum baking is superior to convection baking for the reasons stated above. While the wafers are in a dehydrated condition in the vacuum oven, primer vapors are drawn into the chamber. The wafers are thus primed in the best possible surface condition and each wafer receives intimate contact with the vapors.

Tests have shown no deterioration in adhesion (as measured by etched line widths) after one week's storage. Also, exposure to high humidity conditions will not degrade the adhesion bond. Wafers after etch, exhibit more uniform line dimensions due to the uniformity of the resist adhesion.

Vacuum bake vapor prime also offers cost and production advantages. HMDS use is typically reduced from gallons-per-week to one pint per month. And when a batch vacuum oven is used, the expensive spinner time is freed up for the photoresist spin operation.

## 11.4 PHOTORESIST APPLICATION

The purpose of the photoresist application operation is to uniformly cover the wafer surface with a required thickness of photoresist. Liquids are traditionally applied to surfaces by dipping, spraying or rolling. Dipping is unacceptable for use in semiconductor manufacture because both sides of the wafer would be coated. Spraying does not allow for precise thickness

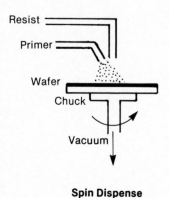

**Spin Dispense**

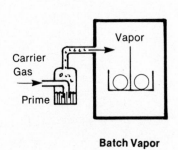

**Batch Vapor**

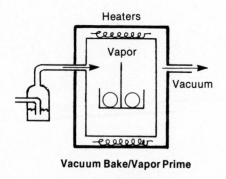

**Vacuum Bake/Vapor Prime**

## Fig. 11.4 Prime Methods

control, and cannot prevent the back of the wafer from becoming splattered. Roll coating is a favored method of coating P.C. boards with photoresist. Again, lack of thickness control limits its use in semicondutor manufacturing. *Spin coating* has emerged as the preferred method of applying photoresist to wafers. However, both spraying and roll coating find use as wafer backcoating techniques.

### 11.4.1 Spin Coating

Spin coating (or *spinning*) is a technique meeting the stringent thickness control requirement of photoresist technology. The typical photoresist layer is 0.5 micron thick with an allowable thickness variation of less than 10%. The film must have less than two pinholes per $cm^2$. First, the wafer is mounted on a vacuum chuck and several c.c.'s (cubic centimeters) of photoresist are placed in the wafer center. The wafer is then accelerated to high RPM (3000 – 9000 RPM). The photoresist "rolls" to the wafer edge under the influence of the centrifugal force of the rotation. The excess photoresist is thrown off the wafer, and a uniform layer of photoresist is left on the wafer.

### 11.4.2 Manual Spinners

The actual equipment (spinners) used to apply the photoresist varies from the simplest one-head manual type to fully automated multiple-head types. A manual spinner is a simple machine consisting of a motor with one to four heads ("head" refers to the wafer vacuum chuck), belt-driven vacuum chucks, a timer and a tachometer. The vacuum is supplied from an external source. Each wafer is blown off with filtered nitrogen to remove any dirt and the wafer is primed (if required). The photoresist is dispensed manually onto the wafer from a syringe or squeeze bottle. Removable catch-cups surround each vacuum chuck to catch the excess resist and prevent splatters from settling on adjacent wafers. After photoresist deposition, the wafer(s) are spun at the required speed to complete the coating. After spinning, the wafers are manually removed from the chucks and loaded back into a carrier.

### 11.4.3 Semi-Manual Spinners

This type of spinner requires manual loading of wafers, but features an automatic dispense system. Automatic dispense can be accomplished by two types of pumping systems. In one, the photoresist is placed in a pressurized container. Dry nitrogen enters the container and "pushes" the resist to the dispense tip. If the photoresist is exposed to high pressure (5 p.s.i., i.e., 5 pounds/square inch) over a long time, the nitrogen will be absorbed into the resist. The other pumping method employs a diaphragm-type pump. A bellows is compressed against the resist, forcing it out the tip.

Drying the resist at the dispense tip is a serious problem associated with automatic dispense systems. The dried resist "ball" deposits on the next wafer to be spun, causing a reject. The problem can be solved by drawing the photoresist back up into the tip between spins. This draw back function removes the liquid resist from contact with the air, reducing the amount of drying.

In both pumping systems, drawback is accomplished by a diaphragm mechanism which puts a small negative pressure on the resist line. A separate dispense line allows the wafer blow-off with $N_2$ prior to prime. The blow-off, primer, resist dispense and spin functions are interconnected with separate solenoids and timers. Once the wafer is placed on the vacuum chuck, one start button activates the whole process. After spin the wafers are manually removed from the vacuum chucks and loaded into a carrier.

### 11.4.4 Automatic Spinners

A fully automatic spinner features the automatic blow-off, primer dispense and spin sequence, and includes automatic wafer load and unload. The wafer carrier is placed in the machine and the wafer is automatically placed on the vacuum chuck, processed and removed from the chuck. After spinning, the wafer may be returned to a carrier or automatically transferred into an oven for soft bake. A typical process sequence is listed in Table 11.1.

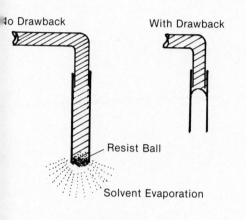

**Fig. 11.5   Automatic Dispense with Drawback**

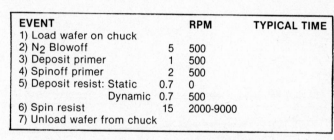

| EVENT | | RPM | TYPICAL TIME |
|---|---|---|---|
| 1) Load wafer on chuck | | | |
| 2) $N_2$ Blowoff | 5 | 500 | |
| 3) Deposit primer | 1 | 500 | |
| 4) Spinoff primer | 2 | 500 | |
| 5) Deposit resist: Static | 0.7 | 0 | |
| Dynamic | 0.7 | 500 | |
| 6) Spin resist | 15 | 2000-9000 | |
| 7) Unload wafer from chuck | | | |

**TABLE 11.1 Typical Automatic Spinner Process**

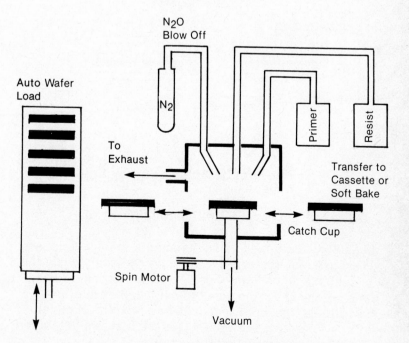

**Fig. 11.6   Automatic Spinner**

## 11.5 SPIN COATING TECHNOLOGY

### 11.5.1 Resist Amount

The amount of resist dispensed on the wafer does not have to be critically controlled. In fact, much more is dispensed than is left on the wafer. For example, a 0.5 micron thick resist layer on a 3 inch diameter wafer is only 0.0023 $cm^3$ of resist. However, to insure complete and even coverage, 5 – 10 $cm^3$ of resist must be deposited on the wafer. A smaller amount of resist would be physically separated by the force of the spinner acceleration and the film would not cover the entire wafer. An excess amount of photoresist will result in a problem only if the resist flows out and over the edge of the wafer. After spin is complete, the back of the wafer would have a rim of resist, which interferes with alignment. Between these two extremes, the amount of resist applied is more of an economic matter. Within these limits, the resist amount does not appreciably influence film thickness, and is therefore not a process parameter.

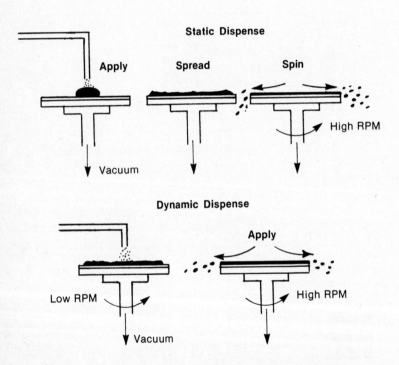

**Fig. 11.7 Photoresist Application by Spinning**

### 11.5.2 Dispense Cycles (Static/Dynamic/Moving)

Spin technology developed using static start manual spinners. *Static dispense* requires that the wafer be stationary while the resist is deposited in the wafer center. After deposition and a brief period required for the resist to spread, the wafer is accelerated to its final spin speed. Five to ten $cm^3$ of resist is required to insure complete wafer coverage (remember that less than 1/100 of a $cm^3$ remains on the wafer).

Most automatic spinners also have the capability of a *dynamic dispense cycle*. The resist is dispensed while the wafer is

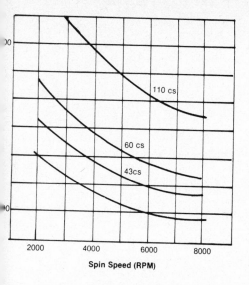

**Fig. 11.8 Film Thickness
vs.
Spin Speed**

spinning at approximately 500 RPM. Dynamic photoresist dispensing is certainly more economical than a static startsprocess, using less resist because the rotation helps spread the resist puddle. Another dispense technique is to move the dispense nozzle from the wafer center he edge during the application. Improved film thickness control and economy are the objects of this method.

### 11.5.2.1 Spinning Speed

The required photoresist thickness is a result of two parameters; the resist viscosity and final spinning speed. Typical film thicknesses range from 0.6 microns to several microns. The resist viscosity is chosen to produce the required film thicknesses with spin speeds of from 3000 – 9000 RPM. The only major consideration on spinning speed is mechanical lifetime. Above 7000 RPM, spinner motors suffer high downtime from extra wear. Spinner design includes controls to easily change the spin speed. It is easier to change spinning speed than resist viscosity to accommodate the thickness requirements of each mask level. Spinning speed becomes a major process variable requiring careful monitoring.

### 11.5.3 Photoresist Thickness

The photoresist thickness is actually determined by several resist-related factors and two spinner-related factors. The photoresist factors, including surface tension, solids content and viscosity govern the degree of "spread" of the resist puddle as the wafer is accelerated to high speed. Surface tension and solids content are constant for a given resist, while the viscosity is the process variable. Acceleration and final spin speed are the two spinner factors. Generally, the spinner acceleration is set at a constant, reaching 5000 RPM in about 1.5 seconds. Photoresist thickness can also be influenced by the amount of photoresist applied and the time of thespin, but only if these factors vary in the extreme. Fortunately, both of these factors have wide ranges and are not normal process variables in determining resist

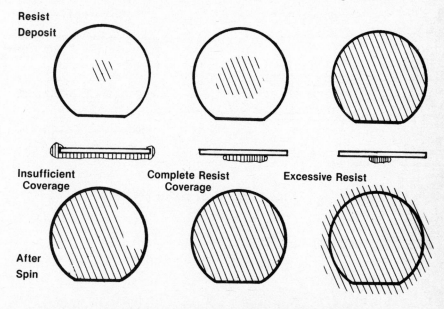

**Fig. 11.9   Example of Resist Coverage**

thickness. For a given viscosity, the film thickness will decrease with increasing spin speed. Increasing the viscosity for the same spin speed will increase the film thickness. The combination of all three factors results in a family of curves as illustrated in

## 11.6 SOFT BAKING

### 11.6.1 Introduction

*Soft baking* is a heating process used to evaporate a portion of the solvents in the resist. The term soft describes the still "soft" resist after baking.

The solvents are evaporated to achieve two results: to avoid retention of the solvent in the resist film, which would interfere in the exposure of the polymer; and to increase the adhesion of the resist to the wafer surface. As in painting, surface adhesion occurs only after the paint is dry (the solvent evaporates).

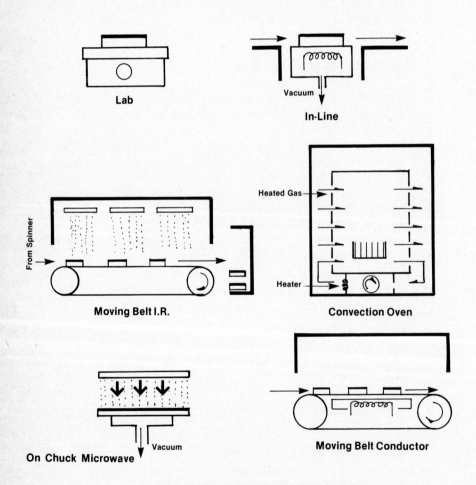

**Fig. 11.10  Soft Bake Methods**

### 11.6.2 Methods of Soft Baking

#### 11.6.2.1 Hot Plate

The three heat transfer methods, explained in the dehydration section, are used in soft baking. The first method, conduction heating on a hot plate, is effective if the temperature/time curve can be controlled. Poor productivity (manual process, limited hot plate size) has limited this method to laboratory operations.

### 11.6.2.2 Convection Ovens

Large convection ovens in which the wafers are batch processed resolve the problem of hot plate baking. Nitrogen or air is heated and circulated throughout the oven to heat the wafers. Consistent and uniform baking requires a constant number of wafer boats and control of the gas flow rate to maintain temperature uniformity.

Nitrogen is the required atmosphere for negative resists and air is used for positive resists.

A problem with convection baking is that the top layer of the resist dries first (crusting or skinning), trapping the solvents inside of the resist film.

This problem can be minimized by "slow" heating of the wafers to allow sufficient evaporation before the crust is formed.

A typical convection soft bake process takes 30 minutes at a temperature between 50° C and 95° C, depending on the resist type used and the other process parameters.

### 11.6.2.3 Vacuum Ovens

Vacuum soft baking has been a popular process in the past. In theory, the vacuum (20–30 torrs) will allow solvent evaporation at lower heating temperatures. The crusting problem is eliminated and the polymer structure is less changed. (Note – the polymers react to heat and radiation as well as to light.) In practice, some heating is required and this presents a problem. Heating in a vacuum takes place by radiation, which requires a direct path (line of sight) to the wafer. Heat radiating from the oven walls will heat the outside wafers faster and hotter than the interior wafers, creating a process uniformity problem.

### 11.6.2.4 Moving Belt IR Oven

The needs for more uniform soft baking, and productivity requirements led to the development of IR ovens, which use direct radiation. Infrared heating of the wafers offers several advantages, including the elimination of the crusting problem. IR waves pass through the resist film and heat the wafer without heating the film, in much the same way as a microwave oven heats the contents of a dish while leaving the dish cool. The heated wafer heats the resist by conduction, allowing solvent evaporation from the bottom of the film (inside-out baking).

Another advantage is increased productivity. The process can be accomplished in a tunnel configuration with the wafers on a moving belt. When mated to a spinner, the process becomes automated, eliminates a storage point and results in a 5 – 7 minute bake per wafer.

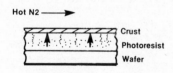

**Fig. 11.11
Crusting Effect of Ovens**

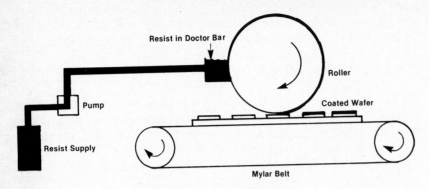

**Fig. 11.12   Roll Coating**

There are two major considerations of IR baking. The first is temperature control. Wafer temperature will vary depending on the number and concentrations of previous diffusions, and on the wafer surface layer. The second is the crust problem. Because the solvent vapors must be removed from the wafer surface by a gas flow, the gas becomes heated from the chamber walls and can heat the resist film, causing a crust to form.

In addition, temperature uniformity is sometimes difficult to maintain due to source variation and chamber wall radiation.

### 11.6.2.5 Microwave Ovens

Microwaves as a soft bake heating source have the advantage of IR heating but are much faster (higher energy). This technology has not been explored in batch oven or moving belt applications due to source uniformity problems and heating control problems. The use of microwaves for soft baking lends itself to on-chuck heating. A microwave source is positioned above the wafer and soft bake takes place immediately after spin.

### 11.6.2.6 Conduction Belt Ovens

Conduction belt ovens combine the bottom heating concept of conduction heating and the productivity of a moving belt. The wafers are transferred from the spinner onto a heated moving belt. Again, removal of solvent fumes must be accomplished with a gas atmosphere and exhaust, without crusting the resist.

| Method | Bake Time Min. | Temparature Control | Productivity Type | Rate Waf/Hr. | Queing |
|---|---|---|---|---|---|
| Hot Plate | 5-10 | Good | single to small batch | 25 | Yes |
| Convection Oven | 30 | Average - Good | Batch | 400 | Yes |
| Vacuum Oven | 30 | Poor - Average | Batch | 200 | Yes |
| I.R. Moving Belt | 5-7 | Average - Good | Single | 90 | No |
| Conductive Moving Belt | 5-7 | Good | Single | 90 | No |
| Microwave | 1-2 | Average - Good | Single in | 60 | No |

**TABLE 11.2 Soft Bake Chart**

# Photomasking Technology Part 2

Chapter 12.

## INTRODUCTION

*Alignment and exposure* is, as its name implies, a two purpose process step. The first purpose is the precise alignment of the wafer to the mask. After alignment, radiation is shined through the mask to expose the photoresist film on the wafer.

The result of these two steps is the transfer of the mask pattern into the photoresist. The exposing radiation changes the photoresist from unpolymerized to polymerized or vice versa depending on the polarity of the resist and mask (see chapter 9).

Alignment and exposure, along with the mask dimensions, establishes the feature size in the photoresist and ultimately on the wafer. It is also the process step *that has seen the majority* of development to achieve micron and submicron imaging.

In the 1970's a photoresist engineer could employ only one A&E method -- contact expose. Now (s)he can choose between five major methods. In this chapter the process of alignment and exposure and the merits of each method are presented.

## 12.1 ALIGNMENT AND EXPOSURE EQUIPMENT

A&E is a machine process. All of the machines for the five methods have in common the following three subgroups:

1. Alignment System
2. Mask/Wafer Relation (Exposure Method)
3. Exposure Radiation

Within these subsystems are the additional options listed in Table 12.1.

TABLE 12.1 Alignment and Exposure Options

| SUBGROUP | METHODS | |
| --- | --- | --- |
| | Mask | No Mask |
| Alignment | Manual<br>Automatic | |
| | | Direct Write |
| Mask/Wafer | Contact<br>Projection<br>Direct Step | |
| | | Direct Write |
| Exposure | Standard UV<br>Deep UV<br>X-Ray | |
| | | E-Beam |

## 12.2 ALIGNMENT PROCESS

### 12.2.1 First Mask

For first mask alignment there is, of course, no pattern on the wafer to align to. The pattern has to be aligned to the crystal structure of the wafer. Since the crystal structure is not visible, the aligment operator aligns the mask pattern to the major wafer flat. This is why all of the patterns are at right angles to the flat.

With manual alignment systems, the wafer flat is positioned on the aligner stage to an accuracy of ±2 degrees. On automatic aligners this step is automatically controlled.

After alignment to the flat, the wafer is automatically positioned under the mask and the exposure subsystem activated. First mask alignment requires no operator attention after the flat is positioned, and is the least critical in the entire process.

### 12.2.2 Subsequent Masks

All subsequent masks are aligned to patterns existing on the wafer. The alighment process begins in the same manner as the process for a first mask alignment. However in this case the mechanical wafer flat alignment must position the wafer "close" to its final alignment. Once the wafer is in place, the operator views the wafer and mask simultaneously by the use of a split field microscope composed of two eyepieces, each with its own objective (the lens closest to the object being studied). The separation of the objectives provides the operator with a simultaneous view of each side of the wafer.

This system (microscopes with 2 objectives) is necessary to observe any misalignment from one side of the wafer to the other. A slight rotation misalignment of the mask and wafer may not be apparent by observing just one side of the wafer. Split field objectives make any misalignment very apparent.

### 12.2.3 Alignment Marks

Due to the complexity of the circuit patterns, alignment by the patterns is very difficult. To simplify this alignment process, alignment guides (or marks) are placed on each die. These marks can take various shapes, with crosses and squares being the most popular.

### 12.2.4 Manual Alignment

Much wafer-to-mask alignment is done manually. These types of aligners have mechanical or electromechanical systems to enable the operator to move the wafer. The controls allow left-to-right (x-direction) and front-to-back (y-direction) motion, and rotation. The movement system has two general modes of operation – course and fine. The designations refer to the amount of wafer movement for a given movement of the control. This alignment process proceeds as follows.

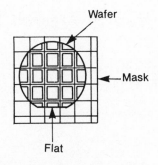

**Fig. 12.1 1st Mask Align**

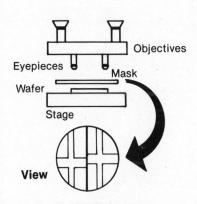

**Fig. 12.2 Split Field Objective**

**Fig. 12.3 Rotation Misalignment**

The operator sees the wafer and mask in the field of view. Using the coarse align mode, the alignment marks are located and a coarse alignment made. When the patterns are "close," the operator switches to fine alignment, which is used to complete the final alignment.

The degree of alignment accuracy varies with the design of the circuit. The smaller the image size, the tighter the alignment required. The accuracy also varies with the mask level. Within a mask set, two or three of the mask levels are more critical than the others. And within a particular mask level there are usually parts of the circuit that are more alignment-sensitive.

The move to automation has also included alignment. Automatic alignment also uses alignment marks. However, the operator's eyes are replaced by a laser or other beam. The beam shines through the alignment mark on the mask and reflects off the wafer alignment mark. A sophisticated servo-feedback system moves the wafer around, until the alignment is correct.

A major advantage of automatic alignment systems is consistancy throughout the shift; whereas misalignment from fatigued operators is a problem with manual systems.

## 12.3 EXPOSURE METHODS

### 12.3.1 Contact

Until the early 1980's, the *contact aligner* was the work horse of the semiconductor industry. With this system, the wafer must be in physical contact with the mask. The goal is to minimize the diffraction of the exposing radiation around the mask, which creates a closer duplication of the mask image in the resist.

Unfortunately, a number of yield and production problems arise from this exposure method. The most serious is the constant physical contact of the mask and wafer which causes damage to both the mask and photoresist layer. Soft emulsion masks experience such a high damage rate that they can be used only about five times. Hard surface masks, such as chrome, are more resistant to damage and can be used for approximately twenty exposures.

Mask and photoresist damage are the major causes of defects in photomasking. The limited mask usage and the interruption of the operation to change masks make contact alignment expensive and slow.

The second major drawback of contact exposure is in *dimensional control.* A number of factors including dirt on the mask, the pressure of the contact and the resist thickness, influence the final image size in the resist. Contact exposure was adequate for MSI level circuits with dimensions in the five micron range. However, as the industry moved to higher levels of integration and smaller feature size, new exposure methods had to be developed.

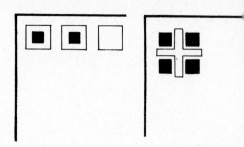

**Fig. 12.4  Alignment Marks**

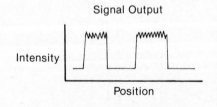

**Fig. 12.5
Alignment of Test Drive**

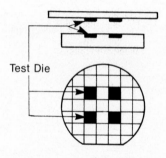

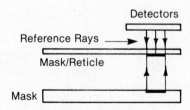

**Fig. 12.6
Automatic Alignment**

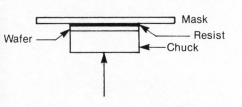

**Fig. 12.7   Contact Alignment**

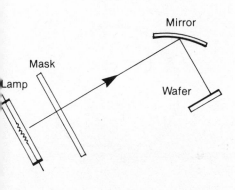

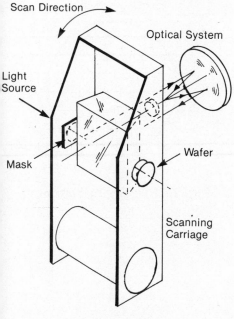

**Fig. 12.8
Projection Exposure**

### 12.3.2 Proximity

One method for minimizing the problems of contact exposure is to position the mask close to, but not touching, the wafer. This method, called *proximity exposure,* is limited in image dimensional control (5 microns) due to the diffraction of the light around the mask. Proximity exposure is usually an option or adaptation of a contact aligner.

### 12.3.3 Projection

*Projection alignment* is an exposure system in which the mask and wafer never touch. The advantages of this system include the following: no mask damage, no photoresist damage, long (infinite) mask life, and no mask change during the operation. An additional advantage is in mask quality. With no mask deterioration, it is economical to spend the money to produce a perfect, or near perfect, mask.

Projection exposure systems have about the same productivity as contact alignment. However, they require more exact temperature and humidity control, as well as attentive preventive maintenance. The system cost is approximately five times that of a contact aligner, but payback due to yield increases can be realized in as little as six months.

For LSI and VLSI level devices, projection exposure has become the standard production method.

### 12.3.4 Wafer Stepping

The yield limiters inherent in projection exposure are mask defects, die fit and image dimensional variation due to variation in the projected light intensity. *Die fit* is the layer-to-layer misalignment that arises from unequal spacing of the die on the mask.

An improved process is to step the reticle (normally used to make the mask) directly onto the wafer. A single reticle can be produced to a lower defect level and with tighter dimension control than an entire mask. And exposure uniformity over one die is greater than over a whole mask.

These machines are known as *steppers* or *direct wafer step systems.* Because it would take forever for an operator to align each wafer die by die manually, the alignment of the reticle to the wafer with a stepper must be automatic. Automatic alignment of each die to one another results in more consistant alignment, higher yield and tighter electrical performance.

The alignment is accomplished by reflecting a laser beam through a special reticle pattern and off a corresponding pattern on the wafer. The stepper automatically positions the wafer to balance the reflected light from the patterns.

### 12.3.5 E-Beam Direct Writing

Eliminating the mask or reticle is the ultimate in defect-free microlithography. An electron beam (E-beam) exposure source allows direct image formation without a mask. As in a TV set (CRT), an E-beam can be deflected by electrostatic plates and thereby directed to precise locations.

You may recall that the image pattern is stored in a computer at the layout stage, in the memory of an E-beam exposure machine. It is used to control the electrostatic plates that in turn direct the E-beam.

Two methods are used to direct the beam to the right location in order to expose the resist. The *raster scanning* method involves scanning the wafer left to right, up and down, and "turning on" the beam only at locations requiring exposure. An alternate method involves exposing small shapes (squares and rectangles) at the required location and building up the desired area and shape.

E-beam direct writing is the preferred method for making high quality masks. Economics and the requirements of smaller dimensions and larger die size make this technique suitable for use in imaging wafers. The major drawbacks of this system -- high cost and low productivity -- determine when, and if, this method will be in general use in wafer fabs.

The *image size (resolution)* possible with E-beam lithography is much smaller than with optical lithography.

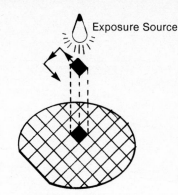

**Fig. 12.9
Direct Step Exposure**

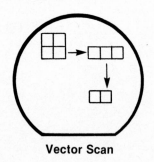

**Vector Scan**

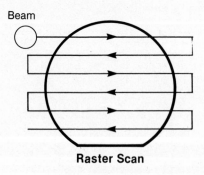

**Raster Scan**

**Fig. 12.10   Beam Scanning**

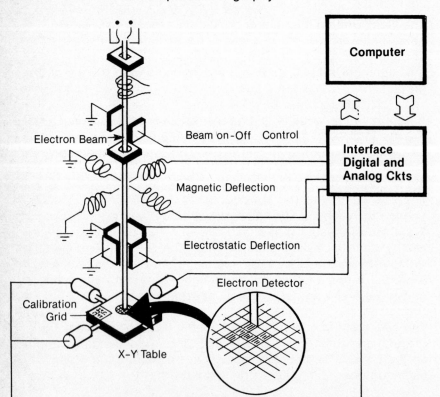

**Fig. 12.11 E-Beam Exposure System**

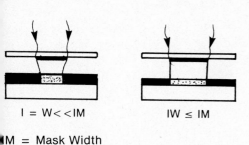

I = W<<IM          IW ≤ IM

IM = Mask Width

IW = Image Width

**Fig. 12.12   Effect of Exposure Wavelength on Image Resolution**

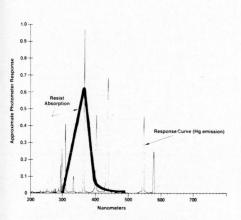

**Fig. 12.13 Spectral Output of Hg Lamp**

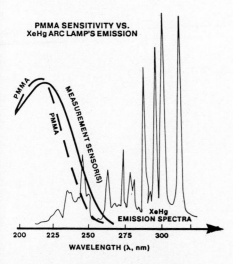

**Fig. 12.14   Deep UV**

## 12.4 EXPOSURE SOURCES

A major limit on the imaging of smaller dimensions (less than 3 micron) has been the wavelength of the exposing radiation source. *Refraction,* the bending of the light around the mask pattern, is a major limiting factor in image resolution.

The bending of the exposing radiation causes a change in the dimension of the image in the photoresist. In the extreme, when the refracted rays touch each other, no image is defined. The usual exposing source is radiation in the U.V. range. With this source, the lower limit on image size in a production environment is approximately 3 microns.

A number of techniques are available to print smaller dimensions. One approach is an exposing source with a small wavelength. The amount of bending (angle of refraction) is less with rays of shorter wavelength, allowing a smaller image definition.

Whatever the exposure source or exposure method, good image definition requires that the radiation impinging on the wafer be in parallel rays. This condition is called *collimated light.* The collimation is created by lenses or specially shaped mirrors in the aligner.

Checking and adjusting the collimation of the light is a daily, even hourly, duty of photomasking process technicians.

### 12.4.1 Ultraviolet (UV)

Traditionally, the exposure source has been a high pressure mercury lamp. Mercury, like all elements, emits radiation when it is excited to a high enough level. The radiation is emitted in wavelengths varying from 150 to 405 nanometers (the range known as the ultraviolet), with the majority being about 365 nanometers.

The ultraviolet range is part of a whole range of radiation wavelengths that vary from very short (x-rays) to very long (radio waves). The full range is called the electromagnetic spectrum.

The most commonly used resists are designed to respond (polymerize or photosolubilize) to the rays in the ultraviolet range. Many are designed to be particulary sensitive to the 365 nanometer wavelength.

### 12.4.2 Deep Ultraviolet (DUV)

Moving down the electromagnetic spectrum, we find, adjacent to the standard UV, the deep UV (DUV) in the range of 180 – 330 nanometers. Several different sources produce DUV, including high pressure Hg (mercury), xenon-mercury, pulsed mercury, and pulsed xenon. Both PMMA and PMIK resists respond to deep UV exposure.

The advantage of DUV exposure sources is their ability to produce smaller image widths. In DUV exposure, the standard mercury lamp in the aligner is replaced by a deep UV source.

### 12.4.3 E-Beam

The advantages of using E-beam as an exposure method have been discussed. E-beam, as an exposure source, also offers some advantages. First, because no mask is used, E-beam exposure does not suffer from any refraction effects. Second, the small beam size allows precise exposure with no variation across the pattern.

An E-beam is similar to a scanning electron microscope, but is used for a different purpose. Obviously, the system is under vacuum and therefore cannot rival the other systems in throughput or price. Table 12.2 is a comparison of the alignment/exposure systems. E-beam exposure requires a resist system (polymer) different from conventional positive or negative resists.

### 12.4.4 X-Ray

X-ray is the ultimate in exposure sources in systems using masks. X-rays, due to their short wavelength, exhibit no detrimental refraction effects. In fact, the collimation is so good that the mask and wafer need not be in contact. X-rays pass through any dust on the surface. A drawback is the special and expensive masks and resists required to use an X-ray source.

Industry futurists predict that either E-beam or X-ray exposure will replace the UV and DUV sources by the mid-1990's.

### 12.4.5 Exposure Control

The degree of exposure is controlled at alignment and exposure by controlling the total energy -- a prduct of the intensity of the source and the time of exposure -- impinging on the resist. In simpler systems, exposure is controlled by setting the intensity (energy) coming from one or two of the major wavelengths, and then controlling the time of exposure.

The above method is adequate when critical control of dimensions is not required. However, energy variation can result from the contribution of the other wavelengths in the spectrum. As the bulb ages, the amount of energy (wavelengths) changes proportionately. Merely setting and measuring the major wavelength does not measure the total energy impinging on the wafer.

A more precise method of exposure control is achieved by using an *integrator*. This system detects the total energy impinging on the wafer and automatically adjusts the time of exposure. It also adjusts the power to the lamp in order to compensate for aging effects.

E-beam and X-ray exposure systems are also controlled with this method.

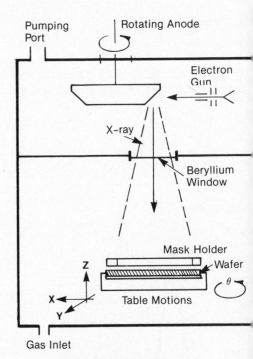

**Fig. 12.15**
**X Ray Exposure System**

Table 12.2  Alignment and Exposure Systems Comparison

| FEATURES | CONTACT | PROJECTION | (DEEP UV) | DIRECT STEP | X-RAY | E-BEAM |
|---|---|---|---|---|---|---|
| Resolution (Microns) | 3.0–5.0 | 1.5–2.0 | 1.0 | 1.5–2.0 | 0.3–0.5 | 0.75–1.0 |
| Throughput (Wafers/Hr.) | 80 | 50 | | 30–50 | 20 | 2 |
| Cost × $1000 | 60 | 370 | | 350–750 | 350–750 | 1500 |
| Mask Required | × | × | | | × | |
| Reticle Required | | | | × | | |

## 12.5 PELLICLES

*Pellicles* are a device used to reduce defects in the photoresist, and to extend mask lifetime. The device is a thin film of an optical grade polymer that is stretched on a frame. The pellicle is attached to the photomask, on either the chrome side or both sides. This solves the problem of airborn dirt collecting on the mask and acting as an opaque spot. Dirt that is in the air falls on the pellicle instead of on the mask surface. During the exposure, the dirt is held out of the focal plane and does not "print".

The use of a pellicle also increases mask lifetime. Once a new mask passes inspection and is covered with the pellicle, the clean surface is protected forever (or until the pellicle breaks). The abrasion and damage that comes from the necessity of cleaning masks between uses is eliminated.

## 12.6 DEVELOPMENT

After alignment and exposure, the pattern that was on the mask is coded in the photoresist layer by regions of polymerized and unpolymerized resist. The next step is to dissolve away the unpolymerized regions of resist. This is achieved with a chemical process, although research is being done in plasma developable resist. The object of this step is to dissolve away the unpolymerized resist and control the degree of development in order to produce the exact dimensions defined in the resist at the alignment and exposure step.

Negative and positive resists develop by different chemical processes. After alignment and exposure, negative resist is changed from polymerized to unpolymerized. The transistion region between these two regions in the resist is fairly definite. The developing chemical rapidly dissolves the polymerized region and the unpolymerized region is dissolved much more slowly.

In positive resists the situation is different. The exposure process renders polymerized regions less dissolvable than unpolymerized regions, but the rate difference is much less than with negative photoresist. This rate difference places a critical dimension control factor on the development process.

If the wafers are left in the positive developer past the determined time, the chemical will dissolve the unpolymerized region. The result can be a significant variation in the dimension of the developed image.

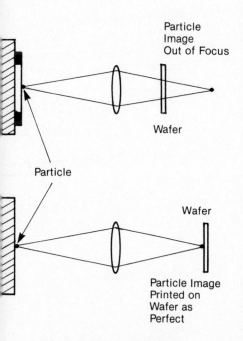

Particle Image Out of Focus

Wafer

Particle

Wafer

Particle Image Printed on Wafer as Perfect

**Fig. 12.16  Pellicle**

## 12.7 DEVELOPER CHEMICALS

### 12.7.1 Negative Photoresist

The preferred developing chemical for negative photoresist is xylene. This is also the solvent that is in the negative photoresist. The development of photoresist after a projection alignment step often requires a less active developer. Usually, a Stoddard solvent is used.

Control of the "developed" image in the resist is influenced by several factors discussed below. The time of the develop step is one important factor to control. The rapid dilution of the developer chemical with a rinse chemical stops the development of the image.

The rinse chemical selected to follow the xylene must be one that will not seriously swell or contract the photoresist film. Mixtures of alcohol and trichloroethylene will serve as a rinse, but do contract and swell the photoresist. The preferred rinse chemical is N-butylacetate.

### 12.7.2 Positive Photoresist

Positive photoresist is easily developed in an alkaline solution, such as potassium hydroxide or sodium hydroxide. The development rate can be closely controlled when these two chemicals are diluted with water to the proper concentration. An advantage of this type of developer is that the only rinse required is water. Unfortunately, sodium and potassium residues left on the wafer can be detrimental to device performance, particularly the MOS devices.

Non-ionic developers are also used on devices sensitive to sodium and potassium contamination. These developers are composed of 2% – 3% tetramethylammonium hydroxide or chlorine ammonium hydroxide in deionized water.

Positive resist developing is sensitive to developer concentration and temperature. A typical operating temperature is 23° C + 1° C with non-ionic developers, whereas the alkaline type developers do not require such tight control.

The table below lists the developers and rinses for each of the photoresists.

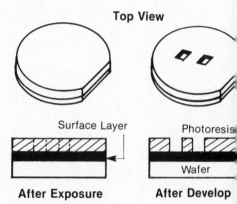

Fig. 12.17    Resist Develop

### Table 12.3    Develop and Rinse Chemicals

|  | Positive | Negative |
|---|---|---|
| Developer | NaOH<br>Tetramethyl<br>ammonium Hydroxide | Xylene<br>Stoddard Solvent |
| Rinse | H$_2$O | N-Butylacetate |

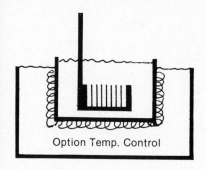

**Fig. 12.18   Immersion**

## 12.8 DEVELOP METHODS

### 12.8.1 Immersion

The *immersion method* is the traditional method of developing photoresist. In the simplest form, a tank of developer and a tank of rinse are set next to each other. The operator immerses the wafers in the developer and the rinse for the required amount of time, and then moves them to the dry operation.

This method is still used for developing positive photoresist because of the problems involved with spraying the positive developers. However, for negative photoresist the spray method is generally used.

The problems which arise from the immersion method are:

1) The development of small dimensions is difficult with an immersion technique because of the surface tension of the liquid and the non-agitation of the wafers.

2) Partially dissolved photoresist pieces stay on the wafer, blocking further development.

3) The baths experience a build-up of contamination as hundreds of wafers are processed through them.

4) The wafers are also subject to contamination that settles on the liquid surface when they are dragged through the liquid interface going into and out of the bath.

5) The necessity of changing the developer several times per shift results in an excessive use of chemicals.

### 12.8.2 Spray Development

*Spray developing* is a preferred method of performing this operation. Normally, it is done with the wafer held on a vacuum chuck, which is the same as a spinner. Instead of dispensing photoresist on the wafer, the developer and rinse chemicals are sprayed onto the wafer.

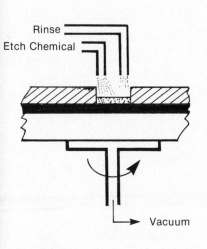

**Fig. 12.19   Spray**

The process requires three cycles. First the developer is sprayed on the wafer. Then the rinse chemical is sprayed on the wafer. Often the rinse cycle will start while the developer is still spraying. This overlap prevents the developer chemical from drying on the wafer. In the final cycle, a high speed spin of the wafer is used to dry off the rinse chemical.

The advantages of spray development are:

1) Small geometries can be resolved due to the physical force of the spray on the photoresist.

2) The wafer is exposed to fresh chemicals, minimizing the chance of contamination.

3) Spinning the wafer under the spray pattern results in a more uniform pattern across the wafer and from wafer to wafer.

4) Partially dissolved pieces of photoresist are swept off the wafer by the action of the spray.

5) Chemical usage is considerably reduced compared with immersion techniques.

6) Spray development lends itself to automation, particularly when mated with a hard bake tunnel oven.

### 12.8.3 Positive Resist Development

One of the problems of automating with spin/spray has been spraying positive photoresist developers. First, the caustic nature of the alkaline developers attacks all metal surfaces, requiring expensive coatings inside the developing machines. Second, the aqueous nature of the developer results in a considerable amount of foaming as it comes out of the spray head under pressure. The third and most critical problem is that the positive developers are more temperature-sensitive than negative developers. Controlling the development temperature on the chuck when the wafer is spinning is difficult. One solution is to heat the chuck to uniform wafer temperature.

Despite these problems, spray development is used because it provides uniformity and increased productivity.

### 12.8.4 Puddle Development

The *puddle technique,* which takes place on a standard spin spray developer, is a compromise method for positive photoresist development. The wafer is positioned on the vacuum chuck and a specified amount of positive developer is deposited on the wafer. The surface tension of the liquid causes it to form a puddle on the wafer. After the required development time, water is sprayed on the puddle to flush the wafer and the wafer is spun dry. Again, developer concentration and temperature are critical factors in this process.

### 12.8.5 Plasma Development

In chemical developing, the unpolymerized photoresist dissolves faster than the polymerized photoresist. When an undeveloped wafer is placed in a plasma environment and exposed to oxygen, the unpolymerized photoresist will oxidize in the presence of the oxygen faster than the polymerized photoresist will. This is an expensive method of developing, but it has the advantage of being dry. There are also some considerations about uniformity, due to the distribution of energies of the oxygen molecules within the reaction chamber.

### 12.9 HARD BAKING

*Hard baking* is the second baking process in the photomasking procedure. Like soft baking, its purpose is to evaporate the

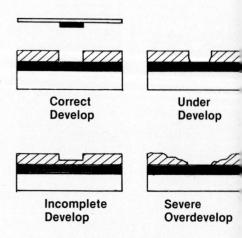

Correct Develop     Under Develop

Incomplete Develop     Severe Overdevelop

**Fig. 12.20**
**Post Develop Conditions**

solvent in the photoresist to increase the adhesion of the resist to the silicon surface.

### 12.9.1 Hard Baking Methods

The methods used to hard bake the resist layer are exactly the same as those in soft baking:

1. Vacuum
2. Convection
3. IR
4. Microwave

Hard bake occurs either immediately after develop or after develop inspect, depending on the method of baking. Tunnel ovens are usually mated to the developer spinners, in which case hard bake occurs immediately after develop. In fact, the favored process is automatic develop/bake.

There are two drawbacks to this procedure. The first and least important is that wafers that fail develop inspection after they have been hardbaked will require a more vigorous stripping process to remove the baked resist.

The second, more serious problem is that while the wafers are waiting at develop inspect and etch, they may absorb moisture into the resist. Poor adhesion and lifting of the resist in the etch operaton can result.

On production lines where this is a severe problem, a second hard bake step is performed on the wafer immediately prior to etch. This is called *pre-etch bake* and generally employs a convection oven.

If hard bake is performed after the develop inspect, serious problems can result. Wafers that were contaminated, underbaked or overbaked during the hard bake step could become rejects if they go through the etch process.

### 12.9.2 Process Specifications

The primary difference between soft baking and hard baking is the temperature. Generally, hard baking takes place at approximately 150° C with a range of ±25 degrees, depending upon the type of photoresist being used and the degree of polymerization required. In the batch processes, baking time is normally 30 minutes. In a tunnel oven, baking time is 5 – 7 minute (similar to that of soft baking). A microwave process, which is much shorter, takes less than a minute.

The amount of heat that the photoresist receives determines the amount of solvent evaporation and the degree of polymerization. The process is time– and temperature-dependant. For example, a longer time compensates for a lower temperature. Above a certain temperature (175° C), photoresist, which is plastic in nature, will soften and start to flow. This is obvious at develop inspection when a slight flow causes a thickening of the photoresist edge. Eventually, at higher levels of resist flow, the edge becomes very sloped and displays fringes when viewed in a microscope. This condition is illustrated in figure 12.7 below. Any appreciable flowing causes dimensional changes in the image dimensions.

High temperature resists are available which allow higher hard bake temperatures (greater adhesion) without flow.

**Fig. 12.21   Resist
Flow at
High Temperature**

# Photomasking Technology
# Part 3

Chapter 13.

## 13.1 DEVELOP INSPECTION

The first inspection in the photomasking process is done after development, or after development/hard bake if an automatic baking system is used. The inspection is called *develop inspection* (or D.I.).

Its purpose is to identify and rework wafers of low yield potential. The estimate of the yield potential made by relating the process parameters (contamination, image quality, critical dimensions and others) to the die sort and final test yields.

Other errors that would make the circuits totally unyielding, such as putting on the wrong mask, are also identified during D.I.

Inspection is done at this point in the process to prevent the creation of unusable wafers. Up to this point in the process, no permanent operations have been performed on the wafer. In fact, only a thin layer of photoresist has been applied and patterned on the wafer surface.

If mistakes or variations in the process have occurred up to this point, we still have an opportunity to remove the photoresist film and reprocess the wafers. This is one of the few places in the process where mistakes are not fatal and rework is possible. The flow diagram below shows the basic photoresist process with the rework loop included.

The inspection at this point is also a major source of process troubleshooting information for the process engineer. Rejects at this point have come from operator error or from a process that is operating "out-of-spec." By correctly identifying the reject type and hopefully its cause, the engineer can quickly fix the offending process.

Rejects (called *reworks*) from the develop inspection operation are sent back to photoresist strip, where they go through the surface preparation operation and back into the process. Reworking wafers back through the process can be a control and accounting problem, especially for a high volume line. Two systems are used to keep track of and process the "reworks." Individual rejected wafers may be collected by device type and mask level until enough are collected to reprocess as a group. Or, rejected wafers can be immediately rerun while holding the parent run at the inspection station. The second method is used on smaller lines or for special "hot lots" that need fast completion.

The number of reworks produced by a photomasking line is a measure of the processing quality. The yield is measured as the percentage of wafers requiring reworking and is referred to as the *rework rate*.

A good yield is 95% or above (a rework rate of less than 5%). Less than a 90% yield causes logistical and cost burdens on the production line. A more critical consequence of an excessively high rework rate is a lower die sort yield. The die sort yield on reworked wafers is typically 70–80% of first run wafers.

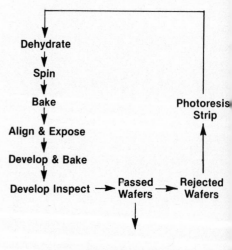

Fig. 13.1   Rework Process Loop

The rework rate is not the same at every masking step. Typically, the easier process steps, such as initial mask and the passivation mask, have a lower rework rate. The more difficult masking steps, such as contact and metal mask, typically run higher, at 5-10%.

## 13.2 INSPECTION PROCEDURE

### 13.2.1 1 × Inspection (Naked Eye)

As the wafer is drawn from the carrier to be placed on the microscope stage, the operator looks at the wafer without the aid of the microscope. The wafer may be inspected in the normal light or placed at an angle under an ultraviolet or collimated light, which will highlight contamination on the wafer as well as scratches and other gross film irregularities.

### 13.2.2 Microscopic Inspection

Assuming the wafer passed the 1 × inspection, it is placed on a microscope stage and viewed for defects at a magnification of between 100 × and 400 ×. For VLSI die, 200 × is the typical inspection magnification. The inspection normally takes place in white light, although for special applications a dark field may be used. (See Chapter 17 for a more detailed discussion of inspection techniques).

### 13.2.3 Critical Dimensions

After the wafers pass the microscopic inspection, a sample of the wafers are measured for *critical dimensions*. Because a major goal of the photomasking process is to make an exact transfer of the mask dimension to the photoresist film and the wafer surface, controlling the dimensions of the patterns is extremely important.

The dimensions are normally measured with an optical instrument. The pattern to be measured is viewed through the microscope or on a CRT, and a mechanical hairline is moved across the opening. The instrument translates the motion into the actual dimensions, either by translating from a vernier or computing it directly with a connected calculator (see chapter 17).

## 13.3 DEVELOP INSPECTION REJECTION CAUSES

There are many reasons a wafer can fail inspection. It is often difficult to determine the process that produced a particular problem, as problems viewed in the microscope can come from rom one of many process causes. Rejected wafers fall into several major categories:

1. Wrong mask or wrong step

2. Film integrity: contamination, scratches, resist bubbles or splatters.

3. Image quality: edge definition of the pattern, line linerarity, grossly expanded or closed down ("bridged")

4. Development quality: the pattern may be under or overdeveloped

5. Critical Dimensions

The next table relates some common reject causes to the process that can produce them. Note that a single cause can come from a number of process steps.

**Table 13.1   Post Develop Inspect Reject Causes**

| Possible Process Cause | Broken Wafer | Scratch | Contamination | Pinholes | MA | Bridging | Lifting Resist | Under Exposed | Incomplete Develop | No Resist | Resist Running | Wrong Mask | C.D. | Reject |
|---|---|---|---|---|---|---|---|---|---|---|---|---|---|---|
| Contamination | | | X | X | | X | | X | | | | | X | |
| Spinner (Resist Thickness) | | | | Thin X | | Thick X | | | | | | | X | |
| Soft Bake | | | | | | | Low X | Low X | High X | | | | | |
| Contact | | X | | | X | | X | X | X | | | | | X |
| Time & Intensity | | | | | | | X | X | | | X | | | X |
| Mask   Align | | | | X | X | | X | | | | | | | X |
| Developer | | | | | | | X Press | | | X | X | | | ·X |
| Hardbake | | | | | | | | | | | X High | | | X |
| Handling Automatic & Manual | X | X | | | | | | | | | | | | |
| Operator Error | | | | | X | | | | | | X | X | | |
| Environment | | | X | | | | X % | | | | | | | |
| Chemicals | | | X | X | | | | | | | | | | |
| Wafer | | | X | | | | | | | | | | | |

## 13.4 ETCHING

The purpose of the etching operation is to remove portions of the top layer of the wafer through the holes, or openings, in the photoresist layer. Hopefully the openings in the photoresist have the exact dimensions required by the design. A second purpose of the etching operation is to transfer the pattern with those dimensions into the top layer of the wafer.

The etch operation must not disturb the underlying surface. Etching down into the underlying layer can drastically change the physical dimensions of the device.

## 13.5 ETCHING METHODS

Etching is done using the following methods:

1. Chemical Etching
2. Plasma Etch
3. Ion Beam
4. Reactive Ion Etch (R.I.E.)

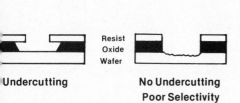

Undercutting                                No Undercutting
                                              Poor Selectivity

**Fig. 13.2    Undercutting**

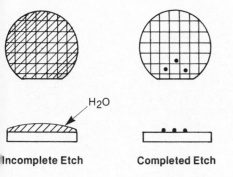

$H_2O$

Incomplete Etch              Completed Etch

**Fig. 13.3    Chemical Etching**

These methods vary in their degree of uniformity of etching across the wafer and from wafer to wafer. Each method offers certain advantages relative to both the degree of etch precision required and productivity factors. One major factor, *undercutting* or *isotropic etching,* results from etching the material to the sides as well as down. Another factor is the *selectivity* of the etch process. Selectivity is the removal of the underlying material or film. The better the selectivity, the less the etch process disturbs the underlying material.

### 13.5.1 Chemical Etching

*Chemical etching* is the most economical and productive of the etching processes. It is a simple beaker process, in which the wafers are loaded into a teflon or teflon-derivative boat and immersed in a beaker of acid. The acid or acid combination is one which dissolves the top layer without affecting those underneath.

The precision of the removal is controlled by the temperature of the etchant, the time of immersion and the composition of the acid etchant. The composition of the etchant is adjusted to produce a controllable etching time, generally between one and seven minutes.

Below one minute, the operator reaction time for removing the wafers from the beaker becomes an appreciable fraction of the etching time, thus introducing variations in the etch time. Above seven minutes, the photoresist tends to lift, resulting in excessive undercutting. A target etching time is typically five minutes.

In some cases the etch process is controlled by frequent visual observation of the wafer surface. The operator periodically lifts the wafer boat out of the etch and observes the amount of etch held on the wafer surface. When the etch process is incomplete the etch covers the entire surface. Upon completion of the etch the surface turns hydrophobic and the etch "beads" on the wafer surface.

If the overetch is long the resist adhesion to the wafer will fail, resulting in a catastrophic undercutting.

The etchant is placed in a beaker or container and maintained at an even temperature. Table 13.2 shows the temperature requirements for the typically used etchants. Room temperature etchants are controlled by the environmental control of the room, while higher temperature etchants are controlled by hot plates or other heating sources.

### Oxide Etching

Hydrofluoric acid (HF) is preferred for etching silicon dioxide formed on silicon, or deposited silicon nitride layers. Unfortunately, hydrofluoric acid etches $SiO_2$ at too fast a rate to be controllable. Diluting the HF with water would result in an etch rate that is slower but still not controllable, because uncontrolled hydrogen ions are generated.

The preferred solution is a mix of HF with ammonium fluoride ($NH_4F$). The ammonium fluoride buffers the HF-silicon dioxide reaction to a controllable level. This solution is known as *buffered oxide etch,* or BOE. These etches are mixed to achieve a range of etch rates.

Quite often a surfactant or wetting agent is added to the BOE solution, to ensure penetration of the etch into the very small openings in the photoresist. Penetration of the openings can also be accomplished by dipping the wafers into a separate beaker of a wetting agent just prior to the etch.

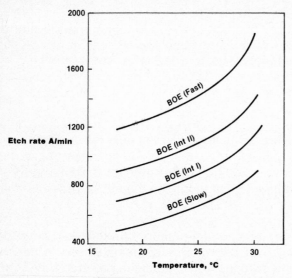

**Table 13.2    Etch Rate vs. Temperature for BOEs**

## Deposited Oxide Etching

Vapox -- or silox -- layers are actually layers of deposited $SiO_2$ and we would naturally think that a good etchant would be BOE solutions. When used as a passivation layer the silox is deposited over an aluminum pattern. Unfortunately, BOE solutions attack the underlying aluminum. The etch of the aluminum takes place on the exposed pads. The etched pads appear to have a color when viewed with a microscope. The condition is known as *brown* or *stained pads.*

The acid solution used to eliminate this etching of the aluminum is a combination of acetic acid and ammonium fluoride. The relative amounts of ammonium fluoride and HF are in a ratio of 4:1.

Both silox and oxide etching take place at room temperature and generally do not require agitation. Etching in an ultrasonic bath is sometimes used to achieve uniformity improvements.

## Aluminum Film Etching

The acid that dissolves aluminum (and aluminum alloys) without attacking the underlying silicon, or silicon dioxide, is phosphoric acid. Unfortunately, phosphoric acid, in its reaction with the aluminum, creates a considerable number of hydrogen bubbles. These bubbles cling to the wafer surface and act as an etching barrier causing incomplete etching.

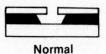

**Normal**

**Over Etch**

**Over Etch and Resist**

**Fig. 13.4
Degrees of Undercutting**

To minimize this problem, nitric acid, acetic acid, water and wetting agents are added to the phosphoric acid. Following the order of the ingredients listed above, a typical aluminum etching solution has the proportion of 16:1:1:2. In this solution strength, heating between 40° C and 50° C is used to achieve a reasonable etching rate (5 – 10 minutes).

The hydrogen bubble generation is such an active process that the agitation of the etching bath is also required to dislodge the hydrogen bubbles. This occurs by stirring the wafers or with ultrasonic baths. An agitation method that actually lifts the wafers out of the etchant takes advantage of the surface tension of the liquid to dislodge the hydrogen bubbles. The typical etchants for the various wafer surface layers are in the table below.

### 13.5.2 Spray Etching

Spray applications, especially those applied when the wafer is rotating, are normally preferred over immersion processes. The combination of the rotation and the spray results in a more uniform process. Etch is one of the few processes that has not been spray automated.

Unfortunately, the use of spray is somewhat dangerous due to the caustic nature of the etchants used in the semiconductor industry. A more practical consideration is the deterioration of the spray etch equipment resulting from the acid. Although over the years various spray machines have been offered to the industry, none have caught on. The most common method of chemical etching is still immersion in a tank.

### 13.5.3 Rinsing

In chemical immersion etching, the etching action is terminated by removing the wafers from the tank and rinsing the etchant from the wafers. The first result of the rinse is to stop the etching process *(process control)*. The second is to remove the etchant chemical from the surface *(contamination control)*. There are several different methods of rinsing:

1. Overflow Rinsing
   In this method, water is introduced into the bottom of a tank and overflows the top, carrying the etchant away from the wafers. Quite often, nitrogen is bubbled through the water to assist rinse efficiency by mixing the etchant into the water. The rinsing time depends upon the tank size and the flow rate of the water.

   An overflow system will often include a resistivity monitor in the waste water stream. Rinsing is carried on until the effluent water exhibits a resistivity of 15–18 meg ohm centimeters.

2. Spray Rinsing
   The advantages of spray rinsing over the overflow system are that the action of the spray increases the physical removal of the etchant, and there are water savings. One problem

## Table 13.3    Summary of Wet Etching processes

| | LIFTING POTENTIAL | COMMON ETCHANT | ETCH TEMP. | RATE A/MIN | METHOD |
|---|---|---|---|---|---|
| $SiO_2$ | 1 | H/F & NH$_4$F (1 : 8) | Room | 700 | Dip & wetting agent predip |
| $SiO_2$ | 2-3 | H/F & NH$_4$F (1 : 8) | Room | 700 | Dip & Wetting agent predip |
| $SiO_2$ (Vapox) | 1 | Acetic Acid &NH$_4$F(2:1) | Room | 1000 | Dip |
| Aluminum | 2 | H$_3$PO$_4$ : 16 HNO$_3$ : 1 Acetic : 1 H$_2$O : 2 Wetting Agent | 40-50°C | 2000 | a) Dip & agitation b) Spray |
| Si$_3$N$_4$ | 3 | H$_3$PO$_4$ | 40-50°C | 80 | Dip |
| POLYSi | 2 | HNO$_3$ : 50 H$_2$° : 20 HF : 3 | Room | 1000 | Dip |

x of Etch
1 = Good
2 = Marginal
3 = Poor

with a spray rinse system is the difficulty of measuring the resistivity of the water. This problem stems from the absorption of carbon dioxide from the air, which reads as though it were an ion on a resistivity meter.

3. Dump Rinsers

In respect to rinsing and water savings, a dump rinser is an extremely effective rinse method. A dump rinser is usually designed with a spray rinse capability. The wafers are placed in the rinse chamber with the spray on, which immediately stops the etchant action.

The chamber quickly fills up with water which is rapidly dumped out of the bottom through a trap door. This cycle is repeated 3–5 times, removing 99 % of the etchant in the first cycle and up to 99.999% in subsequent cycles.

4. Spin/Rinse Dryers

After the wafers are rinsed in one of the above systems, they are transferred to a spin/rinse dryer for final rinsing and drying. A spin/rinse dryer operates on the principle of a centrifuge. The wafer boats are positioned in the chamber and rotated while they are being sprayed by deionized water. After rinsing, the wafers are accelerated to a higher spinning speed to effectively throw the water off of them, leaving them dry for the next step.

Spin/rinse dryers are also designed to process a single wafer boat.

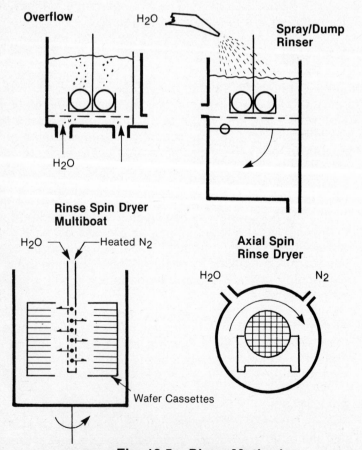

**Fig. 13.5   Rinse Methods**

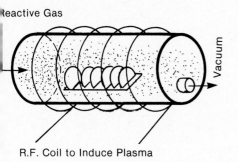

R.F. Coil to Induce Plasma

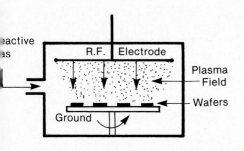

**Fig. 13.6**
**Barrel and Planar Plasma Etching**

## 13.6 DRY ETCHING

There are two significant limits to immersion etching: accurate pattern definition (even with the addition of wetting agents to the etch), and dimensional control problems due to undercutting.

Wet etching by the immersion method also presents a potential health hazard and disposal problem due to the chemicals used. Contamination of the wafers is a further consideration, because the etch baths can become contaminated and contaminate the wafers.

The industry's move to feature sizes less than three microns prompted the development of plasma (or dry) etching technology. A variation of plasma etching has become the favored VLSI etching procedure. To understand this technique, let's examine the principles of wet chemical etching.

In chemical etching one of the components of the etchant has a chemical reaction with the layer being etched and combines with it to create a water rinsable compound. In the case of silicon dioxide, fluorine in the HF combines with the silicon and oxygen to form compounds which then dissolve in the rest of the liquid etchant. Like all chemical reactions, energy is required for the action to take place. In the case of room temperature etchants, it is the internal energy of the etchant that provides the required energy.

Any system with a temperature above absolute zero (minus 278° C) has energy in it. Thus, even snow and ice at the arctic circle contain internal energy.

Plasma etching duplicates the chemical etch mechanism reaction, using an etching gas instead of a wet chemical. The wafers are placed in a quartz chamber and a gas containing an etchant for the particular layer being etched (fluorine in the case of $SiO_2$) is introduced into the chamber.

Sufficient energy must be supplied to the fluorine for it to dissolve the $SiO_2$. In this etching method, the energy comes from a plasma field.

Plasma is actually the fourth state of matter. The sun is not solid, liquid or gas; it is in a plasma state. The sun is in an extremely high energy state. The energy comes from the high level of ionization of the dense gases.

It is possible to induce plasma energies in gases on earth. In a *plasma etcher* (also called a *reactor),* the plasma condition is created by a high energy RF field. The energy of the plasma field excites the gas molecules in the chamber to a high enough level to cause a reaction with the layer on the wafer.

In the case of silicon dioxide, the etching gas used is CF4. The energy imparted to this gas causes the flourine to react with the silicon dioxide, resulting in gases that combine the flourine, silicon and oxygen.

### Table 13.4 Plasma and R.I.E. Etchants

| Film | Etchant | Typical Gas Compounds |
|---|---|---|
| Al | Chlorine | $BCl_3, CCl_4, Cl_2, SiCl_4$ |
| Mo | Florine | $CF_4, SF_4, SF_6$ |
| Polymers | Oxygen $CF_4, SF_4, SF_6$ | |
| Si | Chlorine, Florine $CF_4, SF_4, SF_6$ | $BCl_3, CCl_4, Cl_2, SiCl_4$ |
| $SiO_2$ | Chlorine, Florine | $CF_4, CHF_3, C_2F_6, C_3F_8$ |
| TA | Florine | |
| TI | Chlorine, Florine | |
| W | Florine | |

These vapors are removed from the chamber by a vacuum. (See figure 13.7.) Thus portions of the top surface are removed without using wet chemicals. The wafers enter the operation dry and are removed dry. However, the major advantage of plasma etching is in dimension control. The degree of undercutting is dramatically reduced and the etchant gases penetrate the smallest opening in the resist. In fact, plasma etching or a variation of it is necessary in producing VLSI level circuits.

The plasma method described is called *barrel* or *cylinder etching,* because of the shape of the reaction chamber. This is not the most precise plasma method. Within the chamber there is a variation of energies which results in a variation of the etch results. And at the wafer surface, the gas atoms are somewhat multidirectional. This leads to some undercutting on the etch results. An etch process that exhibits little or no undercutting is called *anisotropic.*

The planar system is a superior plasma etcher design. Instead of in a barrel, the reaction takes place between two parallel plates. The wafer sits on the bottom plate, and the RF field is created between the two. Etchant gases introduced into the system take on a direction perpendicular to the wafer surface. This directionality produces a more anisotropic etch (less undercutting).

The planar design also produces a more uniform etch process and has the advantage of being easily automated. In fact, some "in-line" systems feature a one-wafer planar etch chamber.

The major process drawback to plasma etching is a lack of selectivity. Without controls, a plasma etcher can etch a hole through the wafer. There are two methods for controlling this problem. One is to dilute the etchant gas near the end of the etch time, to lower the etch rate. This reduces the effect on the underlying surface. The second method is end point detection, in which a detector within the etcher senses when the exiting gas stream is free of the elements of the top layer. This condition indicates that the top layer is gone, and that it is time to terminate the process.

A second disadvantage of the plasma etching process is the high temperatures reached in the chamber which make the resist very difficult to remove. The temperature can rise up to 400° C and polymerize the photoresist to a high degree.

Plasma etching is more costly than chemical immersion etching to etch MSI and LSI level circuits. However, the higher yield of plasma etching on VLSI devices makes this method cost effective.

### 13.6.1 Ion Beam Milling

Another "dry" etching method uses ion beams instead of a chemical reaction. Ion beam etching is analogous to sputtering. In this method, Argon gas atoms are ionized and directed towards the wafer which is sitting on a plate that is electrically grounded. The positively charged argon atoms accelerate as they move to the wafers. On impacting the wafer, the top layer, which is exposed through the pattern in the photoresist, is physically removed, or "blasted away" from the surface. Like the plasma method, the ion beam removal method exhibits minimal undercutting. Both exhibit less selectivity. For example, when the wafer is removed, the plasma or ion beam will continue to remove the substrate.

### 13.6.2 Reactive Ion Etching

*Reactive ion etching* (R.I.E.) combines plasma and ion beam removal of the surface. The etchant gas (as in plasma etch) enters the reaction chamber and is ionized. The individual molecules accelerate to the wafer surface. At the surface, top layer removal is achieved by the physical removal and the chemical removal of the material.

The combination results in an etch process that is very controllable and results in reasonable productivity.

Reactive ion etching is the preferred dry etch technique, and continuing development is occurring in this field. The success of R.I.E. is credited with allowing the reliable production of micron size openings.

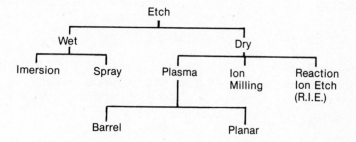

**Fig. 13.7 Guide to Etch Methods**

### 13.6.3 Process Control

Uniform etching depends upon a number of parameters: the thickness and density of the layer being etched, the energy or temperature of the etchant, the adhesion of the photoresist and the uniformity of the etchant at the wafer surface. In the dry etch systems, gas flow rates, pressure and field energy level are parameters which must be controlled.

Since etching variability can exist from lot to lot, in chemical etching a test wafer is often etched first. The operator inspects the test wafer and depending upon the results, the rest of the lot is committed. This procedure would be time consuming with the dry processes.

## 13.7 PHOTORESIST STRIPPING

After etching, the pattern has been transferred into the top surface of the wafer. To complete the process, the photoresist layer, which has functioned somewhat like a stencil, must be removed.

Traditionally, the photoresist has been removed by chemical processing. It can also be removed by using $O_2$ plasma (dry processing). The decision to use either wet or dry processing in photoresist removal depends on several criteria. Wet stripping has the following advantages:

1. A long process history
2. It effectively removes trace amounts of metallic ions
3. It is cost effective
4. It does not expose the wafers to potentially damaging levels of radiation.

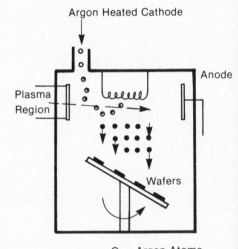

O = Argon Atoms

• = Ionized Argon Atoms

**Fig. 13.8   Ion Milling**

Dry stripping, on the other hand, is favored for the following reasons:

1. There are no chemicals to store, handle or dispose of
2. It does not require the use of wet benches or laminar flow hoods
3. The wafers are never exposed to chemicals or rinse water.

There are several requirements for the photoresist removal process. First, the process must competely remove the photoresist itself. Second, it must be capable of being removed from the wafer through rinse processes. Third, the process must not attack the wafer surface layer or substrate.

The semiconductor surface layers can be a combination of many different materials (silicon dioxide, polysilicon, aluminum, aluminum/silicon, nichrome, etc.). All of the many surfaces used can be divided into two strip categories:

1. metalized layers
2. non-metalized layers.

The non-metalized layers include silicon, silicon dioxide, and silicon nitride layers. Even though silicon is a metal, it is not easily attacked by acids. The removal of photoresist from metallized surfaces is usually a more difficult process because the surface layers themselves are susceptible to etching by the strippers. Two additional considerations in selecting a solution for photoresist stripping, which are not performance related, are operator safety and disposal. Table 13.5 lists the various strippers.

### 13.7.1 Stripping from Oxide Layers

In an attempt to develop more effective photoresist removal processes during the 1960's, the sulfuric acid/hydrogen peroxide stripping system was developed. Sulfuric acid, at a temperature of 125° C, will remove photoresist from a wafer. However, it will not dissolve the carbon present in the resist. The carbon will build up in the sulfuric acid, causing the bath to turn black. After sufficient buildup in the bath, carbon will deposit on the wafers.

To oxidize carbon into carbon dioxide, an oxidant is normally added to the sulfuric acid. The oxidants normally used are hydrogen peroxide, ammonium persulfate and nitric acid.

**Sulfuric Acid/Hydrogen Peroxide System**

Hydrogen peroxide added to sulfuric acid in a ratio of about 1:2 will have two desirable effects. First, the exothermic reaction between the acid and the peroxide will elevate the bath temperature to about 130° C. Second, the oxygen liberated from the hydrogen peroxide will oxidize the carbon to carbon dioxide, which leaves the bath as a gas. Unfortunately, a drawback of the process is that bath temperature peaks quickly at 130° C and then decreases with time.

Fig. 13.10 Temperature Curves

The process effect is a decreasing strip rate. The production effect is to require mixing a new batch every one to three hours.

$$2H_2O_2 \text{-----}\blacktriangleright 2H_2O + O_2$$

The exothermic effect, while liberating oxygen, also reduces the hydrogen peroxide to water. This generation of water has a dilution effect on the sulfuric acid, further adding to an inconsistent strip rate. An alternate method when using hydrogen peroxide as the oxidant is to heat the sulfuric acid to 125° C and add smaller amounts (25 c.c.'s per gallon) to the sulfuric acid.

**Sulfuric Acid and Ammonium Persulfate**

Ammonium persulfate is a crystal having the same effect in sulfuric acid as hydrogen peroxide. It liberates oxygen, which combines with the carbon in the bath. Typically, 40 grams of the ammonium persulfate are added to approximately a one-and-one-half gallon beaker of sulfuric acid with every run of wafers. Ammonium persulfate is safer than hydrogen peroxide. Because it is a crystal, it does not deteriorate like the less stable hydrogen peroxide. This insures a more consistent strip rate. Also, within the bath there is a more uniform temperature from top to bottom. The exothermic reaction of the peroxide in the sulfuric acid starts at the top of the bath, heating the top of the bath and leaving the bottom cooler and less rich in oxygen. Also, ammonium persulfate does not deteriorate to water which dilutes the sulfuric acid, thus resulting in a bath life which is considerably longer than a similar one using hydrogen peroxide.

## Sulfuric Acid/Nitric Acid

The addition of nitric acid to the sulfuric acid, in a ratio of about 1:10, also provides an oxidant function. The main drawback to this solution is that it turns the sulfuric acid slightly orange, making it difficult to detect a buildup of carbon in the bath. Hydrogen peroxide or ammonium persulfate and sulfuric acid baths, however, are always clear; and any color indicates a buildup of photoresist or carbon in the bath.

## 13.7.2 Stripping from Metallized Surfaces

As mentioned in the introduction, stripping from metallized surfaces is a more difficult technology because the metallized layers are subject to attack or oxidation. There are four types of chemicals that are used for this stripping operation:

1. Organic Strippers
2. Chronic Sulfuric Mixtures
3. Aqueous Amines
4. Solvent Strippers

## Organic Strippers

Organic strippers were developed along with the invention of J–100 by Industri Chem in the early 1960's. The stripper is a combination of an organic acid (sulfonic acid) and solvents. Other firms also market organic strippers based on sulfonic acid and solvents. This class of stripper is non-corrosive on metallic films if the wafers and boats are kept dry. Even though used at a higher temperature (90–110° C), with consequent solvent evaporation, the strippers last a minimum of four hours and in some cases much longer, resulting in a highly productive process.

Depending upon the formulation, strippers of this type can either be rinsed from the wafers with flowing deionized water, or require solvent rinses before the final water rinse. The bath life of the organic strippers must be specified to eliminate rinsing problems that arise from the excessive evaporation of the solvents.

The organic strippers have been the workhorse of the photoresist metallic step stripping process for two decades. Many of the organic strippers contain phenol and chlorinated hydrocarbons. Both of these materials are considered hazardous and there has been a move, wherever possible, to minimize the use of these types of organic strippers.

## Chromic and Sulfuric Acid Mixtures

These strippers have the main advantage of being used cold. Generally, they are good strippers from the standpoint of photoresist removal. However, there is always some attack of the aluminum and aluminum alloys even at room temperature. Also, the slightest amount of water on the wafer, or in the stripper, will cause complete removal of the aluminum. In addition, the chromic sulfuric strippers represent a burn danger to the operator and are difficult to rinse completely from the wafer, particularly the chromium ion; and they require stirring or agitation to insure uniform removal.

From an environmental standpoint, the chromium ion is difficult to remove from the waste stream.

**Aqueous Amines**

The resist strippers described above are the universal type. This means they will remove both positive and negative resists. Positve resists that have not been hardbaked during the process are easy to remove with simple solvents. Acetone is the simplest generic chemical that functions as a positive photoresist remover. However, because acetone creates a fire hazard, few production lines use it as a stripper.

One popular positive resist stripper contains an aqueous amine. The stripper is water rinsable, will strip at room temperature and is relativiy easy to dispose of.

**Solvent Strippers**

More vigorous positive resist stripping is available from formulas containing blends of various solvents. These strippers operate over a range of temperatures (to increase the strip rate), and some offer a longer bath life than the amine types.

Solvent strippers are generally disposed of by recycling.

Table 13.5 conmpares the types and uses of the various strippers. The amine types are included with the solvent types, since their process properties are similiar.

## 13.8 DRY STRIPPING

Like etching, the dry plasma process can also be applied to photoresist stripping. The wafers are placed in the plasma chamber and oxygen is introduced. The effect of the plasma field

| Stripper | Operating Temperature | Oxide | Surface Metalized | Bathlife | Resist Polarity | | REMOVAL |
|---|---|---|---|---|---|---|---|
| | | | | | Negative | Positive | |
| 1) Sulfuric Acid & Oxidant a. exothermic | 125°C | X | | 2-3 Hrs | X | X | Neutralize |
| b. heated | 125°C | X | | 8 Hrs | X | X | Neutralize |
| 2) Organic Acids | 90-110°C | X | X | 4-8 Hrs | X | X | Remove & bury |
| 3) Chromic/Sulfuric Acid mixture | 20°C | X | X | 4-8 Hrs | X | X | Remove & bury |
| 4) Solvents | 20°C-90°C | X | X | 4-8 Hrs | X | X | Remove & recycle |

**Table 13.5 Comparison of Wet Photoresist Strippers**

is to excite the oxygen atoms to a high level causing them to "oxidize" the components of the photoresist. The photoresist is converted to its component gases, which are removed through the vacuum outlet of the plasma reactor. Like dry etching, dry stripping is a more expensive process than wet processing, but it does eliminate the need to handle or remove wet chemicals.

The primary drawback of dry stripping is the potential contamination of the wafers from metallic ions. Every photoresist contains some level of the metallic ions (sodium, potassium, etc.) which are not removed or oxidized to a gas by the plasma. Thus the atoms remain in the system or on the wafers. Depending upon the sensitivity of the circuit being manufactured, the contamination level may be high enough to be detrimental to the circuit. MOS devices are more sensitive to this problem. Another device problem is the level of radiation that the wafers can be exposed to. The radiation will generate holes and electrons in the silicon surface which interfere with its intended electrical operation. To minimize this problem, most plasma strippers contain an aluminum shield.

Table 13.6 is a comparison of the general considerations of the two strip methods.

| PRODUCTIVITY | WET | DRY |
|---|---|---|
| Wafer/Hr | | |
| Lot size = 25 | 300 | 150 |
| Lot size = 50 | 600 | 150 |
| COST | X⁵ | RATIO/WAFER |
| METALLIC ION REMOVAL (STRIPPING) | YES | NO |
| RADIATION | NO | DAMAGE |
| WET HOOD REQUIRED | YES | NO |
| CHEMICAL HANDLING STORAGE | YES | NO |
| EXHAUST TOXIC FUMES | YES | YES |

**Table 13.6  Comparison of Wet and Dry Stripping Processes**

### 13.9.1  Introduction

The final inspection step, like the develop inspection, is primarily a visual quality inspection. Also, like develop inspection, it checks for quality of the pattern etched in the top layer, contamination and critical dimensions. It also serves as a check on the quality of the develop inspection. For example, if the wafers exhibit permanent rejects that should have been detected at develop inspection, this provides valuable feedback to the develop inspection station operators.

Also, like develop inspection, the yield at this step is dependent on the difficulty of the layer being patterned. The simpler masks average 99% or better; a very difficult mask averages 97%; thus, the overall average at final inspection should be better than 98%. (Keep in mind, the cumulative effect of a 98% yield over eight masks would be 85%.)

155

### 13.9.2 Final Inspection Methods

Again, like develop inspection, final inspection is done with the same visual methods as were used at develop inspection -- a 1 x inspection, a microscopic inspection (manual or automatic) and then a check on the critical dimensions are performed.

### 13.9.3 Results

Even at final inspection, there are some reject categories that can be reworked. Contamination on the surface of the wafer due to dust in the air, residual photoresist or rinse residues can be cleaned off. Also, if there is an incomplete etching or if the etching was terminated too quickly, it is possible to return to the etching bath and "dip" out the residual oxide. Unfortunately, during this "dipping" process, the field oxide will also be thinned and this may be an intolerable situation. The majority of wafers that do not pass final inspection are rejects which are discarded. Rejects are mainly due to over-etching and problems such as bridging and misalignment, which should have been detected at develop inspection.

### 13.9.4 Sample Size

Again, as in develop inspection, only a portion of each wafer is inspected and only a sample of all of the wafers are inspected.

### 13.9.5 Inspection Procedure

The wafers arriving at the final inspection are first inspected with an incident light for particulate contamination. Wafers passing this initial inspection are then examined with a microscope for contamination, alignment, and other problems. After this inspection, which may be performed with an automatic system, the pattern's critical dimensions are measured.

| Possible Process Cause | Contamination | Misalign | Undercut | Incomplete Etch | Wrong Mask | Pin Holes | C.D.'s | Visual Reject |
|---|---|---|---|---|---|---|---|---|
| Contaminated Etch | X | | | | | | | |
| Contaminated Stripper | X | | | | | | | |
| Contaminated H$_2$O | X | | | | | | | |
| Insufficient Rinse | X | | X | | | | | |
| No Wet Agent | | | | X | | | | |
| Under Etch | | | | X | | | X | |
| Over Etch | | | X | | | | X | |
| Wrong Etch | | | X | X | | | X | |
| Hard Bake Too High | | | | X | | | X | |
| Poor Develop | | | | X | | | X | |
| P$_2$O$_5$ & SiO$_2$ | | | X | | | | X | |
| B$_2$O$_3$ & SiO$_2$ | | | | X | | | X | |
| Low Hard Bake | | | X | | | | X | |
| Develop Inspect Escp | | X | X | X | X | X | | |

**Table 13.7  Final Inspect Rejects Visual Problem**

# Doping –
# Diffusion
# Ion Implantation

Chapter 14.

## INTRODUCTION

The term *diffusion* describes two events: The physical relationship of a substance moving through a medium from a region of high concentration to a region of low concentration, and a process step used to dope a semiconductor wafer.

## 14.1 CONCEPT OF DIFFUSION

In semiconductor manufacturing, diffusion refers to the doping of the solid wafer with dopant atoms. When the dopant atoms are of the opposite conductivity type than the wafer, an N/P junction is formed in the wafer. Chapter 6 explains the physics of the junction formation. The phenomenon of diffusion is illustrated in figure 14.1 by two commonly occurring events.

In the figure drawing on the left illustrates the concentrations in gas molecules when a spray can is used. Initially, there is a high concentration of the gas molecules close to the nozzle. In time those molecules will move through the air with a subsequent decrease in concentration at each position away from the can. This is an example of *gas state diffusion.*

A similar phenomenon takes place when ink is dropped in a glass of water. From its original concentration, it spreads into the water according to the law of diffusion. The concentration of ink decreases as the ink diffuses away from the area of high concentration. This is an example of *liquid state diffusion.*

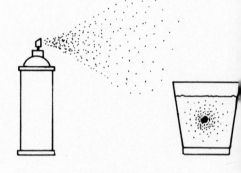

**Fig. 14.1**
**Examples of Diffusion**

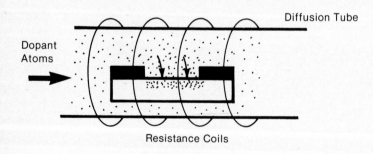

**Fig. 14.2**
**Solid State Diffusion**

## 14.2 DOPING BY SOLID STATE DIFFUSION

Solid state diffusion is one method of doping a semiconductor wafer. This is a two-step process. The equipment used is identical to that used in the thermal oxidation process.

In order for solid state diffusion to occur, the following two conditions must be present:

1. A concentration of dopant atoms adjacent to, or in the wafer.

2. Sufficient energy to cause the diffusion of the dopant atoms into the wafer.

The two-step diffusion process has three goals:

1. To dope the wafer surface with a specific quantity of dopant atoms.

2. To create a specific concentration distribution of dopant atoms at the wafer surface.

3. To diffuse the dopant atoms to a specific depth (creation of junction).

The two major steps in the diffusion process are called deposition and drive-in.

## 14.3 DEPOSITION

Deposition, which is the first step, is also known by the following terms:

Pre-Deposition
Dep
Pre-Dep

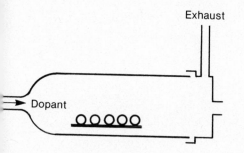

**Fig. 14.3**
**Open Tube Diffusion**

Both steps take place in a furnace similar to the oxidation furnaces.

During the deposition step the dopant is actually introduced into the wafer. Within the source section of the furnace there is a gas, liquid or solid source of the dopant to be diffused. The atoms are converted to a vapor that flows over the wafers in the flat zone of the furnace.

The flow insures that dopant atoms are continuously being replenished at the wafer surface. These atoms enter the surface and move into the wafer at a rate of speed termed Diffusivity.

The amount of atoms that enter the wafer surface is also a function of temperature, up to a limit termed the maximum solid solubility of the specific dopant in the wafer. Solid solubility is different for each dopant element in different semiconductor materials. The concept of solid solubility has a counterpart within the saturation process of liquids. That is a cup of coffee can only dissolve a maximum amount of sugar. To increase the amount dissolved, the temperature of the coffee must be increased.

In the deposition tube, the concentration of dopant atoms is purposely set to exceed the solid solubility limit of the dopant in the wafer at the particular temperature. This condition insures that the deposition always takes place at solid solubility. The result is that minor variations in the source vapor concentration will not change the amount of dopant atoms at the wafer surface.

The variables of the deposition step are:

1. Surface Concentration
2. Diffusivity

3. Time of Diffusion
4. Junction Depth
5. Quantity of Atoms Diffused into the Wafer

Recall that an N/P or P/N junction will occur where the concentration of the diffusing atoms equals the concentration of the diffusing atoms equals the concentration of the dopant atoms already in the wafer.

The five factors above are related mathematically by the relationship termed the *error function*.

### 14.3.1 Dopant Sources

Diffusion takes place when there are sufficient dopant atoms available at the wafer surface. The dopant atoms originate from one of the three states of nature: gas, liquid or solid. Each of the dopants used in silicon technology is available in one or all of the states.

In nature, the dopants exist with other elements in molecule form. In the tube, the molecule containing the desired dopant atom is combined with another gas called the *carrier gas.* Mixing the two results in "liberating" the desired source element. The process is illustrated below for the dopant boron, starting in the form of a gas, $BCl_3$.

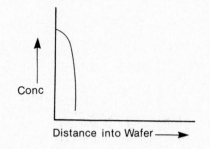

Fig. 14.4    Error Function

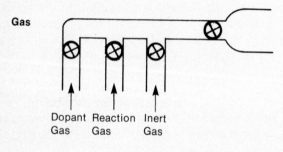

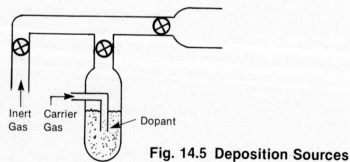

Fig. 14.5 Deposition Sources

$$2BCl_3 + 3H_2 \longrightarrow 2B + 6HCl$$

Source Carrier Gas Dopant Vented

The diffusion source chart at the end of this section lists the reactions for the silicon dopants. Each of the source "states" has different advantages and disadvantages and requires different equipment to create the desired vapor in the deposition tube.

### 14.3.2 Gas Sources

Many of the dopants are available in the gas form. Gas sources (compressed gas cylinders) have the advantage of convenient hookup to the source cabinet, precise dilution control with flow meters or mass flow controllers, and cleanliness.

### 14.3.3 Liquid Sources

Liquid sources are handled in the same manner as an $H_2O$ oxidation bubbler. A carrier gas is "bubbled" through the liquid, picking up the vapor which is added to the carrier gas. The shape of a diffusion "bubbler" is cylindrical.

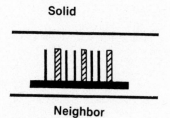

Solid

Neighbor

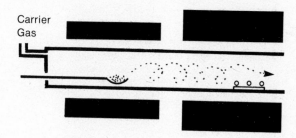

Carrier Gas

**Fig. 14.6**
**Solid Deposition Sources**

### 14.3.4 Solid Sources

Solid deposition sources fall into two categories: local and remote. Boron nitride is a frequently used local solid source. Slugs (wafers) of boron nitride are placed in the deposition boat between every two wafers. Upon reaching temperature, boron diffuses out of the slug and into a neighboring silicon wafer.

A second type of solid source is a powder of the source element. This type of source is used in the capsule technique described below.

A third form of solid neighbor source, called *spin on dopants*, is a glass that contains the required dopant atom. Boron trioxide is an example. The glass is finely ground and suspended in a solvent. The dopant is put on the wafer surface in exactly the same manner as a photoresist, by spinning.

After spin, the solvents are driven off by a heating step. In the deposition tube the element diffuses out of the glass layer into the wafer.

Gold diffusion (gold doped bipolar devices) originates from a thin layer of gold evaporated directly onto the wafer surface.

In a traditional remode solid source method, the source is from glass containing the required element. The vapor is created by heating the "glass" in a small source oven attached to the deposition furnace. (see illustration).

The vapors liberated by the heat are carried in to the deposition part of the tube by a carrier gas. This method of doping has fallen out of favor due to its inherent lack of control. However, many non-critical bipolar N-type subcollectors are still deposited from a solid remote antimony trioxide source.

**Table 14.1 Diffusion Source Chart**

| Type | Element | Compound Name | Formula | State | Diffusion Reactions* |
|---|---|---|---|---|---|
| N | Antimony | Antimony Trioxide | $Sb_2O_3$ | Solid | |
| | Arsenic | Arsenic Trioxide | $As_2O_3$ | Solid | $2AsH_3 + 3O_2 \longrightarrow As_2O_3 + 3H_2O$ |
| | | Arsine | $AsH_3$ | Gas | |
| | Phosphorus | Phosphorus Oxychloride | $POCl_3$ | Liquid | $4POCl_3 + 3O_2 \longrightarrow 2P_2O_5 + 6Cl_2$ |
| | | Phosphorus Pentoxide | $P_2O_5$ | Solid | $2PH_3 + 4O_2 \longrightarrow P_2O_5 + 3H_2O$ |
| | | Phosphine | $PH_3$ | Gas | |
| P | Boron | Boron Tribromide | $BBr_3$ | Liquid | $4BBr_3 + 3O_2 \longrightarrow 2B_2O_3 + 6Br_2$ |
| | | Boron Trioxide | $B_2O_3$ | Solid | $B_2H_6 + 3O_2 \longrightarrow B_2O_3 + 3H_2O$ |
| | | Diborane | $B_2H_6$ | Gas | |
| | | Boron Trichloride | $BCl_3$ | Gas | $BCl_3 + 3H_2 \longrightarrow 2B + 6HCl$ |
| | | Boron Nitride | $BN$ | Solid | |
| | Gold | Gold | $Au$ | Solid (Evap.) | |
| | Iron | | $Fe$ | | |
| | Copper | | $Cu$ | | |
| | Lithium | | $Li$ | | Undesirable impurities from contamination |
| | Zinc | | $Zn$ | | |
| | Manganese | | $Mn$ | | |
| | Nickel | | $Ni$ | | |
| | Sodium | | $Na$ | | |

*Note: Only selected diffusion reactions are listed

## 14.3.5 Choosing a Dopant Element

As the diffusion source chart shows, there is a choice of elements, compounds and states available as dopant sources. The choice is made based upon the following factors.

1. Diffusivity
   For example, N-types like Antimony and Arsenic may be too slow for a deep diffusion.

2. Concentration of dopant required
   N-Types – Antimony does not have a high enough solid solubility in silicon to produce the concentration required for an emitter layer.

3. Concentration Profile
   The distribution of the dopant atoms in the wafer has a major influence on device performance. Some dopant elements, such as arsenic, result in a higher performing emitter structure.

4. State:
   Each state and its delivery system results in different degrees of deposition uniformity. Convenience and cleanliness are additional considerations.

### 14.3.6 Closed Tube Deposition

In the early 1960's there was considerable development of a deposition technique known as *capsule* or *ampule deposition.* In this technique the wafers and powdered source were sealed in an evacuated quartz 'capsule'. When the capsule was brought up to deposition temperature, the dopant evolved out of the source powder and diffused into the wafer.

This method is more costly and time consuming than the open tube techniques described above. Despite the greater uniformity claimed for capsule deposition, the vast majority of depositions are done by open tube. IBM still uses the closed tube method.

In review, deposition is the first step of a two step diffusion process in which:

1. The dopant is introduced into the wafer.

2. The source of dopant atoms is continuous (the mathematical term is *an infinite source*).

3. The surface concentration is at the solid solubility limit.

4. The deposition takes place in the flat zone of a diffusion furnace from a variety of dopant sources.

## 14.4 DRIVE-IN/OXIDATION

The device requirements of surface concentration, total quantity of dopant atoms and junction depth cannot usually be achieved in a one step diffusion. A second step is required. This step also takes place in a diffusion furnace, usually at a higher temperature than a deposition. This second step is called by one of the following names, depending upon the fabrication line:

Drive-In
Diffusion
Drive-in/Oxidation
Reoxidation
ReOx

During this step two things happen. First, the dopant atoms "diffused" into the wafer during the deposition step are redistributed deeper (and more widely) into the wafer. In other words, the diffusion continues into the wafer. There are two major differences between a deposition and a drive-in. First, in the drive-in there is no source, therefore no additional dopant atoms are introduced into the wafer. The side diffusion of the dopant is approximately 85% of the vertical depth.

The second difference is in the carrier gas. The carrier gas in the quartz tube during drive-in is an oxidizing gas. While the dopant is being redistributed, the wafer is being reoxidized, with the exposed silicon surface receiving the most rapid growth. The resultant oxide protects the surface and can serve as a barrier for a subsequent diffusion.

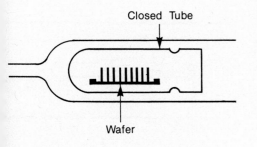

Fig. 14.7   Closed Tube

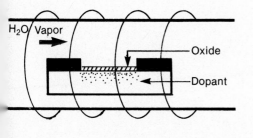

**Fig. 14.8
Drive in Oxidation**

The goals of the drive-in step are: to redistribute the dopant atoms to a specific depth; and to grow silicon dioxide to a specific thickness. The variables available to control these two results are temperature, time and the type of oxidant chosen (wet or dry).

The variables are mathematically related to each other by the Gaussian function.

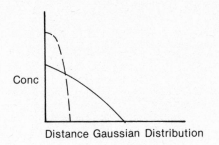

Distance Gaussian Distribution

**TABLE 14.2 Summary of Deposition and Drive-In Steps**

|  | Deposition | Drive-In |
|---|---|---|
| Goals | Introduction of Dopant | 1. Redistribution of Dopant<br>2. Reoxidation |
| Variables |  | 1. Surface Composition<br>2. Junction Depth<br>3. Time<br>4. Diffusivity<br>5. Temperature<br>6. Quantity of Atoms |
| Source Conditions | Continuous Source | No Source |
| Temperature Range | 900 – 1100°C | 1050 – 1200°C |
| Oxidation | No | Yes |

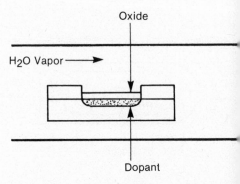

**Fig. 14.9 Redistribution of Dopant**

## 14.5 WAFER FLOW THROUGH DIFFUSION

There are a number of sub-steps that must occur to sucessfully complete a diffusion operation.

Preclean and Etch
Deposition
Deglaze
Evaluation #1
Drive-In, Oxidation
Evaluation #2

### 14.5.1 Preclean and Etch

During deposition the wafer is extremely vulnerable to contamination entering the wafer along with the dopant. To prevent this situation, the wafers are thoroughly cleaned. The sources of contamination may be both airborne dirt and photoresist that is not completely removed at the previous photomasking step.

A typical preclean takes place in a sulfuric acid and oxidant mixture at approximately 100° C–130° C. This solution removes both dirt and organics. A more elaborate clean is the RCA procedure employing both acid and basic solutions.

Exposure of the silicon to the heated cleaning acids will result in the growth of a thin layer of oxide which acts as a diffusion barrier in the subsequent deposition, an unacceptable condition.

The solution to this problem is to follow the preclean with a dip in a diluted HF solution which removes any oxide. Both the preclean and etch (dip) steps are followed by a deionized water rinse and spin dry.

### 14.5.2 Deposition Cycles

The deposition of the wafers actually requires a minimum of three gas *ambiants* (cycles) in the furnace. This requirement is the same as for oxidation. The wafers are slowly loaded in the flat zone in an ambiant of an inert gas, usually nitrogen, to prevent the growth of a diffusion retarding film of silicon dioxide, and to allow the wafers to come up to temperature.

The second cycle contains the dopant vapors.

At the conclusion of the deposition cycle, the furnace is switched back to an inert gas which sweeps out the dopant vapors, thus stopping the deposition. Removal of the dopant gases is also necessary for operator safety.

### 14.5.3 Deglaze

The wafers coming out of deposition have a thin oxide on the silicon that is highly doped with whatever dopant was used. This doped oxide, if left on, could serve as a diffusion source during drive-in and change the intended concentration. The deglaze step consists of an HF dip of the wafers to remove the unwanted oxide and dopant source.

### 14.5.4 Evaluation #1

The amount of dopant in the wafer, the concentration at the surface and the junction depth all must be carefully controlled to guarantee future device performance. The control and monitoring of the deposition process is done by measurements made on test wafers which go into the deposition boat along with the device wafers. Their position on the boat is selected to represent the degree of uniformity of the entire boat. After deposition and deglaze, the test wafers are measured for sheet resistance.

A wafer is doped to change its conductivity type and resistivity. Measuring the wafer's sheet resistance is an indirect measurement of the amount of dopant in the wafer. Either a four-point probe or contactless method is used.

In some cases the junction depth will be measured at this point, although it is extremely shallow after deposition.

For circuits that are very sensitive to metallic ion contamination a *capacitance/voltage plot* will also be performed on the test wafer(s). The measurement techniques are explained in detail in Chapter 17.

### 14.5.5 Drive-In/Oxidation

Like the deposition step, the drive-in/oxidation requires the entrance and exit of the wafers from the flat zone in an inert gas.

### 14.5.6 Evaluation #2

The test wafers from the deposition step are carried along into the drive-in/oxidation step. After drive-in/oxidation, they are again measured for sheet resistance to guarantee that the redistribution of the dopant was accomplished correctly. Junction depth is also measured at this point.

The measurement of junction depth is a destructive test. The measurement could be made on a device wafer but is usually made on a test wafer.

Surface concentration cannot be measured directly. However, it is a fixed quantity in relation to the resistivity and junction depth, by the diffusion laws (Error of Gaussian functions), and can be calculated.

Oxidation thickness is also a critical parameter measured after the drive-in/oxidation on a test wafer.

**Concentration Profile**

The mathematical laws governing deposition and diffusion predict the dopant concentration at every depth in the wafer. From the measurement of sheet resistance (resistivity) and junction depth, the theoretical concentration can be calculated. Under some conditions the actual concentration profile deviates from the theoretical, giving rise to unpredicted device performance.

The effects of concentration profile are more pronounced on shallow diffused devices and those where device speed is important. Two techniques are used for measuring the profile in the wafer:

    3-Point Probe
    Differential Capacitance

The measurement is made on a test wafer. Due to the time and expense of the measurement, it is performed infrequently or when device performance indicates a profile change.

**Table 14.3  Summary of Diffusion Evaluation**

| Evaluation Parameter | Technique |
| --- | --- |
| Resistivity | 4-Point Probe Contactless |
| Junction Depth | Lap & Stain |
| Concentration Profile | 3-Point Probe Capacitance |
| Surface Concentration | Calculated |
| Quantity of Atoms | Calculated |
| Oxide Thickness | Color Interference |
|  | Ellipseometry |
|  | Lap & Stain |
|  | Moving Styles |

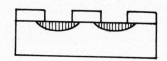

**Fig. 14.10 Side Diffusion**

**Fig. 14.11
Ion Implantation Analogy**

## 14.6 INTRODUCTION TO ION IMPLANTATION

Until 1970, diffusion was the only doping procedure used in semiconductor production. If the world had not needed MOS circuits and higher levels of integration, diffusion would have continued as a satisfactory doping method. However, the industry has moved rapidly in those directions and pushed the limits of diffusion. MOS technology has continually strived toward achieving lower gate voltage operation. One technique used to accomplish this is highly controlled doping of the gate region. At these low concentration levels ($10^{15}$ atoms per $cm^2$ and lower) control is difficult with diffusion.

Another feature of diffused layers that adversely affects MOS device operation is the higher concentration of the dopant at the wafer surface. During device operation, the current travels where the dopants are concentrated. In the case of a diffused layer, the current travels along the top surface of the wafer. Any surface contamination can interfere with the device operation, a situation that is intolerable in MOS devices.

The side diffusion resulting from a diffusion process places a limit on how close individual components can be placed next to each other. This spacing results in a larger chip size, slower circuits and a lower yield.

The high temperature required for diffusion is another yield limiting factor. Each heat treatment (above approx. 400° C) causes some crystal damage in the wafer which limits yield. Another problem in high temperature steps is the diffusion of unwanted contaminants into the wafer.

*Ion implantation* not only overcomes these problems but adds additional process benefits. These additional benefits are the ability to dope the wafer through a thin oxide layer, and the use of photoresist and other layers as the doping mask. As device design heads increasingly toward smaller, shallower and lower concentration dopings, better doping control, and more doped layers per process, ion implantation will become the dominant doping technique. Diffusion will still find a use in the doping of the less critical layers and continue to be the preferred doping method for lower integration level circuits.

## 14.7 BASIC THEORY

Diffusion is a natural phenomenon that occurs when the right conditions of dopant concentration and temperature are present. Ion implantation, on the other hand, is an event that does not occur naturally. The required conditions are created in the ion implantation machine.

An analogy of ion implantation is when cannonballs are shot into a wall. If they have enough momentum, they will penetrate the surface and locate inside the wall. The same process occurs during ion implantation, using ionized dopant atoms instead of cannonballs.

In the ion implanter the dopant atom is ionized (given a charge) and accelerated to a high speed. The stream of ions is swept across the wafer surface. The ions penetrate into the wafer where the wafer surface is exposed through a blocking mask.

The amount of dopant and the depth of penetration are governed by the size of the dopant atom, the velocity of the ion, and the amount of time the wafer is exposed to the beam. Please note: The actual operation is much more complicated than the simple explanation above.

Ion implantation is based on a number of sophisticated techniques borrowed and adapted from other fields, which are explained in the following section.

## 14.8 ION IMPLANTATION EQUIPMENT

Ion implanters are sophisticated and expensive pieces of equipment. They come in a variety of designs and are used for research and development as well as high volume production. Ion implantation is best understood by examining each of the major subsegments. All implanters have the same subsegments.

They are:
Dopant Source
Ionization Chamber
Mass Analysis (or Separation)
Acceleration
Beam Focus
Scanning
Vacuum System
Target Chamber/Loading

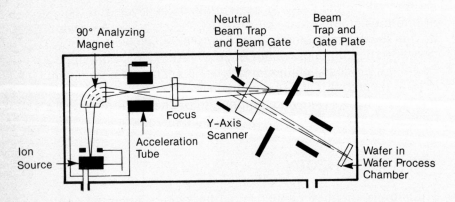

**Fig. 14.12**
**Block Diagram of Ion Implanter**

### 14.8.1 Ion Implant Sources

The dopant elements which are ion-implanted into silicon are the same as those used for diffusion ($A_s$, P,$S_b$, B), and are typically extracted (by the ion implant machine) from gases. While all of the gas sources used in diffusion are eligible for ion implant sources, fluorine-based gases ($PF_5$, $As F_5$, $B_{111}F_3$, $Sb F_3$, $As F_3$, $PF_3$) are preferred.

The selected gas is metered into the ionization section of the machine by mass flow controllers.

Certain solid sources are also used as ion implant sources. Phosphorus pentoxide ($P_2O_5$) is one. Solid sources require heating to produce a vapor containing the dopant element which is released into the *ionization chamber.*

### 14.8.2 Ionization Chamber

The source vapor flows into the Ionization Chamber with the element to be implanted tied up in a molecule. To separate the element out of the molecule and to acceletate the dopant element, it must be in an ionic form. (Remember, an ion is an element or a molecule that has either a positve or negative charge.)

The dopant-bearing molecule is ionized in the ionization chamber. This is accomplished by bombarding the molecule with electrons. Two things happen during the collision process. First the molecule is broken up into a host of molecules formed from the components of the starting molecule. The process is illustrated below for the molecule $BF_3$. The second effect is the ionization of all the species created.

The electrons are created from two types of sources:

    Hot Filament
    Cold Cathode

A hot filament source is a wire of tungsten or tantalum that is heated by an electric current. At a certain temperature, electrons "boil" off the filament. Cold cathode sources require a high electric field between a cathode and anode plate pair which causes the formation of free electrons. In the presence of a high gas pressure, the reaction becomes self-sustaining.

Within the chamber the electrons (which are negatively charged) are attracted to a positively charged plate. During their trip to the positive plate, they accelerate, gain momentum and ionize any source molecules they collide with.

### 14.8.3 Mass Analyzing

The positive ions created are attracted to an oppositely charged plate and drawn into the analyzing section. The term *mass analyzing* comes from the general name of the instrument adapted to ion implantation. During the Manhattan Project, which developed the atom bomb, it was necessary to separate and select certain ions from a gas cloud. The mass analyzer, which is based on the law that different molecules or elements and their ions have different atomic weights, was invented to do the job.

Within this section of the machine is a magnet. The paths of the ions streaming into the analyzer are bent into a curve by the

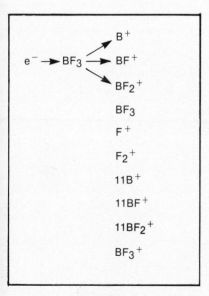

**Fig. 14.13**
**Ionization Species of $BF_3$**

interaction of the charge on the ion and the magnetic field. Exact path shapes are a function of the charge and the weight of the molecule or atom. Bowlers experience an analogous situation when using a different weight ball. Changing ball weight, without changing the amount of force and spin put on the ball, results in a miss of the pocket (gutter ball).

Since the exact weights of the molecules are known, the exact path (radius of curvature) of each molecule and atom can be precisely calculated. To select the desired ion out of the crowd requires positioning the exit port in the correct location or adjusting the strength of the magnetic field to allow only the desired ion to exit. The other ins go crashing into the wall of the analyzer. Another name for this procedure is *mass selection* or *separation.*

### 14.8.4 Acceleration Tube

At this point in the process, the required dopant atom has been separated from its original source and is in an ionized state. The next operation in the sequence is to accelerate the ion to a high enough speed so that it has enough momentum to penetrate into the wafer surface. This happens in the *acceleration tube.* The theory of ion acceleration simple. Negative and positive charges attract. The higher the difference in the "charge" between the two, the faster they will accelerate to each other.

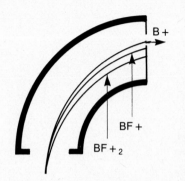

**Fig. 14.14    Analysing Magnet**

The charge difference is created by placing a high voltage (in the 100,000 volt range and abbreviated KV for kilovolts) on the tube.

As the ion enters the tube, it immediately accelerates under the influence of the oppositely charged voltage. The other end of the tube has an opening to allow the accelerated ion to exit. The acceleration level is a function of the weight and charge of the ion and the voltage on the tube. The exiting beam of ions is actually an electric current. Machines are rated by their beam current capabilities. Thus a high current machine has voltage capabilities in the 300KV to 500KV range. The higher the rating, the higher acceleration it can impart to an ion. Higher rated meachines are required to accelerate heavier atoms and can implant a given amount of ions faster and/or deeper.

### 14.8.5 Beam Focus

As the beam exits the acceleration tube, it enters a focusing mechanism. This subsystem uses electrostatic and magnetic lenses to narrow the beam to a diameter of approximately 1 cm.

### 14.8.6 Beam Scanning

At approximately 1 cm in diameter the ion beam must be moved over the wafer surface to achieve uniform doping. Two methods are available to achieve this effect -- *beam scanning* and wafer movement. Production level machines use a combination of both methods. Beam scanning, like mass separation and acceleration, takes advantage of the charge on the ion. The positively charged ion passes between a set of electromagnetic plates. When the charge on the plates is negative, the beam is deflected away from

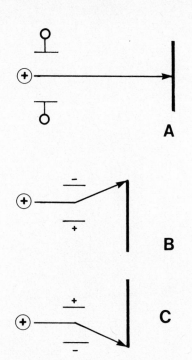

**Fig. 14.15  Beam Scanning**

the plates. When the plates are charged with a positive charge, the beam is bent towards them. The charge polarity is alternated between the plates to cause the beam to sweep across the wafer surface. This is the same principle used to sweep the electron beam across the inside of a TV screen. The beam is moved horizontally across the wafer first and then moved down before being swept across the wafer in the other direction. This method is called *raster scanning.*

### 14.8.7 Vacuum System

The intention of the implant operation is to dope the wafer with only the selected dopant. This requires that the implant operation take place in a vacuum because air molecules that might be in the system can also become ionized and implanted into the wafer. The vacuum level must be very high (greater than $10_{-6}$ Torr). The vacuum is created and maintained by either oil diffusion or cryogenics pumps. Both of these systems are discussed in Chapter 16.

### 14.8.8 Target Chamber/Loading

The first ion implanters used in production were capable of implanting only one wafer at a time, usually relying on beam scanning alone. As implantation became a necessity, one-wafer implanting became a drawback. Because implantation is expensive, implant equipment producers increased productivity by gang loading the wafers on a carousel or wheel and rotating the wafers in front of the beam. These methods also increase the uniformity of the implanted layer.

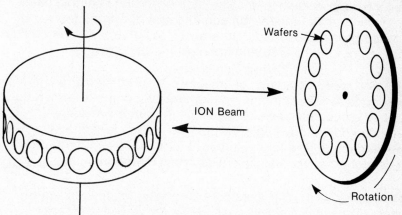

**Fig. 14·16 Batch Implantation Methods**

## 14.9 Ion Implantation Masks

A major advantage of ion implantation is the variety of masks that are effective blocks to the ion beam. Whereas inn diffusion processing the only effective mask is silicon dioxide, most films employed in the technology can be used to block the beam, including photoresist, silicon dioxide, silicon nitride and aluminum.

The use of photoresist as a mask offers additional dimension control to the process. In diffusion processing the silicon dioxide layer has to go through two steps which each cause dimensional variation -- the development and etch processes. The use of the photoresist layer itself as an ion implant eliminates the need for the etch step, and the dimensional variation associated with the etch step. The problems resulting from high temperature oxidations are also eliminated by the use of these other implant masks.

Silicon nitride and photoresist masks both provide comparable blocking to silicon dioxide, with the added benefit of thinner films. Following are the minimum thicknesses required to block a 100KV arsenic implant.

> Silicon Dioxide . . . 1.0 microns
>
> Silicon Nitride . . . 0.7 microns
>
> Negative Resist . . . 0.2 microns

A drawback to using photoresist films as implant masks is the subsequent removal of the film. The combination of the vacuum in the chamber and the implanting of the dopants in the film make it difficult to remove the film.

## 14.10 RESULTS

In the introduction we mentioned that the position of the dopant in the wafer was different than its position in a diffused layer. There are two reasons for this. The first is the physical nature of the process. It is easy to imagine that when firing cannon balls into a wall not all of them will come to rest at exactly the same distance below the surface. Differences in ball weight and charge size result in the balls having different momentums.

The same result occurs in ion implantation. The ions arrive at the wafer surface with different momentums and come to rest in the wafer at varying distances. A typical distribution of ions is illustrated below. The center of the distribution is termed the projected range. The total number of ions and their distribution are described by the Standard (Gaussian) distribution.

Notice in fig. 14.17 that the atoms are located below the wafer surface. Thus, devices using ion implanted regions are less surface-sensitive.

A Gaussian distribution results from the variation of ion momentum and the perfection of the wafer crystal. It is also possible to create other ion distributions. By varying the acceleration of the ion, any distribution shape is theoretically possible.

Ion implantation allows the option of doping through surface layers. Doping through a thin silicon dioxide layer can result in a precise, lightly-doped layer near the surface, and the oxide mask serves to protect the surface from the beam.

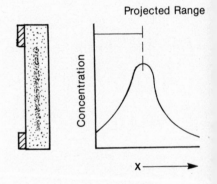

**Fig. 14.17
Distribution of Implanted
Atoms in Wafers**

### 14.10.1 Ion Dose

Ion depth into the wafer is a function of the energy (acceleration) of the ion, its weight, and the crystal condition of the wafer. The amount of dopant implanted into the wafer is called the *dose*.

Consider the exact amount of water required to fill a bucket using a hose. If the flow rate of the water is known it is a simple matter to calculate the time required to fill the bucket. In ion implantation, the "flow rate" is the current density (ions/$cm_2$). The dose required is the current density $\times$ the time of implant.

## 14.11 SUMMARY OF IMPLANT FACTORS

| FACTOR | FUNCTION OF |
|---|---|
| Ion depth | Acceleration<br>Ion weight<br>Crystal condition |
| Ion distribution profile | Gaussian statistics<br>or<br>"Custom" profile |
| Dose (Ion Quantity) | Current density<br>Time |

### 14.12 Crystal Damage/Dopant Electrical Activity

Since ion implantation is a mechanical process, there is some crystal damage resulting from the impact of the ion with the crystal atoms. The amount of damage is in proportion to all of the above factors. Longer, deeper implants cause more damage, as do heavier dopant atoms.

A reduction of the number of electrically active ions in the wafer is another result of the collision process. Dopant atoms become "tied" up in the crystal damage. Some of the damage, and a high proportion of the "tied" up atoms can be restored by a high temperature step called *anneal*. A post-implant anneal is a standard part of the process. Typical anneal processes take place at 1000° C in a nitrogen or hydrogen atmosphere.

Laser pulse annealing is another method used. Rapidly pulsing the wafer surface to the required temperature restores the crystal structure without causing junction movement.

### 14.13 CHANNELING

Shooting the ions into the crystal structure of the wafer is similar to spraying a stream of water into a pile of marbles. Most of the water is blocked by the marbles, but some will penetrate down

174

between the openings. The same situation occurs in the wafer. The ion beam can penetrate into the crystal planes. This phenomenon is called *channeling.*

Prevention of channeling is accomplished by cutting the wafer "off-orientation." The effect is to tilt the crystal planes relative to the beam direction. For each implanted species, implant energy and crystal orientation there is a minimum critical angle required to prevent channeling. The range varies between 3 and 6 degrees. Other Techniques to prevent channeling is to implant through a thin surface oxide or to damage the surface with a high implant layer.

## 14.14 IMPLANT USES

Theoretically, ion implant can replace every diffusion in a semiconductor process. The increase in MOS processing, higher density circuits and automation will elevate ion implantation to the dominant doping procedure in the 1990's. The technique is currently used where ion implantation offers specific advantages. In bipolar devices, implants are used to form buried layers (replaces long diffusions), dope resistors and create high concentration (low resistance) base contacts.

MOS technology first took advantage of implants to precisely control the gate threshold voltage through gate doping. The growth of CMOS circuits has seen the use of implants for most of the doping steps. Deep well doping is particularly advantageous to implant processing.

Both bipolar and MOS circuits benefit from the use of implanted resistors. Diffused resistors are limited to a reproducible range of ±5%. Implanted resistors can be formed with a variation of ±1%. Resistors formed by implantation have a range of sheet resistivities from 50 to 100,000 ohms per cm$^2$. The higher resistivities are difficult to achieve and control with diffusion technology.

One drawback to implantation is the absence of an oxide during the process. In diffusion processing, an oxide is grown during the drive-in step. Many of the implants take the place of the diffusion deposition step. Redistribution and reoxidation take place in the furnace following the implant.

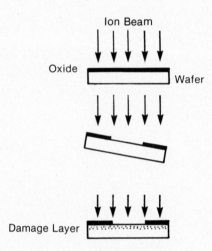

**Fig. 14.18**
**Methods for Preventing Channeling**

# Chemical Vapor Deposition

Chapter 15.

# INTRODUCTION

Semiconductor devices are composed of N or P-type regions formed in the wafer surface by doping, and of various thin layers deposited on the surface. *Chemical vapor deposition* (CVD) is a technique for depositing some of the layers which function as dielectrics or conductors.

In the early days of the industry when device structures were simpler, the added surface layers were primarily silicon used as bipolar collector regions, aluminum as the conducting layer and silicon dioxide as the topside passivation.

Increasing circuit density MOS device development and new bipolar devices created the need for new layer materials and new deposition techniques.

The increased use of non-silicon substrates has also led to increased industry use of CVD. Neither germanium nor II-V compounds has a natural oxide with the functional properties of silicon dioxide. Processing of these type wafers, of necessity, requires the use of high quality deposited films.

This chapter presents the fundamentals of CVD, the CVD processes and equipment and the materials deposited. CVD techniques are used to deposit conductors, semiconductors and insulators.

## 15.1 Basic CVD Processing

CVD processes are simple in concept. A chemical containing an atom(s) of the material to be deposited is introduced into the system reaction chamber. In the chamber, the chemical (in the gaseous state) reacts with another gas, liberating the desired material. The freed material (in atom or molecular form) then "deposits" on the substrate. The unwanted by-products of the chemical reaction leave the reaction chamber and are exhausted to the facility's fume scrubber system. The reaction of silicon tetrachloride with hydrogen to deposit silicon illustrates the concept. This reaction requires the addition of heat to take place.

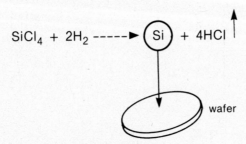

$$SiCl_4 + 2H_2 \dashrightarrow (Si) + 4HCl \uparrow$$

wafer

**Fig. 15-1 Chemical Vapor**
**Deposition of Silicon**
**From Silicon Tetrachloride**

The deposition processes are governed by complex relationships between the various system parameters. The actual process and system design involves tradeoffs and variations from "ideal" conditions, especially when productivity must be considered. The operation of a successful CVD process is a mixture of theory, hands-on experience, and, quite often, luck.

### 15.1.1 Films Deposited

The films and their electrical categories deposited by CVD techniques are listed below.

**Table 15.1    CVD Deposited Materials**

| CATEGORY | MATERIALS |
|---|---|
| Insulators & | $SiO_2$ |
| Dielectrics | $Si_3N_4$ |
| | Phosphorus Silicate Glass (PSG) |
| | Doped Oxide |
| Semiconduc- | |
| tors | Silicon (Si) |
| | Gernanium (Ge) |
| | Gallium Arsenide (GaAs) |
| | Gallium Phosphide (GaP) |
| Conductors | Aluminum (Al) |
| | Nickel (Ni) |
| | Gold (Au) |
| | Platinum (Pt) |
| | Titanium (Ti) |
| | Tungsten (W) |
| | Molybdenum (Mo) |
| | Chromium (Cr) |
| | Tungsten Silicide ($WSi_2$) |
| | Molybdenum Silicide ($MoSi_2$) |
| | Doped Polysilicon |

### 15.1.2  System Components

CVD systems exist in a bewildering variety of designs and configurations. Fortunately all of the systems have common components or sub-systems. Figure 15.2 illustrates a basic system.

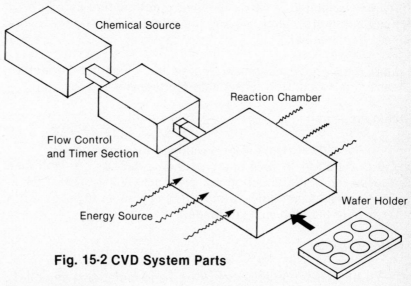

**Fig. 15-2 CVD System Parts**

**Source Sections**

Every CVD system contains a source section where the liquid and/or gas state chemicals are housed and metered into the reaction chamber. These sections are similar, and in some cases identical, to the source sections of diffusion systems. CVD processes, like diffusion processes, require cycles of different gases or gas mixtures. The cycling is under the control of the timer/flow meter (or mass flow meter) equipment. This system subsection is usually controlled by a microprocessor allowing process selection versatility and automated "one button" operation.

### Reaction/Energy Sources

In order for the chemical reaction of the gases in the chamber to take place, energy is required. Different energy sources are used depending upon the reaction requirement, the maximum processing temperature of the wafer, and productivity factors such as growth rate and system cost. The three sources are listed in Table 15.2.

**Table 15.2   CVD Reaction Energy Sources**

| SOURCE | METHOD |
|---|---|
| Heat | Conduction |
|  | Inductive R.F. Field |
|  | Radient |
|  | Convection/Radiation (Diffusion Tube) |
| Plasma | A.C. |
|  | D.C. |
| Ultraviolet | Photochemical |

### Temperature Ranges

CVD reactions take place over a temperature range from room temperature up to 1250° C. The choice of temperature depends on the level required to cause the CVD reaction, film defects induced at high temperatures and the effect of heat on the layers present on the wafer.

In general the process engineer desires the lowest temperature process compatible with reasonable productivity.

### System Pressure

The original CVD systems were developed for atmospheric pressure operation. In 1974 Unicorp, under license from Motorola, introduced the first production low pressure CVD system. This systems operates just below atmospheric pressure (0.5–150 torr) rather than in the high vacuum range.

### Reaction Chamber

A CVD system reaction chamber design and material is selected for compatibility with the method, energy source and temperature range. Horizontal systems employ rectangular tubes of stainless steel or quartz; LPCVD depositions take place in quartz diffusion tubes; and vertical silicon deposition takes place in stainless steel chambers.

**Wafer Holder**

The wafers are mounted on a variety of holders. The design and material of each is dictated by the energy source and system configuration. Materials include graphite (silicon CVD and low temperature pyrolitic deposition), quartz (LPCVD) boats and special design stainless holders.

### 15.1.3 Cold Wall Deposit

Some systems employ a direct heating of the wafer by induction or radiant heating. In these systems only the wafer (and its holder) are hot. The CVD reaction therefore takes place only at the wafer and holder. The chamber walls remain relative to the wafer. These systems are termed *cold wall*.

### 15.1.4 Hot Wall Deposition Systems

The CVD reaction takes place in the gas stream, when there is sufficient energy for the reaction to take place. In systems where the gas stream is heated, such as in a diffusion tube, the reaction product is deposited on every surface in the system, including the walls. Such a system is termed a *hot wall system.*

### 15.1.5 Film Criteria

CVD layers must meet similar criteria, regardless of the film material or the method of deposition. The films must be of uniform thickness and structure to meet the rigid electrical and physical requirements. An important aspect of uniform thickness is *step coverage.* As semiconductor devices become more complicated, their surface topography becomes more varied, which can alter the dynamics of a deposition. This can result in a thinning of the layer over a surface step. This thinning can alter electrical performance of dielectrics.

Two criteria are necessary to prevent shorting between conductive layers and to prevent contamination from reaching the wafer surface: all layers must be free of pinholes and cannot develop stress cracks and the film itself cannot contain any contamination.

## 15.2 CVD SYSTEMS

### 15.2.1 Atmospheric Pressure Systems

Chemical vapor deposition was first developed to deposit the silicon layers required in bipolar device structures. The early systems were operated at atmospheric pressure and the industry favored the horizontal R.F. induction heated system for epitaxial silicon deposit. The hot plate-heated silicon dioxide deposition system was also common.

A system operated at atmospheric pressure relies on the flow dynamics in the chamber to produce uniform films. Since the deposited species is being depleted from the gas stream, the flow rate and design of the system must insure that the wafers at the back receive the same amount of deposit as those in front.

## Horizontal/Induction Heated System

There are several variations in design and reaction energy of atmospheric pressure systems. The workhorse of silicon deposition was the horizontal induction system, which featured a rectangular quartz tube wrapped with an R.F. coil. The wafers were mounted on a graphite holder and positioned in the tube. The R.F. energy passed through the quartz chamber walls and heated the graphite induction block by induction, which in turn heated the wafers by conduction.

The R.F. energy passed through the quartz walls without heating them. Since the reaction occurred only where there was energy (heat), this system was a cold wall system. To insure an even deposition, it was necessary to tilt the wafer holder (called a *susceptor*) up into the gas stream.

## Cylindrical or Barrel/Radient Heated System

The limitations of deposition uniformity and high energy use of the horizontal systems have been overcome by the introduction of barrel systems. In this type of system the wafers are mounted on the face of a graphite holder that rotates inside a cylindrical chamber. The front of the wafer results in a more uniform epitaxial growth.

Deposition uniformity is increased by the rotation of the wafer in the gas filled chamber. This system has become the industry standard for deposition silicon. Both the cylinder and horizontal systems are used for deposition reactions that require higher temperatures (900° C – 1250° C).

## Horizontal/Conduction (Hot Plate) System

For depositions requiring a lower temperature, such as silicon dioxide from silane, the higher temperature capabilities of R.F. and radiant heating are not needed. The required temperature can be achieved with a hot plate arrangement. In one version of the system, the wafers are mounted on a portable hotplate that is positioned in a stainless steel rectangular tube. Power is supplied to the hot plate by attached cables. The reaction gases are introduced into the tube and flow over the wafers. These systems are not very controllable for thickness uniformity or particulates. Because it is a hot wall system, the reaction product forms on the side and top walls. If the system is not cleaned frequently the particle buildup on the walls will deposit on the wafers.

Another version of this system uses a moving hot plate that passes under a head containing a heater. The reaction gases are passed through the plates in the head causing the desired reaction to take place. This design is more productive and is less prone to particulate contamination.

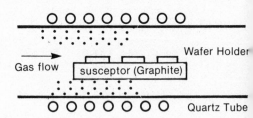

**Fig. 15-3 Cold Wall Induction System**

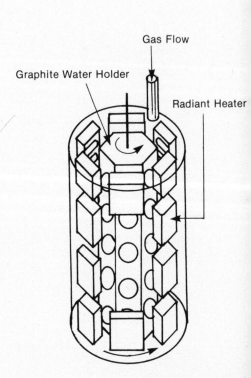

**Fig. 15-4 Cylindrical or Barrel System**

### 15.2.2 Low Pressure (LPCVD)

LPCVD processes have been used in the industry for many years. The original imeptus for their development was the pressure-temperature tradeoff of chemical reactions. Decreasing the pressure at which a reaction takes place in a flowing gas allows a reduction in the temperature. The advantages of lower temperature processing have been discussed in earlier chapters. For the deposition of passivation layers, there is an upper temperature limit of 450° C when aluminum metallization is used. Above that temperature aluminum will alloy down into the silicon, causing shorted devices. (This problem is discussed further in Chapter 16.)

The acceptance of LPCVD as a production technique was delayed for several reasons. Compared to atmospheric systems, LPCVD processes could not deliver the uniformity required for epitaxial deposition. And the device structures of the mid-seventies did not require either high quality conformal passivation layers or silicon nitride layers. Now the increasing dominance of silicon gate MOS and growing levels of integration have made LPCVD an essential process of the 'eighties.

An LPCVD system is similar in appearance to a diffusion system. The reaction chamber is a quartz tube. Unlike a diffusion tube, the gases are introduced into the chamber from the load end. The rear of the tube is connected to a vacuum pump. LPCVD systems operate in a pressure range from 0.1 torr – 100 torr.

The lay-down wafer holders of the original LPCVD systems have given way to more productive stand-up boats. While atmospheric systems are flow-dependent, requiring that wafers lay in a horizontal position, the reduced pressure systems are less so. The lower temperature (below 600° C) reactions are uniform from end to end. In the mid-temperature (600 – 1000° C) range some of the reactions are depletion-limited as the gases move down the tube. Uniform deposition is achieved in these systems by raising the temperature at the rear of the tube.

Lower cost has also contributed to the acceptance of LPCVD processing. The LPCVD systems are cheaper to purchase and operate because they don't require high temperature and high cost energy systems. Many systems are set up in a standard diffusion furnace, saving the expense of a standalone system.

Temperature, pressure, wafer spacing and gas flow affect deposition uniformity in an LPCVD process. Proper definition of these parameters can result in film uniformities of $\pm 2\%$ to $5\%$. This matches the uniformity level of atmospheric systems with the added advantage of increasing the number of wafers per load by a factor of 10.

Improved film quality is also achieved with low pressure systems. The vertical placement of the wafers results in a major reduction in the number of particulates. In atmospheric hot wall systems with laydown wafer holders, particulates deposited on the hot wall chamber walls fall directly down on the wafer surface.

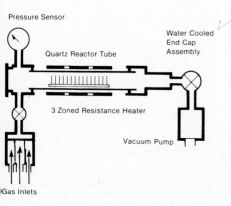

Pressure Sensor

Quartz Reactor Tube

Water Cooled End Cap Assembly

3 Zoned Resistance Heater

Vacuum Pump

Gas Inlets

**Fig. 15-5 LPCVD System**

Because low pressure systems are less dependent on gas flow, step coverage and film uniformity improvements are achieved. The reactant gases backfill the chamber, facilitating a reaction at every wafer surface.

Process control and uniformity also result from the rapid turnover of the gases from one cycle to another. In an atmospheric system the reactant gases have a dwell time in the tube which is a function of the velocity of the gases and volume of the system. In an LPCVD system the spent gases are quickly extracted from the tube by the vacuum.

In review, LPCVD offers the following advantages over atmospheric systems:

1. Low Temperature Processing
2. Higher Productivity
3. Improved Process Control
4. Higher Quality Films

## Resistance Heated Systems

Resistance heated systems are the most popular systems for production deposition of silicon dioxide and silicon nitride. The heating system is the same as a diffusion system. Resistance heated coils surround the quartz tube and heat the gases by conduction (contact with the inside tube walls), which in turn heat the wafers. This system results in a hot wall deposition.

## Plasma Enhanced LPCVD (PECVD)

This system combines the advantages of standard LPCVD processing with those of plasma. The system is configured with parallel graphite slabs in the tube reaction chamber. The slabs are connected to an R.F. generator and the wafers are loaded between pairs of slabs. During the deposition cycle, the R.F. generates a plasma between the plates which enhances the CVD reaction. In effect, each pocket is a mini planar deposition system. The localization and direction of the deposition due to the plasma field improves uniformity and step coverage. The benefits of PECVD have been used primarily in the deposition of polysilicon and silicon nitride.

## Radiant Heat Reduced Pressure

The high quality required of epitaxial films cannot be achieved in standard stand-up LPCVD reactors. However, the advantages of low pressure are gained by reducing the pressure in a standard radiant heated cylinder style system.

Reduced pressure allows reduction of the deposition temperature. Lower temperature is less damaging to the crystal structure and reduces the outdiffusion of dopants from the back of the wafer which can become incorporated into the CVD film. This phenomenon is called *auto doping.* Higher resistivity films with greater uniformity are the other major advantages resulting from this approach to epitaxial deposition.

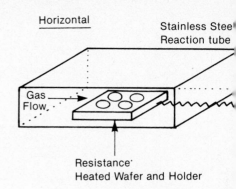

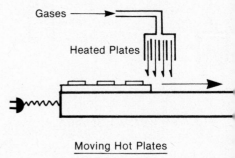

**Fig. 15-6 Conduction Heat C.V.D. Systems**

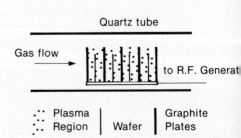

**Fig. 15.7 Plasma Enhanced CVD**

Typical Reduced Pressure Epi Cycle

1. Load System
2. Evacuate System to 40 torr
3. Heat System to 1200° C in $H_2$
4. Switch System to HCl for Etch
5. Reduce Chamber Temperature to 1080° C
6. Purge Reactant gases with $N_2$
7. Turn off Heaters
8. Return Chamber to Atmospheric Pressure
9. Unload wafers.

**Photochemical (Ultraviolet) LPCVD**

Photochemical systems utilize an ultraviolet light to disassociate the reactant gases into the desired film material. The major advantage of the photochemical CVD is the lower reaction temperature required. Both silicon dioxide and silicon nitride can be deposited at temperatures between 50° C and 200° C.

The lower temperature can result in a deposited film with fewer stress cracks and very good step coverage. Compared to higher temperature systems there is less thermal damage to the device, and compared to plasma systems no radiation damage.

Unlike most LPCVD systems the reaction chamber is not a diffusion tube. The systems, which are stand alone with a horizontal reaction chamber, are heated by a hot plate. They operate at the low end of the LPCVD pressure range, between 0.3 torr and 1.0 torr. Due to the chamber design the productivity of photochemical systems is less than that of diffusion tube systems, with standup wafer boats.

## 15.3 SILICON DEPOSITION

The development of thin low-resistivity epitaxial films was a major step in the advancement of bipolar integrated circuits.

The lightly doped (low-resistivity) layer solved the device performance problem. The electrical isolation problem was solved by growing the epitaxial layer with a conductivity type opposite to that of the wafer. Diffusing a narrow ring of dopant of the same conductivity type as the wafer completely through the epi layer leaves pockets of the epi layer totally isolated from each other. The bipolar circuit components are individually formed in the pockets. This isolation scheme was the development that paved the way for higher levels of bipolar circuit integration.

The term *epitaxial* comes from the Greek word meaning "arranged upon." In CVD silicon deposition, the term describes the crystalline structure of the film. During the deposition the silicon atoms created in the gas stream deposit on the wafer and orient themselves in the same arrangement as the atoms in the host wafer. Thus, the crystal orientation of the wafer is extended into the epitaxial layer.

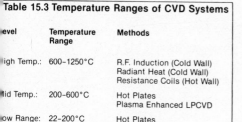

**Table 15.3 Temperature Ranges of CVD Systems**

| Level | Temperature Range | Methods |
|---|---|---|
| High Temp.: | 600–1250°C | R.F. Induction (Cold Wall) Radiant Heat (Cold Wall) Resistance Coils (Hot Wall) |
| Mid Temp.: | 200–600°C | Hot Plates Plasma Enhanced LPCVD |
| Low Range: | 22–200°C | Hot Plates P.E. CVD Photochemical |

To achieve a high quality single crystal layer on the wafer, many factors must be controlled. The wafer surface must be immaculate, the source must be very pure, the growth rate critically controlled and the system free of leaks and contamination.

MOS device structures also require deposited silicon layers. The usual use is as the top layer gate electrode. The silicon is deposited on top of the gate oxide, by the same processes used to deposit epitaxial films.

However, the oxide film has no crystal structure and the deposited silicon film has a polysilicon structure. These films are referred to as *polysilicon* or simply *poly*.

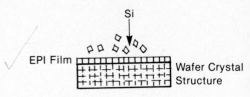

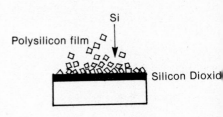

**Fig. 15-8 Epitaxial and Polysilicon Film Growth**

### 15.3.1 Epitaxial Deposition Systems

Early epitaxial deposition development took place in horizontal/induction heated systems. The cold wall system allowed the deposition of particle-free films and guaranteed the extreme temperature control required (± 1 C). Much work went into determining the optimum flow rates, system configuration and temperature required to produce uniform epitaxial films. However, these systems have low wafer throughput due to the requirement of laying the wafers flat on the boat. Also, maintaining film uniformity is a constant battle requiring precise control of flow rates and gas stream composition. adjustment. The introduction of the cylinder/radiant heated systems resolved the drawbacks of the horizontal systems. The cylinder design allowed many more wafers to be processed per run. Film uniformity became easier to achieve and maintain as a result of the rotation capabilities of the system.

Film structural quality also improved in the radiant heating system. In an induction-heated system the wafers are heated by conduction from the susceptor. As the film grows, the film surface becomes slightly cooler, changing the deposition rate and structure. In the radiant heated system, however, the lights are always shining on the wafer surface, maintaining a constant temperature.

Cylinder/radiant systems have replaced the older systems as the mainstays of production silicon deposition. LPCVD systems have not yet been able to produce the quality and uniformity required for epitaxial silicon films, although a great deal of development effort has been expended toward this end.

### 15.3.2 Silicon Source Chemistry

The following silicon-bearing chemicals are used as the source of silicon to deposit epitaxial films.

| Table 15.6   Silicon Dioxide Source |
|---|

**Deposited Silicon Dioxide (Silox):**

$$SiH_4 + O_2 \longrightarrow SiO_2 + 2H_2$$
$$SiHCl + 2O_2 \longrightarrow SiO_2 + 2H_2$$

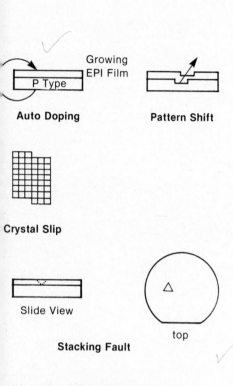

**Fig. 15-9 Epitaxial Film Growth and Problems**

Deposition temperature, film quality, system design and process control are the general considerations used to select a silicon source. Deposition temperature influences the deposition (or film growth) rate, the formation of crystal defects, energy consumption and auto doping (the most critical factor). Any dopant from either the wafer itself or a diffused region will out diffuse during epi growth. The "out diffused" atoms will be recombined in the growing epi film, changing its resistivity.

The growth rate is critical in the maintenance of single crystal growth and the prevention of pattern shift. If the growth rate is too fast, the epi on {111} wafers will grow at an angle to the wafer surface. In bipolar devices the base and emitter must be lined up over the subcollector. This alignment is accomplished by referencing the depression in the epi surface. Figure 15.8 illustrates the effect on alignment when the epi and the surface depression "shift." The lowest temperature possible, consistent with the other film requirements, is most desirable.

Another crystal defect resulting from poor system control is *slippage* (or *slip*) of the crystal planes. A poor or dirty wafer suface can cause a film crystal defect called a *stacking fault*. The fault starts at the wafer surface and propagates to the film surface. Stacking faults are detected by etching the surface.

Silicon tetrachloride is the source most used for epitaxial deposition. While this source requires the highest deposition temperature, it is also the best known and results in the highest quality epitaxial films.

Silane, the next choice as an epi source, continues to receive a lot of development effort due to the lower required deposition temperature. The silane reaction is simple, requiring only heat to decompose (*pyrolyze*) it into silicon and hydrogen.

While considerable development has gone into both dichlorosilane and trichlorosilane, neither is used in general production.

### 15.3.3 Epitaxial Film Doping

The required resistivity of the epi film is achieved by the mixing of dopant atoms in the gas stream. The atoms become incorporated in the growing film. The dopant atom sources are the same gas and liquid sources used for diffusion.

15.3.4 Typical Epitaxial Process

Wafers for epitaxial deposition follow the same process flow as wafers for diffusion.

1. Precleaning
2. Deposition
3. Evaluation

The epitaxial process starts with an extensive wafer cleaning process in which all particulate contaminants and surface stains or residues must be removed. This process usually includes mechanical scrubbing and chemical cleaning to remove both organic and inorganic contaminants. Particular care must be taken during spin-rinse-drying steps to insure that particulates resulting from the wafers "shaving" the teflon boats do not get on the wafers. Typical cleaning solutions are listed in Table 15.4.

### Table 15.4    Typical Pre-Epi Cleaning Process*

| Contaminate | Removal Process |
|---|---|
| Particles | Scrubber |
| Organics | $H_2O_2 + NH_4OH + H_2O$ |
| Inorganics | $H(+H_2O)$ |
| | $HCl + H_2O_2 + H_2O$ |
| | $H_2SO_4 + H_2O$ |

*Cleaning processes vary depending on cleanliness required*

In the epitaxial reactor the wafer undergoes a lengthy process as shown in table 15.5.

### Table 15.5    Typical Epitaxial Deposition Process

| Cycle | Temperature | Gas | Purpose |
|---|---|---|---|
| 1 | Room | $N_2$ | Purge air from system |
| 2 | Room | $H_2$ | Reduce any organic contaminants of wafers in system |
| 3 | (Heating) | $N_2$ | Bring system to deposition temperature |
| 4 | Deposition Temperature | HCl | Etch wafer to prepare surface for epi deposition |
| 5 | Deposition Temperature | Source + Dopant + Carrier | Grow epitaxial film |
| 6 | (Heat Off) | $N_2$ | Purge system of reactant gases |

## 15.3.5 Evaluation of Epitaxial Films

The critical role of the epitaxial film in the device dictates a well-monitored and controlled process. Part of the control process is the characterization of the films and continual feedback to the operator.

Five parameters are evaluated:

1. Surface Quality
2. Resistivity
3. Film Thickness
4. Doping Profile
5. Crystal Quality

### 15.3.5.1 Surface Quality

Surface problems such as particles, haze, stains and crystal irregularities could cause device failures. Particles and stains stem primarily from poor wafer cleaning and system housekeeping. Haze, which may arise from a number of sources associated with growth rate, results primarily from oxygen from leaks in the system. Small amounts from the tiniest leak can cause major surface disruption.

Crystal irregularities derive from poor surface cleaning or poorly defined growth rates. A highly accelerated growth over wafer surface spots, which results in film surface "spikes," is the most common irregularity. These spikes can grow to several times the film thickness.

Every wafer in the run is given a surface inspection under a collimated UV light. Selected wafers receive a more detailed inspection by microscope. Periodically sample wafers are examined for actual crystal structure by X-ray techniques.

**Resistivity**

The doping level (*resistivity*) of the epitaxial film is a critical device parameter. Wafers from each run are resistivity–measured using a *four point probe.* This test qualifies the run and functions as a process monitor. Since the sheet resisitivity of the film is a function of the film thickness as well, the sheet resistance measurement also serves as a control of the thickness and ultimately the entire process.

**Film Thickness**

In conjunction with the doping level and doping profile, the epi thickness is a critical device component. Control of thickness is mandatory.

Several thickness measurements are used. The traditional method is the *lap and stain* technique, also used to measure diffusion depths. Because it is a destructive test method, it is made on a partial wafer chip which is included in the run specifically for this purpose.

The measurement of *stacking fault* dimensions is another thickness measurement. A stacking fault is a disruption of the crystal which originates at the wafer surface. The fault is propagated to the surface where it is revealed by a preferential etch. The shape of the fault is orientation dependent. At the surface a {111} film grows a triangular shaped fault and on a {100} wafer the fault is square shaped. The length of the sides of the fault are related to the thickness by the laws of geometry. This method is less accurate than lap and stain, and is also less destructive.

The preferred method is infrared (IR) interference which is similar to the interference method used to measure the thickness of silicon dioxide and photoresist layers. In this application, the radiation is in the IR range and reflects off a buried layer in the host wafer surface. The development of software to automatically handle the calculations, and the non-destructive nature of the test, account for its popularity on LSI and VLSI lines.

**Doping Profile**

In bipolar technology, the wafer going into the epi reactor has subcollector regions diffused over the surface. During the epi film growth the dopant in these regions will "out diffuse" into the growing film. The profile of the out diffusion also plays an important role in the device operation.

Periodically the dopant profile is determined by the destructive spreading resistance probe method.

### Crystal Quality

During the epitaxial growth cycle various defects, including dislocations, can occur in the film. These dislocations are a primary cause of soft junctions in the finished wafer. Dislocation density can be ascertained by etching the epi surface to reveal dislocations. Their density is counted with the aid of a microscope. Other crystal defects are revealed by using a scanning X-ray technique.

## 15.4 POLYSILICON DEPOSITION

Polysilicon layers are the primary conductor (metal) component in silicon gate MOS structures. They are deposited on top of a layer of silicon dioxide. The chemistry of the deposition is exactly the same as an epitaxial silicon deposition. The difference is in the effect of the underlying oxide on the growing silicon film. Since the oxide does not have a crystal structure, the silicon atoms deposit in a random fashion, forming a polysilicon structure.

The role of the polysilicon in the MOS gate does not require the same stringent thickness control as an epitaxial layer in a bipolar structure. And the crystal uniformity has more of an effect on the etching process than the device performance.

### 15.4.1 Deposition Systems

All of the systems used for epitaxial deposition can be used for polysilicon deposition. The trend is toward greater use of LPCVD deposition. LPCVD deposited poly films meet uniformity requirements while offering lower temperature deposition and greatly increased productivity.

### 15.4.2 Source Chemistry

The less stringent requirements of a polysilicon layer also allow the use of all the silicon sources listed in Table 15.3. However, the trend to LPCVD systems favors the use of silane as the source.

### 15.4.3 Film Doping

The primary use of polysilicon as an MOS electrode (conductor) requires the lowest resistivity possible. Since phosphorus has the highest solubility in silicon it is the preferred doping element. The preferred source is phosphine, which provides adequate doping uniformity along with the control and convenience a gaseous source provides.

## 15.5 SILICON DIOXIDE DEPOSITION

### 15.5.1 Uses

Deposited silicon dioxide layers are used in a variety of ways in semiconductor structures. Traditionally they have been used as the final passivation layer. Deposited on top of the metal layer, the silicon dioxide serves as a scratch protector. When doped with phosphorous, it acts as a sodium barrier and also protects the circuit from general contamination and water vapor.

In multilayer metal schemes silicon dioxide is deposited on top of the first metal layer and acts as the intermetallic dielectric.

Silicon dioxide is used to a lesser extent as a diffusion source. The film is deposited directly on the exposed wafer with either an N or P-type dopant. In the diffusion furnace, the dopant diffuses out of the silicon dioxide into the wafer.

Silicon dioxide is also used as an etch barrier. Films like sie difficult to precinhusi rmazhinz vslfzause the etchants required are aggressive and etch times are long. The effect on a photoresist layer can be devastating. The resist is attacked or lifted from the surface, causing pattern dimension changes. By depositing a layer of silicon dioxide on top of the silicon nitride the problem can be solved. The pattern is transferred to the silicon dioxide layer by conventional photomasking techniques. In the etch bath the silicon dioxide takes the place of a photoresist film, with the advantage of not being attacked by the etchant or lifting.

On non-silicon wafers, deposited silicon dioxide films serve all of the functions that thermally grown oxide films serve in silicon devices: surface passivation, surface dielectric and doping barrier.

Deposited silicon dioxide films are known by the names *Vapox* or *Silox*. The former term was coined by Fairchild engineers while the latter is a trademark of Applied Materials Inc. Sometimes the films are simply called "glass," or if doped with phosphorus, "phosphorus silicate glass" (often abbreviated as P.S.G.).

When phosphorus is present at a high level it causes photoresist adhesion problems which can be solved by doping only the lower portion of the layer, leaving the top free of phosphorus. Some processes require a three level sandwich of undoped, doped, undoped silox.

### 15.5.2 Source Chemistry

Silicon dioxide films can be deposited from several sources as listed in Table 15.6. The traditional and most common source is silane. The original use of deposited oxide films was as the top level passivation layer. This deposition required a temperature below the eutectic temperature of aluminum and silicon (577° C). Silane forms silicon dioxide at room temperature when exposed to oxygen in the air. In actual practice a deposition temperature between 200° C and 450° C is required to achieve a practical deposition time and to produce quality films. Silicon dioxide films deposited at these low temperatures have come to be known as *LTO*'s.

---

**Table 15.7    Silicon Source Table**

**Epitaxial Silicon:**

$SiCl_4 + 2H_2 \xleftrightarrow{} Si + 4HCl$

$SiH_4 + Heat \longrightarrow Si + 2H_2$

$SiH_2cl_2 \xleftrightarrow{} Si + 2H_2$

**Poly Silicon:**

$SiH_4 + Heat \longrightarrow Si + 2H_2$

---

The reaction applies to both atmospheric and low pressure systems. In photo initiated systems the silane is reacted with ammonia or nitrous oxide to form the silicon dioxide film.

### 15.5.3 Deposition Techniques

Although any CVD system can be used to deposit silicon dioxide, low temperature requirement and productivity considerations cause the conventional silicon deposition systems to be seldom used. The industry originally favored hot wall, atmospheric, conduction systems which were difficult to control to produce high quantity clean and uniform films. The advent of LPCVD technology, the dominant deposition technique, has solved both of these problems.

The more recently introduced photochemical process also promises quality and uniformity advantages.

### 15.5.4 Film Doping

Silox films are doped with either N or P type-dopants, depending on their function in the device. Passivation layers are doped with phophorus as a sodium barrier. On devices with a highly varied topography, high levels of phosphorus (up to 10%) are added to allow the silox to flow and create a more planar surface.

Oxide diffusion sources are doped with the appropriate dopant.

## 15.6 SILICON NITRIDE

### 15.6.1 Uses

The densification of integrated circuit design, accompanied by a reduction of film thicknesses, and the requirement for higher quality films is leading the industry away from silicon dioxide to silicon nitride layers.

As is often the case in semiconductor development, the need for improved conductor materials was outweighed by the difficulty of patterning the materials. Plasma etch now appears to offer a solution to that problem.

Silicon nitride has always been considered a superior passivation layer. A silicon nitride layer is functionally superior to silicon dioxide in every critical aspect, including:

1. Dielectric Strength
2. Mechanical Strength
3. Water Vapor Barrier
4. Sodium Barrier
5. Fewer Pinholes

The general use of silicon nitride was deterred by the lack of a reliable method of deposition that could occur at 450° C or below, and by the difficulty of high resolution etching of the layer. These impediments have been overcome by the development of LPCVD, oxide etch mask techniques and plasma etching.

The tendency of silicon nitride films to trap charge is a drawback. However, this property is used advantageously in some MOS devices, where the trapped charge creates a non-volatile memory.

### 15.6.2 Source Chemistry

Silicon nitride is created in the reactor from the reaction of silane with ammonia.

$$3SiHCl_4 + 4NH_3 \longrightarrow Si_3N_4 + 12H_2$$

Photochemical deposition can take place by reacting the silane with nitrous oxide. The choice of a carrier gas depends on the temperature of the deposition.

### 15.6.3 Deposition Techniques

Like the silicon oxide films, silicon nitride can be deposited in any of the existing CVD systems. In situations where a higher deposition temperature can be tolerated, conventional LPCVD systems are employed. In the presence of aluminum films and other low temperature requirements, plasma enhanced LPCVD and photochemical systems are utilized.

## 15.7 REFRACTORY METALS AND THEIR SILICIDES

### 15.7.1 Uses

**Table 15.8**

**Refractory Metals**

Molybdenum
Platinum Silicide
Titanium Silicide
Tungsten Silicide

The decreasing feature size of integrated circuits is requiring new metals to replace polysilicon conductors. As the devices decrease in size, the contact resistance between the polysilicon and the silicon increases to a level that seriously affects circuit response time.

Early in MOS development, refractory metals (transition elements) and their silicides were considered for semiconductor metal systems. Their positive benefits included low resistivities and resistance to high temperature processing. These materials may replace both silicon and aluminum as the favorite conductors.

Ongoing development to determine the best process of depositing these films is occurring. The processes being considered are evaporation, sputtering and PECVD.

### 15.7.2 Source Chemistry

The source gases for the deposition of tungsten, molybdenum and tungsten silicide are high vapor pressure halides or carbonyls.

### 15.7.3 Deposition Techniques

The deposition of these materials takes place in a conventional plasma enhanced LPCVD system. Reaction temperatures vary from 60° C to 900° C.

| Fig. 15.9 Overview of C.V.D. Techniques | | |
|---|---|---|
| **Atmosphere** | **Low Pressure** | |
| Cold Wall/Induction Heated | Cylinder | 1 |
| Cylinder/Radient Heated | Resistance Heated "Diffusion" Tube | 2 |
| Conduction (Hot Plate) | Plasma Enhanced | 3 |
| | Photochemical | 4 |

# Metalization

Chapter 16.

## INTRODUCTION:

Semiconductor device structures require a number of different layers or films. These layers can be dielectrics, semiconductors or conductors and are placed on the wafer by a variety of techniques. During the past ten years there has been a dramatic increase in the uses and number of these layers.

The materials and techniques used to deposit conductive layers on the wafer are explained in this chapter. Deposited conductors are an integral part of every device, in the role of surface wiring. Conductors also provide other functions in I.C. structures, such as fuses and back side electrical contact for the packaged die. *Metallization* is the general term used to describe this segment of semiconductor processing.

## 16.1 METAL FILM USES

### 16.1 Conductors

Metal films are used in semiconductor technology to wire together the various components formed in the wafer surface. The wiring is accomplished by the deposit of a thin (10 to 15 thousand angstroms) layer of metal on the wafer. This metal layer, after being patterned through a photomasking process, connects the devices as required by the circuit operation. The metal strips on the wafer surface are called *leads* or *interconnects.* Generally, a wafer heating step called *alloy* follows deposition to insure good electrical contact between the metal and the wafer surface.

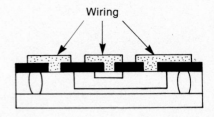

Patterned conductive films serve two other roles in device structures. They function as the gate electrodes in MOS structures, and are used as electrodes in thin film capacitors.

**Fig. 16.1    Thin Film Wiring**

The following metals and alloys are used for these purposes:

1. Aluminum
2. Aluminum Alloys
3. Titanium/Tungsten
4. Doped Polysilicon
5. Refractory Metals and their Silicides
6. Gold

### 16.2 Aluminum and Aluminum Alloys

Aluminum has been the traditional "wiring" metal. In fact the development of thin film aluminum technology has been one of the major contributions to planar technology. Aluminum achieved this status because it meets the requirements that a metal must have to be compatible with silicon technology.

1. Good Current carrying Density
2. Superior Adhesion to $SiO_2$
3. Ease of Patterning

4. High Purity
5. Good Electrical contact with Silicon

Aluminum meets all of the above requirements. It has good conductivity, adheres very well to silicon dioxide, can be patterned with conventional photomasking techniques and is obtainable in high purity. Aluminum has to be purified to between 99.9999 and 99.99999% for semiconductor use. Electrical contact of aluminum with silicon, while adequate for LSI level technology has reached its limits in the VLSI era. This subject is addressed in the section on alloying.

### 16.2.1 Electromigration

Aluminum has another drawback; *electromigration.* This is a phenonenom that occurs in aluminum leads while the circuit is in operation. In other words it is a field failure, not one that occurs during processing. Electromigration is caused by the diffusion of the aluminum in the electrical fields set up in the lead while the circuit is in operation. It is also enhanced be thermal gradients that arise in the lead from the heat generated by the flowing current.

The metal thins and eventually separates completely, causing an opening in the circuit. Electromigration occurs over time and may not show up until a device has had many hours of operation. This problem can be overcome by designing wide overlap regions at contacts, using a consistent film thickness, or adding copper (=4%) to the aluminum.

Electromigration becomes more of a worry as the level of integration increases. The higher number of components in the circuit create more current flow and generate more heat. This problem and the alloying problem discussed next is pushing the development of aluminum alloy uses and nonaluminum metal systems.

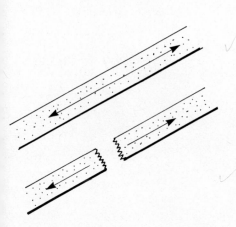

**Fig. 16.2   ElectroMigration**

### 16.2.2 Aluminum/Silicon Alloys

Another aluminum related problem arises during the alloying step. The alloy is a heating process required to insure good ohmic contact. There is an upper limit to the temperature of this step. At 577° C a curious phenomenon occurs between the aluminum and the silicon. While each will not melt individually at this temperature, in combination they do. In metallurgy this is known as a *eutectic point.* Physically, a liquid alloy forms down into the wafer. In structures with deep diffusions the alloyed region may not pose a problem. However, in shallow structures (and this is the trend) the junction is shorted out by the alloy.

Three solutions to overcome this serious problem are used.

1. Alloy Temperature:
   The alloy temperature is limited to 450° C. At 450° C the alloying is sufficient to insure good contact, yet is low enough to prevent major eutectic alloying. However this is a

compromise solution. The contact is not always as good as desired and there is some alloying.

2. Aluminum Alloys:
   Aluminum with 1–2% Silicon added is used instead of pure aluminum. During the alloy step the aluminum alloys with its "own" silicon, rather than the silicon in the wafer.

3. Barrier Metals:
   A thin layer of a metal (or metals) is deposited into the contact region prior to the deposition of the aluminum. Its function is to separate the aluminum and silicon. The metals used are titanium tungsten (TiW) alone, or TiW on top of a layer of platinum silicide.

### 16.2.3 Other Metal Materials

Higher current carrying density requirements associated with higher levels of integration have led to investigations of other metal systems. Gold/molybdenum/platinum metal systems have been around the industry for years. This system was originally developed as a solution to the aluminum electromigration problem. Its main drawback is the expense of a three metal system, especially one that includes gold and the softness (scratch prone) of the gold.

Silicon gate technology incorporates a polysilicon lead as the gate electrode. Circuit designers have taken advantage of the available polysilicon layer and put it to use as a conductor. To achieve the degree of conductivity required the poly must be doped. The preferred dopant is phosphorus since it has the highest concentration level in silicon.

Early in the industry the refractory metals;platinum tungsten and titanium were identified as possible semiconductor metals due to their high conductivity levels. The other advantages of aluminum and lack of an economical deposition method shelved development until the late 1970's. Advancing circuit density and the development of sputtering and CVD technology have given the refractory metals and their silicides new life.

## 16.3 FUSES

Fuse technology is the basis of *Programable Read Only Memories (PROM's)*. A fuse is located in the circuit at every memory cell location. The user uses a programming unit to "blow" selected fuses, leaving in the circuit a series of memory cells that hold the desired memory information.

The fuses are formed by two techniques. One is based on a thin (160 – 200 angstroms) metal layer patterned and connected into the memory cell by aluminum leads. The other technique uses a thin polysilicon or oxide layer in the contact hole.

In the metal technique the narrow neck design allows the "blowing" of the fuse when a programming current heats the

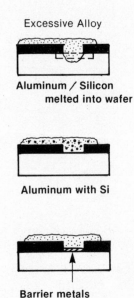

Excessive Alloy

Aluminum / Silicon melted into wafer

Aluminum with Si

Barrier metals

**Fig. 16.3  Alloying Process**

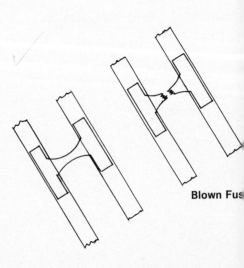

Blown Fus

**Fig. 16.4  Thin Film Fuses**

to withstand the low pressures that are ($5 \times 16^{-5}$ torr, or 0.00005 mm Hg).

neck portion to a high enough level to vaporize it. Metals used include nichrome and titanium tungsten. The same technique is used to "blow" the poly or oxide fuses in a contact hole.

## 16.4 DIE ATTACH AND LIFETIME CONTROL

Gold and some silver compounds are used to attach chips into the package, providing an ohmic back contact. Gold contacts are provided from a layer that is evaporated on the back of the wafer during fab processing.

In bipolar transistors, gold is evaporated onto the wafer (usually prior to base diffusion) and diffused into it during a diffusion step. The gold that locates in the base region acts as a trap for moving electrons, reducing their lifetime. The result is a faster turnoff of the device.

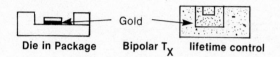

Die in Package      Bipolar $T_X$    lifetime control

**Fig. 16.5   Uses of Gold Films**

## 16.5 DEPOSITION METHODS:

Metallization techniques, like the other fab processes, have undergone improvement and evolution in response to the demands of the new circuits. The mainstay of metal deposition techniques was and is *vacuum evaporation.* Aluminum, gold and the fuse metals are deposited by evaporation. The newer metal systems as well as the dielectrics and semiconductors can be deposited by sputtering. This technique offers superior film composition and thickness control and will become the dominant deposition method by the end of the century.

The two systems are similar in construction and operation. Each requires a source of the material to be deposited, a method to convert the source to atoms and/or molecules, wafer holders to insure even film deposition, an evacuated chamber and a pumping system to remove the air.

### 16.5.1 Evaporation Theory

The evaporation of metal onto silicon relies on the same process by which water will evaporate out of a glass. At the liquid air interface some of the water atoms have enough internal energy to break the surface and escape into the air. Over time, enough atoms will escape from the water and remain in the air, reducing the volume of the water. This same evaporation process can also occur in a solid. When the temperature is raised high enough; atoms of the solid material will "evaporate" into the atmosphere.

Three methods are used to provide the external energy needed to evaporate aluminum and the other metals. They are:

1. Filament
2. E-beam
3. Flash

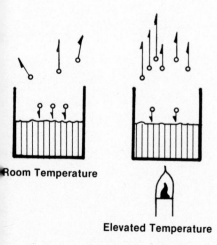

Room Temperature

Elevated Temperature

**Fig. 16.6
Evaporation Principle**

198

## 16.5.2 Evaporation Methods

### Filament

The filament technique is used primarily for gold and nichrome evaporation. An electrical current is passed through a tungsten filament of wire or pan design. The metal to be evaporated is wound on the wire or placed in the pan and is raised to the evaporation temperature by the current flowing through the filament. Atoms from the source material are "evaporated" into the atmosphere. In alloys, such as nichrome, each of the elements in the alloy will evaporate at a different rate. Each rate is characteristic of the evaporation rate of the element at the particular temperature of the filament. In the case of nichrome, the composition of the nickel and chromium on the wafer will differ from the composition in the source alloy.

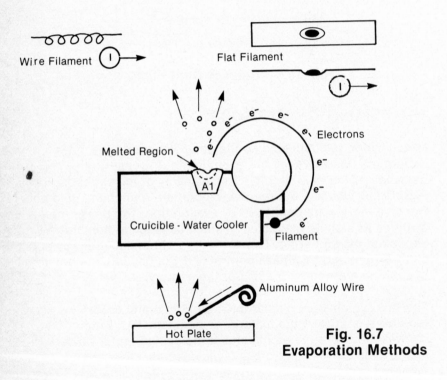

**Fig. 16.7
Evaporation Methods**

### E-Beam

This evaporation source consists of a copper crucible (water cooled) with a center cavity to hold the aluminum. A filament, located on the side of the crucible is heated to "boil off" electrons. The path of the released electrons is bent into an arc by a positive pole magnet. The electron beam is directed to impinge into the center of the aluminum. The high energy electrons heat a pool of aluminum in the center of the crucible to the evaporation temperature. The water-cooled crucible maintains the outside of the aluminum at a cool temperature. This method prevents any impurities from the crucible from diffusing into the melted aluminum and ending up on the wafer.

The evaporation of aluminum alloys can be a problem with a one gun E-beam source. Since each element in the alloy will have a different evaporation rate, the composition of the metal on the wafer will vary. More consistent film composition is realized by using two E-beam guns. For example, to evaporate an aluminum/silicon film one gun would hold the aluminum and another would hold silicon. In operation the power to each gun would be adjusted to control the evaporation rates to achieve the desired film composition on the wafer.

**Flash System**

This method is used primarily to evaporate aluminum/silicon alloys. The source is a wire of the alloy. A mechanical feeder automatically pushes the wire onto a hot plate. Upon contact the end of the wire very quickly evaporates or "flashes" into the gas state. Since all of the elements in the wire are evaporated instantaneously the composition of the film on the wafer is very close to the source composition.

### 16.5.3 Evaporation Chamber

The evaporation must take place in an evacuated chamber. If the evaporation took place in air, the high energy aluminum would combine with the oxygen in the air to form $Al_2O_3$, an insulator. The chamber itself is made of heavy wall quartz or stainless steel Chamber design is either the familiar bell jar or the refrigerator style hinged configuration. Bell jars have the advantage of maximum strength and good vacuum sealing from the bottom circular gasket, but the disadvantage of slower productivity due to the time required to raise and lower the jar. The front opening styles have the opposite advantages and disadvantages.

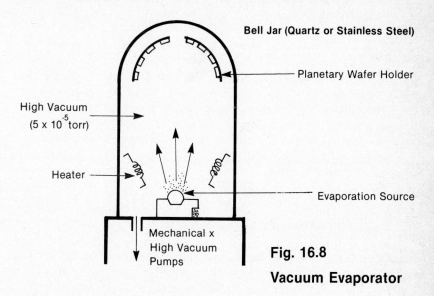

Bell Jar (Quartz or Stainless Steel)

Planetary Wafer Holder

High Vacuum
($5 \times 10^{-5}$ torr)

Heater

Evaporation Source

Mechanical x
High Vacuum
Pumps

**Fig. 16.8**

**Vacuum Evaporator**

### 16.5.4 Wafer Holders and Step Coverage

An important goal of the metal deposition process is uniform film deposition. This goal becomes more difficult to achieve when depositing the thin films over a thick step on the surface. As the device structures become more complicated the number and height of the steps will increase. In fact this situation also poses a problem in the photomasking process where the steps must be covered with photoresist.

Uniform thickness over the steps is mandatory to prevent electromigration and high resistance pathways. Three methods are used to enhance good step coverage. In situations where the step height is particulary high all three of the methods are used.

1. Planetary Wafer Holders
2. Heaters
3. Sloped Sides

1. The deposition of gold films and, sometimes, fuse films is done with the wafers held in a fixed nonrotating flat plane holder. When the surface topography is fairly flat this type of wafer holder is adequate. Step coverage is improved if the holder is of a domed design.

   Good step coverage using aluminum or the aluminum alloys requires a rotating, planetary, domed fixture. Typically three domes are connected into a rotating mechanism. The mechanism rotates around the inside of the chamber. Each of the domes also rotates on its own axis, giving a planetary motion. The planetary rotation exposes the wafer surface to the evaporation source at many different angles. No surface steps block the evaporating material.

2. Quartz heaters in the deposition chamber bring the wafers to a temperature of approximately 400° C. (Recall that the maximum allowable temperature is 450° C.) The aluminum atoms arriving onto the heated surface remain mobile for an instant before cooling and fill in the step corners by a capillary action.

3. A third technique is *slope etching* (controlled undercutting) of the oxide steps to minimize step shadowing. During the etch process in photomasking the sides of the contact holes are purposely overetched. The effect in the evaporator is a reduction of the shadow effect of the side wall and a reduction of the thinning of the film at that point.

## 16.6 VACUUM SYSTEMS

### 16.6.1 Vacuum/Pressure Measurement

The vacuum requirement for sucessfully depositing metal films is very stringent. There cannot be any contaminants inside the chamber that will interfere with the deposition itself or can become incorporated into the film.

The term *vacuum* describes a low pressure condition. Vacuum and pressure work as opposing forces. When one goes up, the other goes down. Vacuum is measured in pressure units; there are no separate vacuum units. The transition point from pressure to vacuum conditions starts at atmospheric pressure. Anything above that point is postive pressure; anything below is low pressure or vacuum. The use of the terms "high" and "low" vacuum are somewhat arbitrary. Operations such as vacuum

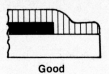

Good

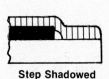

Thin at Step

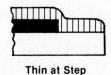

Step Shadowed

**Fig. 16.9    Step Coverage**

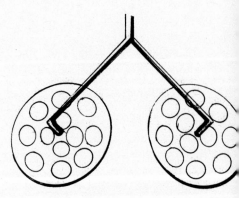

**Fig. 16.10
Planetary Wafer Holder**

Oxide

Wafer

**Fig. 16.11
Sloped Side and Step Coverage**

dehydration bake are at "low" vacuum, while metal deposition and ion implantation are performed at "high" vacuum.

The pressure in a vessel exists in proportion to the energy and amount of gas atoms or molecules it contains. Measurement of the pressure exerted is done by an indirect method, and expressed in units of "mm of Hg" (millimeters of mercury).

To understand the relationship of a length measurement to pressure, we must review an old method of pressure measurement -- the barometer. A barometer is a glass tube having an open end which is inserted in a dish of mercury or water. Air has been eliminated from the tube by filling it with the liquid, covering the end, and inserting it under the surface of the liquid in the dish.

If the apparatus is sitting in the open, the pressure of the air (Remember, our atmosphere is some 13 miles high. We all walk around with a column of air sitting on us.) will push down on the liquid in the dish and raise the liquid up into the tube. The height of the liquid in the tube is proportional to the pressure. Originally the liquid used in barometers was mercury and the standard unit of pressure became the mm of Hg. Torrichelli, an Italian researcher in pressure phenomenon, was honored by the use of his name as the unit of pressure measurement. And since Torrichelli is long (and difficult to spell) the name has been shortened to Torr. One Torr is equal to the pressure that would raise a column of mercury up 1mm.

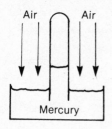

**Fig. 16.12    Barometer**

Low vacuum can theoretically be measured by this method, although the technique is inaccurate. Consider the effect of placing a glass bell jar over the barometer and evacuating some of the air. The height of the column would be less than the open air height (which is 760mm at sea level). As the air amount, and therefore pressure is reduced, the height of the column is also reduced. It has become common practice to measure high to medium pressure levels in microns. Ten (10) microns of pressure or vacuum corresponds to the pressure level if the height of mercury was only 10 microns high. Ultra high vacuum conditions would raise the column a very small amount. Vacuum depositions take place in a vacuum of $5 \times 10^{-5}$ Torrs or lower! If the barometer was placed in the evaporation chamber, the column of mercury would rise only 0.00005 mm of mercury! A number of modern instruments are used to measure the vacuum level and calculate the results in the units of microns or Torrs.

### 16.6.2 Vacuum Pumps

A number of different pump designs are available to achieve the pressure levels required for metal deposition. The pump selected depends on the level of vacuum required, the speed of pumping and the other equipment factors of reliability, cost and process up-time.

### Mechanical Rotary Oil Pumps

This type of pump features an eccentric rotating vane in the pump cavity. Every time the vane rotates it "sweeps" out more of the gas molecules from the deposition chamber. The compressed gas is forced out of the cavity into the oil reservoir. The oil prevents backstreaming of outside air molecules. Each sweep of the vane removes more gas molecules from the chamber.

Rotary oil pumps are effective in producing vacuum levels in the mid-pressure range, down to $10^{-3}$ Torr (1 micron).

## Oil Diffusion Pump

The oil diffusion pump has been the mainstay of the deposition vacuum systems. To achieve the high vacuum levels it is necessary to first remove the bulk of the atmosphere from the chamber with a mechanical rotary oil pump.

At the bottom of an oil diffusion pump is an oil reservoir. External heaters bring the oil up to its evaporation temperature. The oil vapors rise in the inside column and exit through the ports with a downward direction. The lower pressure created by the mechanical pump, called a forepump in this application, also causes the oil molecules to drift downward. During the journey any gas molecules or atoms from the chamber are "pushed" out of the pump by the oil molecules. This process occurs continously until the vacuum level of the pump, about $1 \times 10^{-7}$ Torrs is reached.

To protect the deposition chamber from oil back-streaming, a *cold trap* is inserted between the diffusion pump and the chamber. The trap is designed exactly like a liquid source bubbler but is operated with out any liquid inside. A jacket filled with liquid nitrogen surrounds the cold trap which reduces the temperature of the trap to $-278°$ C. Any volitile gases from the pump or the chamber are frozen to the inside wall of the trap.

Evacuation of the chamber with an oil diffusion pump is a three stage procedure.

1. Fill Cold Trap
2. Evacuate to 1 micron with Rotary Pump
3. Evacuate to $1 \times 10^{-7}$ with Diffusion Pump

## Cryogenic High Vacuum Pump

This type of pump works on the same principle as the cold trap. Gases freeze onto very cold surfaces. In a cryogenic pump, a series of vanes are maintained at the low temperatures provided by liquid nitrogen or helium. Gas molecules from the chamber adhere to the vanes. Eventually the number of molecules in the chamber is reduced, creating the high vacuum level.

Cryogenic pumps (or *cryopumps*) offer a number of advantages over diffusion pumps. The most important one is their ability to produce a vacuum down to the $10^{-10}$ Torr range, the same level as the vacuum of space. Another advantage of cryopumps is they don't require either a forepump or a cold trap. These two factors, combined with the faster pumping speed of cryogenic pumps, result in faster wafer through-put time. Another factor increasing

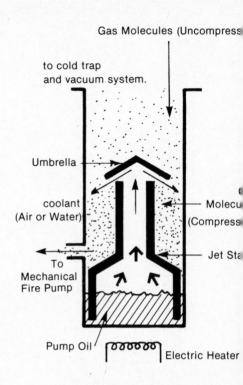

Fig. 16.13   Oil Diffusion

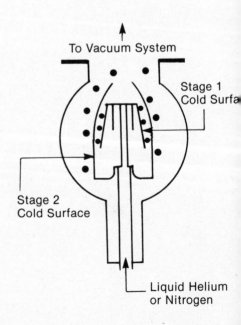

Fig. 16.14   Cyrogenic Pump

pumping speed is the ability of this type of pump to evacuate water vapor faster than oil diffusion pumps.

The total capture nature of the pump and oil-less operation drastically reduces the possibility of contamination. However when the pump is brought back to room temperature by mistake or for maintenance, the frozen gases are released and care must be exercised to vent any toxic or flammable gases trapped on the vanes.

The build-up of the gases also affects the pumping speed. Cryopumps must be monitored for pumping speed and require periodic cleaning when the speed falls off.

### 16.6.3 Evaporation Process Steps

**Wafer Precleaning and Etch Dip**

Successful, clean metal deposition requires clean wafers. Typically, this includes a pre-evaporation clean to remove particles and stains. The wafers are precleaned in a sulfuric/oxidant solution similar to the solution used in pre-diffusion cleans. An unwanted result of this procedure is the formation of a thin oxide (50–200 Angstroms) on the bare silicon in the contact hole. This oxide is thick enough to block the electrical contact between the aluminum and the silicon.

The oxide is removed in an HF acid and water solution. Typical mixtures are 1:10 and 1:100. The step is called a *dip* or *etch* because the HF attacks the surface oxide along with the oxide in the contact holes. Bipolar devices that require a heavily phosophorus-doped oxide are particularly vulnerable at this step. Overetching of the contact hole silicon can also remove the phosphorus-doped oxide.

**Evaporation Process**

Immediately after preclean and dip, the wafers are mounted on the dome planetaries which are fixed in the chamber. After the air is evacuated from the chamber, the wafers are heated (if heaters are used). The source is then heated to evaporation temperature. During the source heatup, a shutter shields the wafers until full power is reached and a steady evaporation rate is established.

Once the aluminum puddle is at temperature and evaporation starts, the shutter opens automatically and the material evaporates onto the wafers. When the predetermined thickness is achieved, the shutter automatically closes and the heaters turn off. Control of the evaporation rate and thickness is achieved with monitors mounted in the top of the chamber. All of these steps are programmed into the controller. The operation is automatic from load to unload.

**Evaluation**

The evaporated film is measured for thickness by a variety of techniques including four-point probe, a moving stylus instrument or interference techniques. See Chapter 17 for an explanation of these measurements.

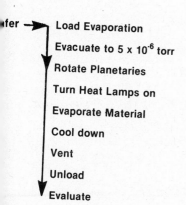

**Table 16.1**
**Vacuum Evaporation Process**

Wafer →
Load Evaporation
Evacuate to $5 \times 10^{-6}$ torr
Rotate Planetaries
Turn Heat Lamps on
Evaporate Material
Cool down
Vent
Unload
Evaluate

After aluminum metallization and patterning, the wafer will be alloyed (heat treated) to insure good electrical contact between the aluminum and the silicon.

## 16.7 SPUTTERING

*Sputtering* is another method of depositing both thin metal films and insulators onto the wafer. Sputtering is a physical process. Unlike evaporation, the material to be sputtered does not have to be heated. There are two important benefits of sputtering: the deposition of alloys and insulators. Sputtering has other benefits as a deposition technique when compared with evaporation. They are best understood after a discussion of the principles of sputtering.

### 16.7.1 Principles of Sputtering

Sputtering is a physical process that can be compared to throwing steel balls at a concrete wall. Upon impact the ball tears away fragments of the concrete, resulting in fragments which retain the chemical and physical properties of the concrete. If the process is continued, surfaces in the vicinity of the impact are covered with a layer of concrete dust. In sputtering the "steel balls" are ionized argon atoms, and the "wall" is a plate of the material to be sputtered, called a *target*.

The sputtering process takes place in an evacuated chamber. Ionized argon atoms are introduced into the chamber which contains the wafers and the targe of the film material to be sputtered. The target is maintained at a negative potential relative to the positively charged argon atom. In ion implantation, when this situation was created, the positive ion accelerated towards the negative charge. The same thing happens in the sputter chamber.

Unlike the ion implantation process, in the sputtering process the argon atom does not become imbedded in the target. Instead, it slams into it and like the steel ball, tears off some of the target material. Since the chamber is maintained at a vacuum, the liberated material settles on everything in the chamber, including the wafers.

### 16.7.2 Sputtering Equipment

A sputtering machine or "rig" is composed of four principle subsections.

1. Gas Source
2. Sputtering System
3. Vacuum System
4. Deposition Chamber

### Gas Source

Argon is the principle gas used in semiconductor sputtering, although neon can also be used. The gas used must meet very

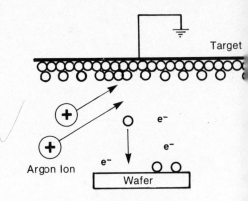

**Fig. 16.15**
**Prinicple of Sputtering**

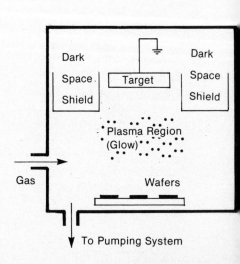

**Fig. 16.16**
**Typical Sputtering Equipment**

stringent cleanliness and low water content specifications. The presence of contaminants can change the film composition and seriously affect the sputtering process. Water vapor can cause unwanted oxidation of the chamber and the film material.

The gases are metered into the systems by gas flow controllers like those used for oxidation, diffusion and ion implant.

**Sputtering Methods**

**Three sputtering methods are used in semiconductor depositions. They are:**

1. **Diode**
   **Direct Current (D.C.)**
   **Radio Frequency (R.F.)**
2. **Triode**
3. **Magnetron**

The first two methods called *diode sputtering,* are simple in concept. The target is connected to a negative potential, with a positively charged anode present in the chamber. The negatively charged target ejects electrons which accelerate towards the anode. Along the way they collide with the argon gas atoms, causing them to be ionized. The positively ionized argon atoms then accelerate to the target, initiating the sputtering process.

The ionized argon ( + ) and the target (–) form a diode. This arrangement is called *diode sputtering.*

A secondary effect of the ionization process is the impact of the electrons with the gas atoms, resulting in a plasma condition. (Plasma is a region of highly energized gas ions.) This is a glowing purplish region just in front of the target surface, or *plasma glow region.* The other regions in the chamber, where there is no plasma region, are called the *dark spaces.* Dark spaces exist right in front of the target surface and to the sides. Sputtering efficiency is enhanced when the plasma is confined to the region between the source and the wafers. This situation is enhanced by dark space shields to the side of the target, which prevent a plasma region from developing and creating target atoms that will not deposit on the wafers.

Another problem arises from the out-gassing of contamination from the chamber walls in the vacuum. To prevent contamination of the film in D.C. sputtering, a small negative bias (charge) is put on the wafer holder. Ions are created at the wafer surface and have the effect of dislodging stray outgassed atoms from the growing film. D.C. biasing is used primarily for the sputtering of metal films.

Improved sputtering is gained by connecting the target to the negative side of an R.F. generator. The required gas ionizing condition is set up near the target surface without requiring a conductive target. R.F. sputtering is required to sputter non-conductors and is also used for conductors. The same film "cleaning" effect is achieved for the non-conductive films with R.F. biasing.

R.F. biasing offers another advantage to the sputtering process -- etching and cleaning of the exposed wafer surface. When the bias polarity is reversed, the argon atoms impinge directly on the causing the argon atoms to impinge directly on the wafer. Upon impact the argon atoms remove any contamination from the contact area and a very thin layer from the wafer surface. The result is a better electrical contact between the sputtered film and the wafer. This procedure is also called *sputter etch, reverse sputtering* or *ion milling.* This is the same as the process used to etch photoresist-defined patterns in the photomasking step. Most D.C. sputtering systems will include an R.F. biasing capability for this critical cleaning step.

In diode sputtering, a number of processes occur at or near the wafer surface. After impact of the argon atom, a number of electrons are created. These electrons cause heating of the substrate (up to 350° C) which can cause uneven film deposition. Radiation, which can have serious effects on radiation-sensitive devices, is also created in this system arrangement.

Diode sputtering is not used to deposit the most frequently used semiconductor conductor – aluminum. Residual oxygen in the target material and in the chamber combines with the aluminum to form aluminum oxide which creates two problems. Aluminum oxide that is formed is an insulator which is unwanted on the wafer surface. Second, the aluminum oxide requires higher energy to be broken up by the impinging atoms. D.C. diode sputtering cannot achieve the required energy. In effect the target becomes sealed by the aluminum oxide and the sputtering process stops. Two methods which overcome the problems of D.C. sputtering are triode and magnetron sputtering.

## Triode Sputtering

In triode-designed sputtering systems a separate high current filament is used to create the electrons necessary to ionize the gas. The benefits of this method include lower vacuum requirements in the chamber. The sputtered film undergoes less evaporation during deposition and is therefore denser. The filament is housed in the deposition chamber or in an adjacent chamber. In the latter case the wafers are isolated from the electrons and any radiation damage resulting from them.

## Magnatron Sputtering

In diode sputtering, not all of the electrons escaping the target contribute to the ionized plasma glow area. The wasted electrons fly around the chamber causing radiation and other problems, like the heating of the target. A magnatron sputtering system addresses the electron problem by placing magnets behind and sometimes at the sides of the target. These magnets capture the escaping electrons and confine them to the immediate vicinity of the target.

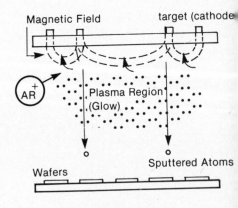

**Fig. 16.17
Magnetron Sputtering**

The ion current (density of ionized argon atoms hitting the target) is increased by an order of magnitude over conventional diode sputtering systems, resulting in faster deposition rates and lower pressure deposition. The lower pressure in the chamber helps create a cleaner film. Target temperature is lower with magnetron sputtering enhancing the deposition of high quality aluminum and aluminum films. This method is becoming the favored aluminum deposition technique.

### Vacuum System

The sputtering process takes place in the presence of the ionized argon gas. All other gases must be eliminated from the system or they will be incorporated in the film or interfere with the deposition. They are drawn from the system immediately after the wafers are loaded in the chamber. The vacuum level reached is in the same range as in evaporation, $10^{-7}$ Torr.

Both of the vacuum techniques (oil diffusion and cryogenics) employed in the evaporation systems are used in sputter systems. However, the continued flow of argon into a sputtering system requires fast response pumping to maintain the pressure. The faster speed of a cryogenic pump is favored for this application.

### Deposition Chamber

The basic parts of the deposition chamber have been identified and discussed. Design of the chamber interior reflectsthe requirements of film uniformity and production productivity. The classic wafer holder is a flat plate that rotates under the target. Other designs feature carousel holders that continually rotate the wafers in and out of the target area. Automated production machines require only operator cassette loading. The machine automatically loads the wafer holder, directs the vacuum pumping, the power to the sputtering system, deposition, venting and unloading.

In-line systems are another approach to automation. These systems operate in the same manner as the batch type described above, with one exception. In in-line systems deposition is done on one wafer at a time in a smaller chamber. This approach can produce a more uniform film composition and higher productivity.

### 16.7.3 Sputtering Process

Because clean wafers are essential, the wafers receive a chemical clean prior to loading in the sputterer. A typical machine sequence is listed in Table 16.1. After the deposition, the films are evaluated for conductivity, thickness, thickness uniformity and purity.

## 16.8 METALLIZATION OVERVIEW

A short time ago, the field of metallization was synonomous with the E-beam evaporation of aluminum and some filament evaporation of gold and nichrome. Today this process includes

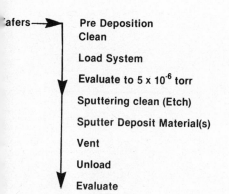

afers ⟶ Pre Deposition Clean

Load System

Evaluate to 5 x 10⁻⁶ torr

Sputtering clean (Etch)

Sputter Deposit Material(s)

Vent

Unload

Evaluate

**Table 16.2
Typical Spluttering Process**

many materials and two major techniques. The number of film combinations used is multiplying, as is the number of sputtering system designs. Chemical vapor deposition techniques are also vying for a share of metallization processes. It is expected that metallization processes will continue to undergo extensive development and improvement.

Table 16.3   Metalization Overview

| METAL | USE | | | DEPOSITION METHOD | | |
|---|---|---|---|---|---|---|
| | Conductor | Fuse | Other | Evaporation | Sputtering | CVD |
| Aluminum | X | | | X | X | |
| Aluminum/Silicon | X | | | X | X | |
| Aluminum/Copper | X | | | X | X | |
| Aluminum/Copper/Silicon | X | | | X | X | |
| Gold/Molybdenum/Platinum | X | | | X | X | |
| Titanium/Platinum/Gold | X | | | | X | |
| Titanium/Tungsten | | X | Barrier | | | |
| Nichrome | | X | | X | | |
| Gold | | | Die Attach/ Lifetime Control | X | | |
| Doped Silicon | X | | | | | X |
| Molybdenum | X | | | | X | X |
| Platinum Silicide | X | | Barrier | | X | X |
| Titanium Silicide | X | | | | X | X |
| Tungsten Silicide | X | | | | X | X |

# Wafer Test and Evaluation Methods

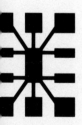

Chapter 17.

# INTRODUCTION

The wafer fabrication process requires a high degree of precision. Because one mistake can render the wafer completely useless, it is imperative to identify out-of-spec or potentially low-yield wafers as soon as problems arise. Therefore, as the wafer proceeds through the fabrication process steps, it undergoes a variety of tests and evaluations.

Characterization of the process itself and the circuit parameters is also required for line and product stability. Good characterization can warn of a process about to go out of control. Good characterization of the component characteristics is essential to analyze circuit performance.

Therefore, every significant process step is followed by an evaluation of the results. These tests have been identified in previous chapters. Here, we will explain the basic theory, parameters measured, range of sensitivity and frequency of measurement of those tests.

The term *test wafer* refers to blank wafers or wafer pieces that are included on the process wafer holders. Many of the tests are destructive and cannot be performed on the device wafers.

## 17.1 Resistance/Resistivity

The object of the fabrication process is to form, in and on the wafer surface, solid state electrical components (transistors, diodes, capacitors and resistors) that are wired together to form the circuit. Each of the individual components must meet certain electrical performance specifications if the entire circuit is to function. Throughout the process, electrical measurements are performed to judge the process and the electrical device performance.

Figure 5.1 plots the change in silicon resistivity with dopant concentration. Note that there are two curves: N and P. This implies that by adding exactly the same amount of N-type and P-type dopant to silicon, different resistivities will occur. This is due to the greater amount of energy required to move the holes in P-type material.

Wafers are purchased and Q.A. tested to a specific resistivity specification before being put in the line.

Although theoretically we can measure the resistivity of the wafer with a multimeter, the resistance to the current between the probes and the material invalidates the reading from this type of instrument.

An instrument with four probes is required to accurately measure the resistivity of semiconductor materials.

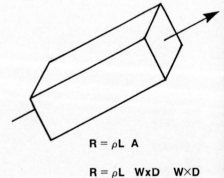

$$R = \rho L \ A$$

$$R = \rho L \ W \times D \quad W \times D$$

**Fig. 17.1
Relationship of Resistance
To Resistivity and Dimensions**

### 17.1.1 Resistivity Measurements

The addition of dopants to the wafer, both during crystal growth and during the doping process, alters the electrical characteristics of the wafer. The altered parameter is the resistivity, which is a measure of a material's specific "resistance" to the flow of electrons.

Whereas the resistivity of a given material is a constant, the resistance of a volume of the same material is a function of its dimensions and resistivity.

This relationship parallels that of density and weight. For example, the density of steel is a constant, whereas the weight of a particular piece depends on its size. The formula for the resistance of the object is illustrated below:

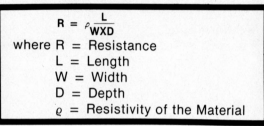

$$R = \rho \frac{L}{W \times D}$$

where R = Resistance
L = Length
W = Width
D = Depth
$\rho$ = Resistivity of the Material

The units of resistance are ohms ($\Omega$) and the units of resistivity are ohm/cm($\rho$).

Since adding dopants to a wafer will alter its resistivity, measurement of resistivity is actually an indirect measure of the amount of dopants added.

### 17.1.2 Four Point Probe

In a four point probe, the two outside probes are connected to a power supply and the inside probes are connected to a voltage meter. During operation, the current passes between the outer probes and the voltage drop is measured between the inner probes. The relationship of the current and voltage values is dependent on the resistance of the space between the probes and the resistivity of the material.

Thus, adding more dopant reduces the resistance (resistivity) of the wafer. The reduced resistance permits the current to flow with less force (voltage). In Ohm's Law, the three parameters are related in the following way:

R = V/I

Using a four point probe, the voltage and current are related to the resistivity by the relationship:

$\rho = 2\pi s d V/I$

where s is the distance between the probes.

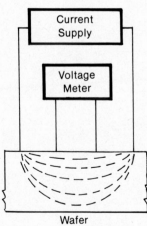

Ohms

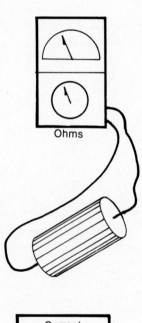

Current Supply

Voltage Meter

Wafer

**Fig. 17.2 Multimeter and 4-point Probe**

### 17.1.3 Sheet Resistance

The four point probe measurement described above is valid for measuring the resistivity of wafers and crystals. During the processing, thin doped layers of material are deposited on the surface and thin doped layers are formed down in the surface.

When a four point probe measurement is made on the thin layer of added dopants, the current is confined in the thin layer. A *thin layer* is defined as a layer thinner than the probe spacing (distance between probes).

The quantity measured on a thin layer is called sheet resistance (R). This quantity has the units of ohms/square.

### 17.1.4 Four Point Probe – Thickness Measurement

The thickness of uniform conducting layers on an insulating layer can be determined using a four point probe. For thin films the formula is:

$$T = \varrho_s/R$$

Where T = Layer Thickness
$\varrho_s$ = Resistivity
R = Sheet Resistance

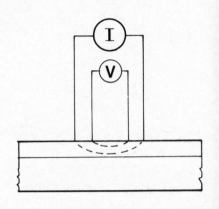

**Fig. 17-3 4-point Probe measuremen of a thin layer**

Since the resistivity is a constant for pure materials such as aluminum, the sheet resistance measurement is actually a measurement of the film thickness.

### 17.1.5 Summary of Four Point Probe Measurements

| QUANTITY MEASURED | FORMULA | CONDITIONS |
|---|---|---|
| Resistivity | $\varrho = 2\pi S V/I$ | Layer thickness greater than probe spacing. |
| Sheet Resistance | $R = \pi V_{In} = 4.53\ V/I$ | 1. Layer thickness much smaller than probe spacing 2. Sample area larger than probe spacing. |
| Thickness | $T = \varrho_s/R$ | 1. Layer thickness less than probe spacing 2. Uniform resistivity |

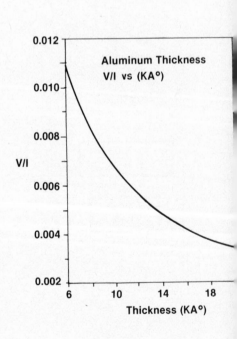

**Fig. 17-4**

**Thickness vs Rs of Aluminum**

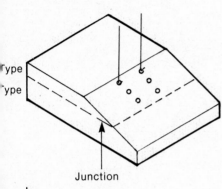

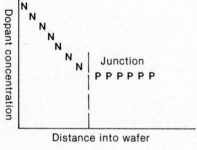

**Fig. 17-5 Spreading Resistance**

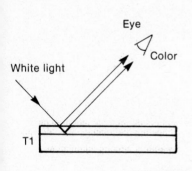

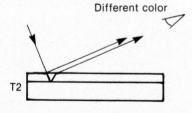

**Fig. 17-6 White light interfere interference**

### 17.1.6 Concentration Profile

The distribution of dopant atoms in the wafer is a major influence on the electrical operation of a device. The distribution or dopant concentration profile is determined by the *spreading resistance technique.*

After doping, a test wafer sample is prepared by the *Bevel Technique* (Section 17.3.1). A two point probe is marched down the bevel. At each point the vertical drop of the probes is recorded and a resistance measurement made. The resistance value at each point is the result of the concentration of dopants at that level.

A computer is used to perform the calculations and to relate the depth and resistance values to determine the concentration profile. This measurement is usually made periodically or when electrical device performance indicates that the dopant distribution may have changed.

## 17.2 LAYER THICKNESS MEASUREMENTS

### 17.2.1 Color

Both silicon dioxide and silicon nitride layers exhibit different colors on the wafer. We know that silicon dioxide is transparent (glass is silicon dioxide), yet it has a color on a wafer. The color is actually the result of an *interference phenomenon,* the same phenomenon that creates the colors of rainbows.

The silicon dioxide layer on a silicon wafer is actually a thin transparent film on a reflecting substrate. Some of the light rays impinging on the wafer surface reflect off of the oxide while others pass through the transparent oxide and reflect off of the mirrored wafer surface. When the light rays exit the film, they combine with the surface-reflected ray, resulting in a color.

The exact color is a function of three factors. One, which is a property of the transparent film material, is the *Index of Refraction.* A second factor is the viewing angle (rotate an oxidized wafer and the surface color will change). The third factor is the thickness of the film.

The color of a thin transparent film becomes an indication of the thickness when the nature of the viewing light is specified (i.e. daylight, flourescent), along with the viewing angle. The classic color vs. thickness chart (at the end of this chapter) is a regular feature at oxidation and diffusion stations. Color alone is not an exact indication of thickness, due to the consequences of the interference phenomenon.

As the film gets thicker the color changes in a specific sequence and then repeats itself. Each repetition of the color is called an *order.* To determine the exact film thickness, a knowledge of the color order is necessary. A principle use of color charts is for process control.

Each oxidation or silicon nitride process is designed to produce a specified thickness. Naturally the thickness will vary run to run. Operators quickly become sensitive to the usual color. When a variation occurs, a quick check of the chart will indicate if the film thickness is out of specification. Rarely is a process so far off that the film thickness is a whole order (same color, different thickness) out of specification. The accuracy of color chart thickness determination is limited to the accurate perception of the colors (what exact is red-orange?). A typical chart is accurate to ± 300 angstroms.

## 17.2.2 Fringes

When the order is not known, a fringe counting technique can be used. The test wafer edge is dipped in HF acid for a few seconds. The acid quickly eats through the oxide from the top down to the bare wafer. When the wafer is viewed in white light, colored fringes cover the area between the wafer surface and the top of the film. Thickness determination is made by first determining the order of the film thickness. It is easy to see the repeated sequence of colors. If three blue-red fringes exist, then the thickness corresponds to the surface color in the third order.

A more accurate fringe counting method uses *monochromatic light* as the viewing light. Monochromatic light consists of one color (wavelength), whereas white light is *polychromatic* (many wavelengths). The sample is prepared in the same way as it is for color fringe counting.

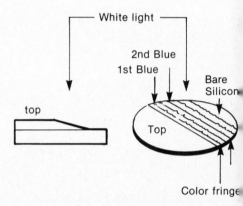

**Fig. 17-7 Color Fringes**

However, in the monochromatic light the fringes appear as alternating, evenly spaced black and white stripes. Film thickness is determined by counting the number of fringes and multiplying by a correction factor. The correction factor is determined by the wavelength of the monochromatic light used. For sodium light wavelength = 5,890 angstroms.

## 17.2.3 Spectrophotomoters

Film thickness interference measurement techniques can be automated. To understand the method, let's review the interference effects. Light is actually a form of energy. The interference phenomenon can also be described in terms of energy. White light is really a bundle of rays, each with different energies. When the rays interfere through the transparent film, the result is a ray of one wavelength or one energy level. Our eyes interpret the energy as a color.

In a spectrophotometer, which is an automatic interference instrument, a photocell takes the place of the human eye. Monochromatic light in the ultraviolet range is reflected off the sample and analyzed by the photocell. To insure accuracy, readings are made at different conditions. The conditions are changed by either using another monochromatic light (to change wavelength) or changing the angle of the wafer to the beam. Spectrophotometers specifically designed for use in semiconductor technology have on-board computers to perform the thickness calculations from the data.

Spectrophotometers are also used to measure silicon film thickness. Since silicon is opaque to U.V. light, an infrared source (I.R.) is used. The accuracy of spectrophotometer type instruments stems from multiple measurements and changed conditions. Spectrophotometers lose their accuracy for film thicknesses in the first order (below 1100 angstroms). For thinner transparent films, ellipseometers are the preferred measuring instrument.

### 17.2.4 Ellipseometers

*Ellipseometers* are film thickness instruments that use a laser light source and operate on a different principle than a spectrophotometer. The laser light source is polarized. The effect of polarization is to create a wave that is traveling in only one plane. Polarization can be imagined by considering looking into the beam of a flashlight. In an ordinary beam light rays come to your eyes in many planes, like an arrow with many feathers. A polarized beam has all of the light in only one plane, or an arrow with only one feather.

In the ellipseometer the polarized beam is directed to the oxide covered wafer at an angle. The beam enters the transparent film and reflects off of the reflective wafer surface. During its passage through the film the angle of the beam plane is rotated. The amount of rotation of the beam is a function of the thickness and index of refraction of the film. A detector in the instrument measures the amount of rotation and an on-board computer calculates the thickness and index of refraction.

Ellipseometers are used to measure thin oxides (50 to 1200 angstroms.) Their accuracy in this range is unequalled by other techniques.

### 17.2.5 Stylus

Some thin films such as aluminum cannot be measured by optical techniques. And in the case of aluminum and other very thin conductive films, the four point probe thickness measurement is not sufficiently accurate.

In these situations a moving stylus apparatus is used. The method requires that a portion of the film be removed. This is normally done by a masking and etching step. The prepared sample is mounted and leveled on the pivoting stylus instrument stage.

**Fig. 17-8 Sample Preparation**

After leveling, the measuring stylus is lowered gently onto one of the surfaces. Upon activation of the measuring cycle, the stage is slowly moved under the stylus.

The stylus itself is linked to an inductor that generates an electrical signal in response to the stylus position. This signal is amplified and fed into an X-Y recorder.

While the leveled wafer is moving under the stylus, it does not move in the verticle direction and no change in signal is produced. The trace on the X-Y plotter is a straight line.

When the stylus reaches the surface step it changes position, causing a change in the signal output. This change is evidenced by a change of pen position on the X-Y recorder. The size of the change in pen position is reactive to the step height, which is read directly from the calibrated X-Y chart.

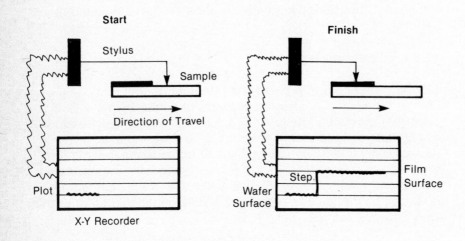

**Fig. 17-9   Step Height Measurement**

## 17.3 JUNCTION DEPTH

### 17.3.1 Groove and Stain

Junction depths are measured by the *groove* or bevel *and stain* technique. The extreme shallow depth of the junction requires either grooving or beveling of the wafer to expose the junction.

The junction itself is not visible to the naked eye. Two techniques, called *junction delineation,* are available to make it visible. Both techniques utilize the electrical difference of properties of N and P type regions. The first technique -- the *etch technique* -- starts with the placement of a drop of HF and water mixture over the junction. A heat lamp is shined on the exposed junction. The heat and light cause holes or electrons to flow in each region. As a result of the flowing current, the etch rate of the $HF/H_2O$ mixture on the silicon, the N-type side of the junction appears darker.

The second delineation technique is *electro staining.* A mixture containing copper is dropped on the exposed junction. Again, the heat lamp is directed onto the junction. A battery is formed, with the poles of the junction being the poles of the battery and the copper solution being the electrical connection. The current flowing in the drop causes the copper to plate out on the N-type region side of the junction.

The final step, after exposure and delineation of the junction, is depth measurement. An interference method is used, in which a monochromatic light is directed through a thin piece of glass positioned over the groove or bevel.

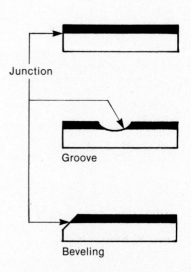

**Fig. 17-10 Exposure of Junction**
**or**
**By Groove or Beveling**

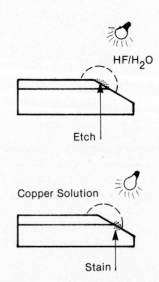

**Fig. 17-11 Etching or Staining of Junction**

The fringes are normally created with the use of an attachment to a microscope. The fringes are observed through it. The junction depth is read by counting the number of superimposed fringes from the surface down to the junction. For a given wavelength, each fringe represents a specific depth. A common source is sodium, with each fringe representing a depth.

Accurate fringe counting is important. Usually a photograph of the fringes superimposed over the junction is made through the microscope, and the fringes are counted from it.

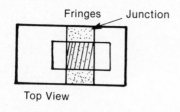

Top View

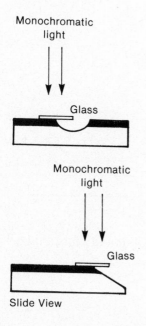

Slide View

**Fig. 17-12 Creation of Fringes**

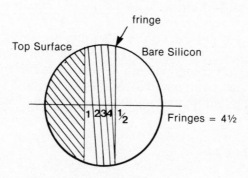

**Fig. 17-13 Fringe Counting**

### 17.3.2 S.E.M. (Scanning Electron Microscope)

The S.E.M. technique (described in section 17.4.7) can also be used to measure junction depths and film thickness. The wafer is scribed and broken at the point of measurement. The cleaned wafer edge is polished smooth and the wafer exposed junction delineated by one of the methods described in Section 17.3.1.

The delineated junction is positioned at right angles to the wafer surface and a photograph taken. The depth is determined from the photograph and the scale factor of the S.E.M.

### 17.3.3 Spreading Resistance

*Spreading resistance* is a technique used for measuring the dopant concentration profile in a wafer (Section 17.6.6). As the probes pass through the junction, they sense the change in conductivity type (N or P). This information, when plotted on the profile curve also gives the junction depth.

## 17.4 CONTAMINATION DETECTION

Detection of contamination in and on the wafer is essential to maintain high yields and to measure the effectiveness of the contamination control procedures. Particulate contamination on the wafer is detected primarily by visual techniques, from high intensity light and manual inspection to S.E.M. Chemical contamination is detected and identified by both auger and E.S.C.A. techniques. Mobile ionic contamination in the wafer is detected by C-V plotting and by interpretation of the transistor and diode electrical tests. Many other sophisticated techniques can be used make these inspections. The ones described here are those employed in a typical wafer fabrication line.

### 17.4.1 1 × Visual Inspection

The first line of defense in (1 × power) colimated detection is to look at the wafers. Operators quickly become sensitive to the way "normal" wafers look. Even minor changes in the surface appearance are picked up by the experienced eye.

### 17.4.2 1 × Collimated Light

The resolving power of a naked eye (1 ×) can be assisted by using a collimated white light, like the beam of light from a slide projector. Particulate contamination is highlighted in the light beam when the wafer surface is viewed at an angle. The effect is similar to the highlighting of dust in the air by light streaming through a window.

### 17.4.3 1 × Ultraviolet

Particulate contamination (and stains) are made even more visible if the viewing light is an ultraviolet source. The smaller wavelength and monochromatic nature of the light highlights very small pieces of contamination. The lamps are a regular fixture at photomasking inspection stations as well as at process stations. Operators view wafers both prior to loading on the process holder and after the operation is complete.

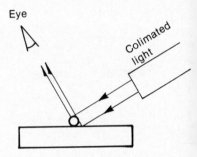

**Fig. 17.14**
**Colimated Light Inspection**

### 17.4.4 Light Field Microscope

The metallurgical microscope is the workhorse tool of surface inspection. The term *metallurgical* differentiates it from the standard microscope found in biology labs. A biological microscope illuminates the transparent samples by shining the light up through the sample. In a metallurgical microscope, the light is passed down to the non-transparent sample through the microscope objective. The light reflects off the sample surface and is transmitted through the optics to the eyepieces. With white light illumination, the picture in the field of view exhibits the actual surface colors. Use of filters will change the surface colors.

A typical fab microscope is fitted with 10 × or 15 × eyepieces and a range of objectives from 10 × to 50 ×. Increasing the total viewing power (eyepiece power × objective power) reduces the field of view. This reduction requires more inspection time of the operator to look at the required sample inspection area on the wafer. The consequence is a slower inspection process. A trade-off power level, when inspecting LSI/VLSI devices, is 200–300 magnification.

The industry typically uses a microscope inspection procedure requiring the operator to look at three to five (3–5) specific locations on the wafer. This procedure is easily automated with motorized stages. Most of the automated microscope inspection stations feature automatic wafer placement on the stage and automatic binning of the completed wafers. At the touch of a button, the operator can direct each wafer to a boat for passed wafers or into one of several boats for different reject categories. Obviously, a microscope inspection is determined to judge surface and layer quality and (in masking) pattern alignment.

### 17.4.5 Dark Field Inspection

Dark field illumination is achieved by fitting a metallurgical microscope with a special objective. In this objective, the light is directed to the wafer surface through the outside of the objective body. It impinges on the surface at an angle and passes up through the center of the objective. The effect on the "picture" in the eyepieces is to render all flat surfaces black. Any surface irregularities, such as a step or contamination, appear as bright lines. Dark field illumination is more sensitive than light field to any surface irregularity. It has the drawback of limiting the operator's ability to discern the nature of the surface irregularity. A passable surface dimple may look the same as a rejectable piece of contamination. In practice, dark field illumination is rarely used in standard inspections, but is reserved for diagnostic purposes.

### 17.4.6 Advanced Microscope Techniques

Optical technology is capable of providing many evaluation techniques beyond simple light and dark field viewing such as phase contrast. Each allows the viewer to determine additional information about the surface. In practice, these instruments are confined to quality assurance laboratories. Their use and interpretation require technicians trained beyond the level of production operators.

### 17.4.7 Scanning Electron Microscope (S.E.M.)

Conventional optical microscopes are limited in their ability to provide accurate information about the wafer surface. First, their resolving power is limited by their white light source. The ability of a viewing system to distinguish detail is related to the wavelength of the light (radiation used). The shorter the wavelength the smaller the detail that can be seen.

Depth of field is another viewing factor which relates to the ability of the system to keep two planes in focus simultaneously. A conventional photograph with the subject in focus and the background out of focus has a background beyond the depth of focus limit of the camera.

In a microscope, the depth of field decreases as the power (magnification) of the system is increased. If the power is increased to see the surface "closer", the operator may not be able to see the top and bottom surfaces in focus. Constant refocusing results in loss of information and a slower inspection time.

Magnification is the third limiting factor of optical microscopes. An optical system with white light illumination is limited to about 1000× magnification with conventional objectives. The oil

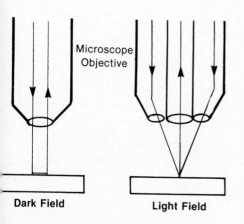

**Dark Field**          **Light Field**

**Fig. 17-15 Light and Dark Field Inspection**

immersion technique pushes the limit up, but it is unacceptable because it is too slow, too messy and a possible source of contamination to the wafer.

All three limitations are overcome by using a scanning electron microscope. The microscope varies from an optical one in many aspects. The "illumination" source is an electron beam scanned over the wafer or device surface. The impinging electrons cause electrons on the surface to be ejected. These secondary electrons are collected and translated into a picture of the surface.

S.E.M. requires that the wafer and beam be in a vacuum. The secondary electrons are viewed on a C.R.T. or used to expose a standard photographic film.

The electron beam has a much smaller wavelength than white light, and allows the resolution of surface detail down to submicron levels. Depth of field problems do not exist; every plane on the surface is in focus. Magnification is similarly very high with a practical limit of 50,000 ×.

A tilting wafer holder in an S.E.M. allows the viewing of the surface at angles which enhance the three dimension perspective. Surface details and features can be viewed at advantageous angles.

Some materials do not give off secondary electrons in response to E-beam bombardment. A photoresist layer in an S.E.M. requires the evaporation of a thin layer of gold on top of the resist-covered wafer surface. The gold layer conforms to the topography of the photoresist layer. Under E-beam bombardment the gold gives off secondary electrons, thus resulting in an S.E.M. picture of the underlying photoresist layer.

### 17.4.8 Auger Analysis

In an S.E.M., a range (spectrum) of secondary electrons is released by the impinging electron beam. One portion of this spectrum is of electrons that are released from the top several nanometers of the surface. These electrons, known as Auger electrons, have energies characteristic of the element that emits them.

The consequence of this characteristic of Auger electrons, allows the identification of the surface materials, including contamination. In operation the E-beam is scanned across the wafer. The ejected Auger electrons are analyzed for their energies (wavelengths) and printed out on an X-Y plotter. Energy peaks at specific wavelengths indicate the presence of elements on the surface.

Scanning Auger Microanalysis (S.A.M.) is limited to the identification of elements. This technique cannot identify the chemical state of the element, what it may be combined with or the quantity on the surface.

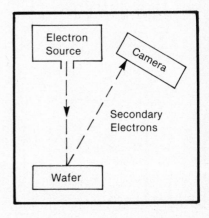

**Fig. 17.16 SEM Analysis**

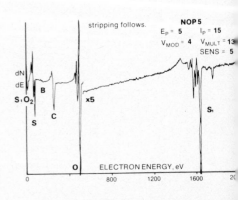

**Fig. 17.17 Typical Auger Trace**

### 17.4.9 Electron Spectroscope for Chemical Analysis (E.S.C.A.)

Often, solving surface contamination problems requires a knowledge of the state of the contaminant. An Auger detection of chlorine on the surface does not reveal whether the chlorine is present as hydrochloric acid or a trichloro benzene. Knowledge of the form of the chlorine expedites locating and eliminating the process source of contamination.

The electron spectroscope for chemical analysis (E.S.C.A.) is an instrument used to determine surface chemistry. The instrument works on principles similar to the Auger technique. However, X-rays instead of electrons are used for the bombarding radiation. Under bombardment the surface gives off. The element analysis of this information leads to the determination of the chemical formula of the contamination.

Unfortunately the E.S.C.A. X-ray beam is wider than I.C. features. The beam diameter limits the technique to a macro surface analysis. By contrast, an Auger electron beam can zero-in on specific bits of contamination.

### 17.4.10 Laser Scanning

The detection of smaller and smaller sized particles on the wafer surface has led to the use of laser beams as a detection illumination. Two advantages accrue from the use of lasers. First is the obvious ability to detect smaller particle size due to the smaller wavelength of the laser. (Helium and neon are the usual sources.)

The second advantage is automation. Laser inspection equipment is easy to automate such that the inspection is automated from cassette to cassette and the quantity and size of the contamination on the surface can be quantified. This last factor is a big help in process control.

Laser inspection of masks has become the favored production technique.

### 17.4.11 Cold Plate

Wafer surface stains from solvents and water are often difficult to detect using conventional microscope techniques. An alternative method to detect them is a cold plate method. This technique is also called the *freeze plate method*. The apparatus consists of a wafer vacuuam chuck that is cooled by circulating cold water, circulating freon or a thermal electric device. The wafer is placed on the chuck and rapidly cooled to below room temperature.

The rapid cooling causes water in the air to condense on the wafer surface. Actually, the condensation occurs first on hydrophyllic regions such as stains. Observation of the wafer surface as condensation begins reveals any surface stains or other anomalies.

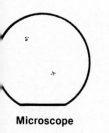 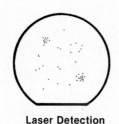

Microscope          Laser Detection

**Fig. 17-18 Laser Detection of Defects**

This technique is also used prior to metallization deposition to indicate the lack of oxide in the contact holes. In this version of the test, the contact holes are observed through a microscope as the condensation begins. If the contact holes are free of oxide the condensation will occur initially on the field oxide.

In both uses of the test the observation must be made immediately as the condensation begins. After a minute or so the entire wafer surface becomes covered with condensation and any indication of surface stains is obliterated.

## 17.5 CRITICAL DIMENSIONS MEASUREMENT

The goal of creating the exact dimensions required of each component in the circuit is controlled at ALL processes. In the doping area, the depth of each doped layer is controlled by the process conditions. Likewise, CVD processes are set to produce the required layer thicknesses.

The horizontal surface dimensions are produced in the photomasking area. As part of that process the dimensions are measured at both develop inspect and final inspect. Two measurement techniques are used.

### 17.5.1 Filar Measuring Eyepiece

The *Filar measuring eyepiece* is a dimension measuring instrument that is fitted to a microscope. The eyepiece features a movable hairline that requires calibration to an outside standard, usually a *stage micrometer.*

In manual operation, the pattern to be measured is focused in the field of view. The eyepiece is rotated to position the hairline perpendicular to the measuring location path. Once oriented, the hairline is moved to the starting point of the pattern to be measured, and the value on the micrometer barrel is noted. The hairline is then moved in a smooth continuous motion to the other side of the pattern. The ending value is also noted.

The actual width is calculated by subtracting the starting value from the ending value and multiplying the resulting number by the previously determined correction factor. This system is highly accurate and is used by the National Bureau of Standards. Accurate measurements require good operator techniques.

Filar systems are easily automated. The hairline movement mechanism is motorized. The correction factor is put into an onboard computer, resulting in a direct digital read-out of the actual width. Operator fatigue is minimized by displaying the pattern to be measured and the hairline on a monitor.

### 17.5.2 Image Shearing

An image shearing attachment to a microscope is another method of critical dimension measurement. In the manual version, the operator rotates the pattern to be measured to a vertical position in the field of view. A control on the unit allows

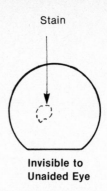

**Invisible to Unaided Eye**

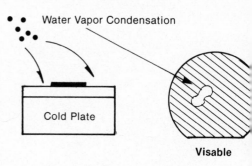

**Fig. 17-19 Cold Plate**

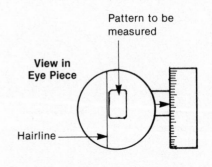

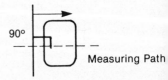

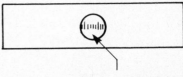

**Fig. 17-20 Manual Filar Measurement**

the operator to separate (shear) the pattern into two images. To start the measurement, the two images are butted against each other. The operator notes the value of this position on the shearing control. In step two, the shearing control is rotated until the images are rejoined into one. Again the ending value on the shearing control is noted. The difference between the starting and ending values is the width of the pattern in "image shearing units" multiplied by a previously determined correction factor. The correction factor is determined by use of a *stage micrometer,* exactly like the calibration of a filar eyepiece.

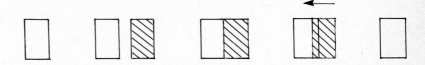

**Fig. 17.21 Single Image Shearing**

The procedure described above is called *single image shearing,* because the pattern is sheared once. Shearing the image twice is another technique. This is accomplished by following the same procedure used in single shearing, but continuing the shear until the image is again doubled. The pattern is actually sheared twice and the calculated width must be divided by two.

**Fig. 17.22 Double Image Shearing**

This procedure can be automated for production work. The images are displayed on a C.R.T. and the shearing motion motorized. And like the filar automated measurement, a correction factor is programmed into the unit. The width of the pattern is read directly from the unit.

### 17.5.3 Reflectance

Both the Filar and image shearing techniques require some operator decision, which can be a source of error. A third type of dimensional measurement instrument is based on *reflectance.* Like the other two, the operator locates the pattern to be measured on a monitor. One edge of the pattern is positioned under a marker on the screen. The measurement is actually made automatically by the instrument after that. A laser beam is swept along the direction of measurement and the reflection energy of the beam recorded. When the beam comes to the edge of the pattern, it steps up (or down) to a new surface. The new surface causes a different reflectance of the beam which is recorded by the detector. The width of the pattern is the difference between the starting point and the point where there is a change in reflectance. This value is read out automatically. Operator decision is limited to determining the starting point, resulting in a more constant accuracy.

The limitation of this method is with patterns that have a step in them, such as metal steps. The instrument is designed to read to the first change in reflectance it senses.

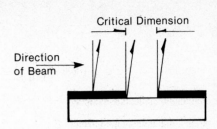

Fig. 17.23 Reflectance C.D. Measurement

## OVERVIEW OF SURFACE INSPECTION TECHNIQUES

| Method | Visual contamination | Surface Defects | Alignment | Contamination Elements | Contamination Compounds | C.D.'s |
|---|---|---|---|---|---|---|
| 1x Incident White Light | X | X | | | | |
| 1x Incident U.V. Light | X | X | | | | |
| Microscope– Lightfield | X | X | X | | | |
| Darkfield | X | X | X | | | |
| S.E.M. | X | X | X | | | |
| Auger | | | | X | | |
| E.S.C.A. | | | | | X | |
| Filar | | | | | | X |
| Image Shearing | | | | | | X |
| Reflectance | | | | | | X |

# 17.6 DEVICE ELECTRICAL MEASUREMENTS

During the process, it is necessary to make measurements of the actual device parameters. These measurements are usually made on special devices in the test die. At the end of the process, the actua devices are more fully characterized. This operation has various names, including *Electrical Test, E-Test, and Pre-sort.* Readers unfamiliar with semiconductor device operation should read Chapter 18.

A great deal of information about the process is available from these tests. In this section we will explain the basic tests and several of the more obvious and frequent device failures. A complete device and process trouble shooting guide is beyond the scope of this text.

## 17.6.1 Equipment

The basic equipment required to perform these tests are a probe machine with the capability of positioning needle-like probes on the devices, a switch box to apply the correct voltage, current and polarities to the device, and an oscilloscope to display the results.

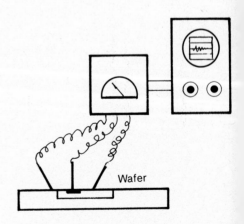

Fig. 17.24 Device Measurement Equipment

In advanced systems, the probe station may be automated to sequentially test several die. The switching can also be automated to allow the equipment to perform the tests in a predetermined sequence. In some systems the device output to a specific test may be displayed as an absolute number rather than displayed on an oscilloscope screen. Automated systems also include hard copies of the test results as well as analysis of the data.

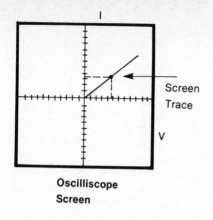

Oscilliscope
Screen

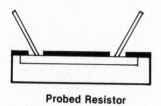

Probed Resistor

**Fig. 17.25 Resistor**

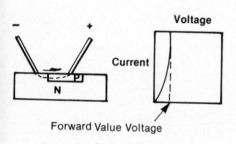

Forward Value Voltage

**Fig. 17.26 Diode Forward Bias**

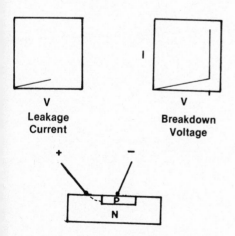

V
Leakage
Current

V
Breakdown
Voltage

**Fig. 17.27 Diode Reverse Bias
Measurement**

The individual tests will be explained, as performed on manual equipment. The shape and relationship of the traces displayed on the oscilloscope are very helpful for understanding device operation.

The device measurements apply a voltage to the component and measure the resulting current. The current is modified by the resistance of the component or the presence of junctions.

The fundamental relationship is that of OHM's Law:

$$R = V/I$$

### 17.6.2 Resistors

Resistor measurements are made by contacting each end of the resistor and applying a voltage. The current passing through the resistor is a result of the resistance value.

The oscilloscope allows the variation of the applied voltage, from zero to higher values. On the screen the voltage value is displayed on the X-axis, with current measured on the Y-axis.

The value of the resistance is calculated by dividing one of the voltage values by the corresponding current value. One might ask, "why not determine the resistance by simply measuring the voltage and current values with a meter?" In other words, why display the values on the screen? The answer lies in the quality information gained from the trace. A resistor's V/I relationship should be a linear one. Any deviation from linearity could indicate a process problem, such as high contact resistance.

### 17.6.3 Diodes

Diodes function as switches in a circuit. This means that a diode will pass current in one direction (forward bias) and not in the other (reverse bias).

Checking diode operation in the forward direction requires probing the diode with the proper polarities, as shown.

As the voltage is increased, current immediately starts flowing across the junction and out of the diode. The initial resistance to that flow comes from contact resistance and the junction. At some voltage level, there occurs a "full" flow of current through the diode. A diode is designed to have this condition occur at some minimum voltage value. If the diode forward voltage value exceeds the design value, it is out of specification.

In the reverse direction, the diode is designed to block the current flow up to the breakdown voltage value.

Actually a small current, called a leakage current, does flow across the junction. Eventually a voltage value is reached that causes a breakdown of the junction, allowing "full" current flow. The breakdown voltage is a designed value of the diode. Circuits are designed to operate at a voltage level below the designed breakdown voltage of the diode. If improper processing results in a breakdown voltage lower than the circuit operating voltage, the diode will pass current in the circuit instead of blocking it.

Junction breakdown is normally a temporary condition. Exceeding the breakdown voltage does not permanently damage the junction, unless the applied voltage is extremely high.

A second value determined during this test is the leakage current or current at breakdown. A small amount normally occurs as illustrated above. Contamination and/or improper processing can result in additional leakage current.

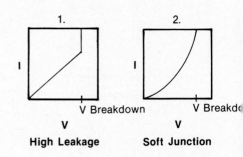

**Fig. 17.28 Junction Leakage**

Trace #1 in the figure shows a diode with a small amount of leakage. The amount of current increases as the voltage is increased. Eventually, the breakdown voltage is reached and the diode becomes fully conducting. In Trace #2, gross leakage is demonstrated. The junction leaks current with every increase in voltage, and the problem is so severe that a breakdown is never reached.

### 17.6.4. Oxide Quality (BVox or Rupture Voltage)

An electrical measurement, $BV_{ox}$, is used as a measure of oxide quality. The test structure used is the same as for C/V analysis. In this case, the voltage is continually increased until the oxide is physically destroyed and current flows freely from the aluminum dot to the silicon. The maximum voltage that the oxide can withstand before breakdown is a function of its thickness, structural quality and purity.

### 17.6.5 Bipolar Transistors

Transistors, as explained in Chapter 18, are three region, two junction devices. Electrically, they can be thought of as two diodes back-to-back.

Many tests are performed to characterize bipolar transistors. The individual junctions are characterized separately and whole transistor operation measured. The parts (or junctions) are probed for forward and reverse characteristics. The breakdown voltage (BV) test is followed by the probing of the transistor regions.

$BV_{cbo}$ indicates the breakdown voltage measured between the collector and base regions. The "o" indicates that the emitter region is "open" – it has no voltage applied to it. $BV_{ceo}$ is the breakdown measured between the collector and emitter. For this test, the collector base junction is reverse biased forward voltages ($VB_e$ and $VB_c$).

The forward voltages of the two bipolar structure junctions are also measured. VBe is the forward voltage of the emitter/base junction and Bc is the forward of the base/collector junction.

$BV_{iso}$ probes the collector-isolation junction.

The principal electrical measurement of a bipolar transistor is the Beta (B) measurement. This is a measurement of the amplification feature of a transistor. In Chapter 2 transistor operation was compared to the flow of water through a valve. In a bipolar transistor, the current flows from the emitter to the collector, through the base. The base current is varied to change the resistance in the base region. The amount of current flowing out of the collector (from the emitter to base) is regulated by the base resistance.

The amplification of the transistor is defined as the collector current divided by the base current. This number is known as Beta. Thus a Beta of 10 means that a 1 milliamp base current will give rise to a 10 milliamp collector. The Beta of a transistor is determined by junction depths, junction separations (base width), doping levels and profiles and a host of other process and design factors.

Measurement of Beta (or hfe) is done by a variation of the $BV_{ceo}$ measurement. A $BV_{ceo}$ measurement at a specific base current is performed. In this mode, the emitter base junction is forward biased.

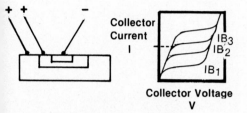

**Fig.17.29 NPN Transistor Beta Measurement**

The collector characteristic of the transistor is displayed on the oscilloscope screen. The almost horizontal lines represent increasing base current values (I). With every increase in base current, a corresponding increase in collector current occurs. Calculation takes place from the data displayed on the screen. Collector current is determined from the vertical axis (dotted line). The base current is calculated by multiplying the number of horizontal lines (steps) by the scale value for each step (from the oscilloscope).

$$(\beta E) = (\#steps) = (miliamps/step) \, I$$

## 17.6.6 M.O.S. Electrical Measurements

M.O.S. circuits are also made up of resistors, diodes, capacitors and transistors. The first three are measured by the same methods used to measure the similar bipolar circuit components.

Like the bipolar, the M.O.S. transistor is composed of three regions: in this case called the source, gate and drain. Measurement of these consists of determining the reverse and forward values of the source and drain junctions. The functioning of the gate is determined by the threshold voltage test.

An M.O.S. transistor has the source region forward based -- the current flows from the source into the gate region. Due to the high resistivity of the gate region, the forward current does not reach the drain. A voltage applied to the gate at a specified level (threshold) will cause enough charges to appear in the gate region to allow the source current to reach the drain region. Every M.O.S. transistor is designed to operate at a specific threshold voltage. This value is measured using the capacitance/voltage technique. The gate voltage is continuously increased, while the capacitance of the gate structure is monitored.

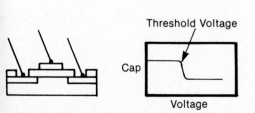

**Fig. 17.30 Threshold Voltage Measurement**

A capacitor is a storage device. Initially, during the voltage increase portion of the measurement, the capacitance does not change. At the threshold voltage level, the inversion layer forms

228

and acts like a capacitor. Since two in-series capacitors have a combined lower capacitance than the sum of the two, the result is a drop to a combined lower capacitance.

M.O.S. transistors also exhibit amplification characteristics. The gain is defined as the source/drain current divided by the gate current. The source drain characteristic for various gate currents is shown.

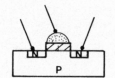

**Fig. 17.31 Grain Characteristic of an MOS Transistor**

## 17.7 CAPACITANCE/VOLTAGE PLOTTING

A variation of the threshold voltage test is used to test for the presence of mobile ionic contamination in the oxide. The test is performed on specially prepared test wafers. A thin oxide is grown on a "clean" silicon wafer. After oxide growth, aluminum dots are formed on the wafer by evaporation through a mask. Dot evaporation is usually followed by an alloy step to insure good electrical contact between the aluminum and oxide.

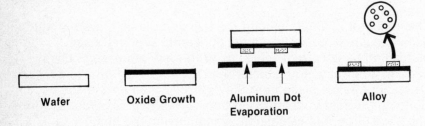

| Wafer | Oxide Growth | Aluminum Dot Evaporation | Alloy |

**Fig. 17.32 Preparation of C/V Test Wafer**

The "dotted" wafer is placed on a chuck and a probe placed on the aluminum dot. The structure is actually an M.O.S. capacitor. A voltage is applied to the dot and gradually increased, as the capacitance of the structure is simultaneously measured. The results are printed out on an X-Y plotter with capacitance on the Y-axis and voltage on the X-axis.

At a voltage level known as the *threshold voltage* or *inversion voltage,* charge starts to build up at the silicon surface. The charges "invert" the conductivity type from N-type (see example) to P-type. The inverted layer has a capacitance of its own. Electrically, the structure now has two capacitors in series. The total capacitance value of the two is less than the sum of the two by the relationship.

$$1/C_{total} = 1/C_{ox} + 1/C_{inversion}$$

The trace on the X-Y plotter drops vertically to the new capacitance level.

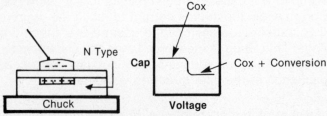

**Fig. 17-33 C/V Plotting 1st Plot**

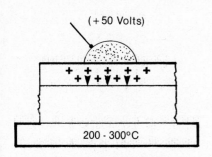

(+50 Volts)

200 - 300°C

**Fig. 17-34 C/V Plotting Ionic Charge Collection**

Original Plot
Second Plot
Voltage Shift
or Drift

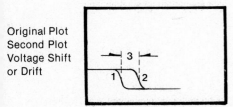

**Fig. 17.35 C/V Replot**

The second step in the process is to force the mobile positive ions in the oxide to the $SiO_2$/silicon interface. This is done by simultaneously heating the wafer to the 200–300° C level and placing a positive 50 volt bias on the structure. The elevated temperature increases the mobility of the ions and the positive bias "repels" them to the oxide silicon interface.

The last step in the process is a repetition of the initial C/V plot. However as the voltage increases, inversion does not start at the same level as in the initial plot. The positive charges at the interface require additional negative voltage to "neutralize" them before inversion can happen. The result is a C/V plot identical to the original but displaced to the right.

The additional voltage required to complete the plot is known as the "drift" or "shift."

The amount of the shift is proportional to the amount of mobile ionic contamination in the oxide, the oxide thickness and wafer doping. C/V analysis cannot distinguish the element (Na, K, Fe, ...) that was in the oxide, only the amount. Neither can this test determine where the contamination came from. It may have come from the wafer surface, any cleaning step, the oxidation tube, the evaporation process, the alloy tube, or any process the wafer has been through.

C/V analysis is usually a part of any process change evaluation that may contaminate a wafer, like a new cleaning process. To make the evaluation, C/V wafers are divided into two groups. One group receives normal processing as detailed above. The second group goes through the proposed cleaning process, usually between oxidation and aluminum oxidation. The drift on the standardly processed wafers is compared to the drift of the experimental group. An increased drift on the experimental wafers would indicate that the proposed cleaning process actually contaminated the wafers with mobile ionic contamination.

Acceptable C/V drifts vary between 0.1 and 0.5 volts, depending on the sensitivity of the device being made. C/V analysis has become a standard test in a fab area. The test is made after any process change or maintenance or cleaning that could have the potential of contaminating the wafers. The C/V plot provides a wealth of other information, such as *flat band voltage* and surface states to the process engineer, in addition to the voltage drift.

## 17.8 PINHOLE COUNTING

A photoresist film will contain circular discontinuities too small to be resolved at normal magnifications. To test for pinholes the resist is spun on an oxidized wafer. The determination of which "dots" are actually pinholes is made by processing the wafers through a photomasking step. The resist-coated wafer is either flood exposed or exposed through a blank mask. After exposure and develop only the actual pinholes are left in the resist film.

These pinholes are transferred into the oxide layer at an oxide etch step. One more step is necessary to differentiate the real pinholes from oxide film surface irregularities. The step is a silicon etch.

The etch penetrates through the pinhole in the oxide layer and etches the silicon underneath. The hole in the silicon is visible with a microscope as a pattern around the pinhole. The shape of the pattern is either a triangle for {111} material and a square for {100} wafers.

Normally a grid is inserted in the microscope eyepiece and the pinholes within the grid counted. Pinhole density for a VLSI resist typically runs 1 or per cm$^2$.

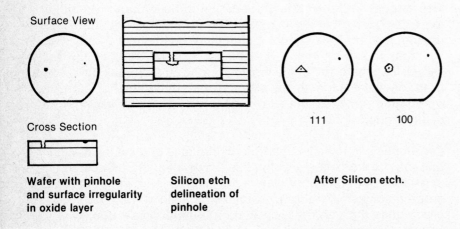

Surface View

Cross Section

Wafer with pinhole
and surface irregularity
in oxide layer

Silicon etch
delineation of
pinhole

After Silicon etch.

111          100

**Fig. 17-36 Pinhole Relination by Silicon Etching**

# Semiconductor Devices

Chapter 18.

## INTRODUCTION

A VLSI circuit can contain up to a million separate components or semiconductor devices. Yet for all its complexity, an integrated circuit is composed of only six types of components:

1. Resistors
2. Diodes
3. Transistors
4. Capacitors
5. Fuses
6. Conductors

In this chapter, we will study the fabrication of these basic components by planar technology techniques and examine their basic operation(s) and function(s).

## 18.1 RESISTORS

Resistors limit current flow within a circuit. The following types of resistors occur in a typical circuit:

1. Diffused
2. Metalic Thin Film

### 18.1.1 Diffused Resistors

The performance values of every semiconductor device are dependent on the physical dimensions of the device. We can examine a diffused resistor to illustrate this dependence.

The circuit designer will specify a required resistor value using the standard schematic symbol for a resistor.

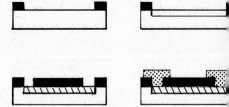

**Fig. 18.2
Diffused Resistor Formation**

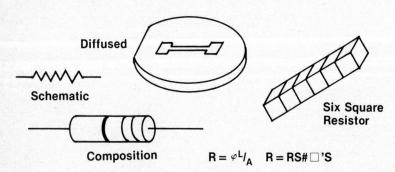

**Fig. 18.1    Resistors**

If we were to manufacture a discrete resistor we would apply Ohm's Law in the form:

$$R = r/L \times A$$

where: $\varphi$ = Resistance (ohms)
r = Resistivity of the Material
L = Resistor Length
A = Resistor Cross-sectional Area

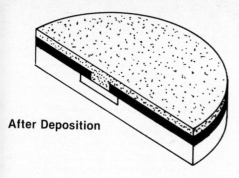

**After Deposition**

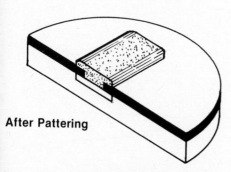

**After Pattering**

**Fig. 18.3   Metal Film Deposition and Patterning**

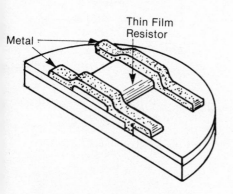

Metal

Thin Film Resistor

**Fig. 18.4   Formation of a Thin Film Resistor**

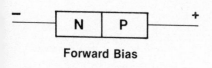

| − | N | P | + |

**Forward Bias**

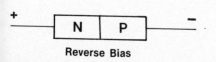

| + | N | P | − |

**Reverse Bias**

**Fig. 18.5 Forward and Reverse Biasing**

To duplicate that same resistance in a semiconductor, we would diffuse into the wafer the appropriate quantity of N or P-type atoms. For a diffused resistor Ohm's Law takes the form:

$$R = R_s \times \# \square \text{'s}$$

where: R = Resistance (ohms)
R = Sheet resistance of the diffused region
# □'s = Number of squares = Length of resistor divided by its width

In effect, a selected doped volume of the wafer is utilized as the resistor. Abstracting that volume from the wafer, it is obvious that it conforms to our standard Ohm's Law. The r and depth parameters are incorporated into the sheet resistance specification. The length and width of the resistor are accounted for by the calculation of the number of □'s = L/W.

The sheet resistance is controlled in the diffusion process. The surface dimensions of length and width are created and controlled by the photomasking process. Figure 18.2 shows the basic planar process steps needed to create a resistor. The resistors can be utilized separately or connected together into an integrated circuit.

The point to remember is that the electrical parameters of an electrical device are directly related to its three-dimensional physical parameters. The depth dimension is determined by the diffused junction depth or the thickness of an added film (aluminum, epi, etc.). The width and length dimensions are created by the photomasking process.

### 18.1.2 Metallic Thin Film Resistors

In a radiation environment, diffused resistors generate unwanted holes and electrons which cause leakage in the circuit. A "non-leaking" (or radiation hardened) resistor is one can be formed from a thin metallic film on the wafer surface. Typically, the metal film (nichrome, titanium, tungsten) is evaporated on the oxide surface, patterned by either an etching or liftoff technique and processed through a metalization sequence, to connect it into the circuit.

### 18.2 DIODES

A diode is a two-region (using different conduction types) device, separated by a junction. A diode can either pass current or block current. If a positive current is applied to the P region of a P/N diode, current will flow. The arrangement is known as *forward bias.* If a negative current is applied to the P-region, no current will flow. However, reverse flow can occur if the applied voltage exceeds the design limit of the diode.

The diodes shown are *bar diodes.*

A *planar diode* is formed by changing the conductivity type in a local region of the wafer by a basic doping sequence followed by a metallization sequence.

Note that a diode is a two-contact device and that the current crosses one junction. A diode is formed at every junction, but not every junction is used as a diode. Isolation junctions are an example of a P/N junction not used in the circuit as a diode.

The first conductivity type indicated (P or N) in the designation of the diode is the region more highly doped.

### 18.2.1 Schottky Barrier Diodes

One special form of planar diode is called a *Schottky Barrier Diode* after its inventor. The diode is formed by shorting the junction on the surface with a metal contact. The operational speed of the diode is increased by this structure.

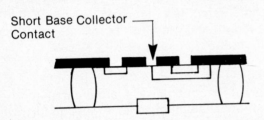

Short Base Collector Contact

**Fig. 18.6   Schottky Barrier Diode**

A primary use of the Schottky diode is in bipolar integrated logic circuits. Their effect in the circuit is also to increase its speed.

## 18.3 TRANSISTORS

### 18.3.1 Water Analogy

Transistors are the central component in an I.C. circuit. They are two-junction devices, requiring three electrical contacts to function, and act in the circuits as an amplifiers or switches. A simple water system illustrates transistor operation.

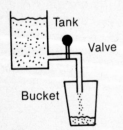

Tank

Valve

Bucket

**Fig. 18.8
Water System – Transistor Analogy**

In the system above water flows from the tank to the bucket through the valve, which controls the flow. Large flows of water can be directed to the bucket with little effort expended in opening the valve. This illustrates the principle of amplification: a "little" effort or input causes or controls a large output. Closing the valve completely shuts off the system.

### 18.3.2 Bipolar Transistors

In electrical devices the flow is electrons or holes. As in the water system, the electrons or holes originate in one location and flow through a control section to another location.

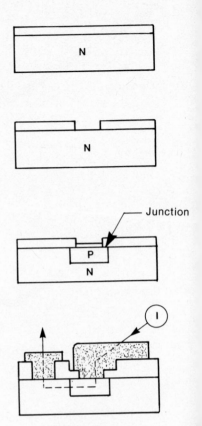

Junction

**Fig. 18.7
Formation of a P/N Planar Diode**

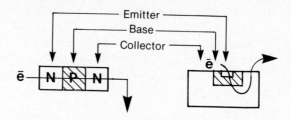

**Fig. 18.9   Bipolar Transistor Operation**

In Figure 18.8 a bipolar transistor is shown in both bar and planar configurations. The electron flow is from the more heavily doped emitter region through the base to the collector. The resistance of the base is varied electrically to control the current flow. Recall that the first name of a transistor was "transfer resistor."

During operation there is both electron and hole flow in the base region. This dual current is the origin of the term *bipolar* (two current polarities). In fact, the word "transistor" stands for The amplification of a bipolar transistor is computed as the ratio of the total current flowing out of the transistor divided by the control current flowing in the base. A small change in base current can result in a large increase in total current.

Note that the base is opposite in conductivity type from the emitter and collector. Transistors are also fabricated in a PNP configuration, although NPN transistors are more common due to their superior functioning (see Chapter 19.1.9).

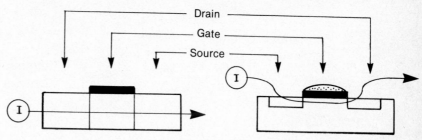

**Fig. 18.10   MOS Transistor Operation**

### 18.3.3 MOS Transistors

In an MOS transistor, the current (holes or electrons) originates in the diffused source region. A voltage applied to the gate region causes a conductive channel to form between the source and the drain, resulting in current flow. The amount of gate voltage controls the amount of flow.

If the source and drain are N-type, the channel required to allow current flow must be an N-channel. The MOS transistor described above is called an N-channel device. A P-type source and drain would result in a P-channel resistor.

A close examination of the physical structure of the gate reveals the origin of the term *MOS*. The gate is actually a thin film capacitor composed of two metal conductors separated by a thin

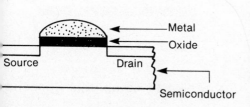

**Fig. 18.11   MOS Gate Structure**

film oxide. One of the metals is a semiconductor; hence the initials M(etal) O(xide) S(emicondcutor).

As in a bipolar transistor, a small change in the control structure (gate voltage) can give rise to a large change in the voltage output of the device. Whereas bipolar transistors are current devices, MOS transistors are voltage devices.

### 18.3.4 Field Effect Transistors

The MOS transistors described are actually a variation in a class of transistors known as *field effect transistors*. These devices work as the result of the electric field set up in the gate region by the applied gate voltage. In the MOS version the field causes a channel to form, allowing current flow between the source and drain.

Another popular form of a field effect transistor is the *junction* type, or JFET. This structure is formed with a junction under the gate. When the voltage is applied to the gate a region forms under the junction. This region is depleted of charge and has the effect of shutting off current flow between the source and drain. The region is called a *depletion region*.

Current flow is cotrolled by gate voltage as it is in a MOS device.

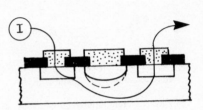

**Fig. 18.12**
**Junction Field Effect Transistor**

### Table 18.1    Control System Flow

| TECHNOLOGY | FLOW | | | CONFIGURATIONS |
|---|---|---|---|---|
| | From | Through (Control) | To | |
| Water | Tank | Valve | Bucket | |
| Bipolar | Emitter | Base | Collector | NPN or PNP |
| MOS | Source | Gate | Drain | N– or P-Channel |

## 18.4 CAPACITORS

Capacitors are electrical devices that have the ability to store charge. Their physical structure is the same as that of an MOS gate -- two conductors separated by a dielectric or insulator.

The simplest method of construction is to pattern a section of the conduction metal on top of the oxide and use the underlying semiconductor as the other conductor.

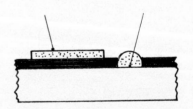

**Fig. 18.13    Monolithic Capacitor**

## 18.5 FUSES

In a normal electrical circuit a fuse is used to protect the circuit from an overload. In an I.C. circuit, a fuse finds application in PROM circuits. A fuse is connected to every memory cell in the array. The array is programmed by blowing fuses at specific locations, thus "disconnecting" the cell from the circuit. The resulting condition in the array of cell/no cell is the required go/no go or on/off situation required for information storage.

The fuses themselves are thin films of metal or silicon dioxide. Each of the materials is inserted in series in the circuit path.

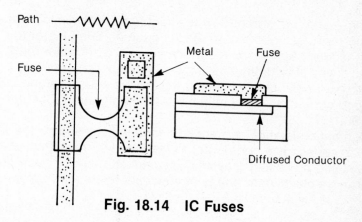

**Fig. 18.14   IC Fuses**

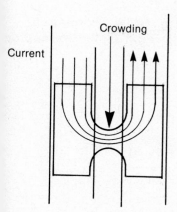

During operation, a current pulse is sent through the circuit to the cell where the fuse is to be "blown". Because the current is concentrated in the fuse, heating occurs and subsequently results in the rupture of the fuse from overheating.

Construction of the metal fuse begins with depositing a thin film onto the wafer. The metal, most often nichrome (NiCr), is patterned by a liftoff or conventional photomasking technique. The conducting metal is evaporated or sputtered over the fuse and patterned.

When using an oxide fuse, a thin film of $SiO_2$ is grown in the contact just prior to evaporation of the conducting metal. The process sequences for metal and oxide fuse fabrication are shown below.

| METAL FUSE | OXIDE FUSE |
|---|---|
| Contact Mask | Contact Mask |
| Deposit Fuse Metal | Grow Oxide in Contact Hole |
| Pattern Fuse | Deposit Conducting Metal |
| Deposit Conducting Metal | Pattern Conducting Metal |
| Pattern Conducting Metal | |

## 18.6 CONDUCTORS

After the individual solid state components are formed in the wafer surface, they must be "wired" together. The wiring is actually very thin layers of conductive metal(s) deposited and patterned on the wafer surface. This procedure is described in Chapter 2. The various metals used are described in Chapters 15 and 16. For review, they are:

Aluminum
Aluminum Alloys
Doped Polysilicon
Refractory Metals

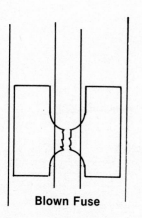

**Fig. 18.15   Blowing Current of Thin Film Fuse**

Electrically a conductor conforms to the same laws as resistors. The difference is that conductors have much lower resistivities. The result is that they allow high levels of current flow.

Like resistors, current flow is affected by the physical dimensions and thickness of the patterned conductor. Thinning of the conductive film at wafer surface steps is a situation that adversely affects the flow. Most conductor patterns are dimensioned much wider and thicker than necessary to insure good current flow and minimize electromigration (Chapter 16).

Contact resistance between the conductive lead and the wafer or fuse surface is a contributor to restricted current flow. Elaborate cleaning processes (chemical, reverse sputtering), good control of process cleanliness and pure materials are required to minimize contact resistance.

### 18.6.1 Silicon on Sapphire and Silicon on Insulator Circuits

Operating speeds of circuits are dependent on a number of design and process factors. For circuits formed in epitaxial layers a speed factor is the conducting property of the underlying wafer. Certain types of circuits cannot operate at the required speeds with this type of structure.

A solution to this problem is a structure of a layer of epitaxial semiconductor material on an insulating substrate. The most popular substrate is sapphire, although others are used. These structures go by the initials SOS and SOI. SOS wafers are startling in appearance. The sapphire is translucent, as is the epi layer (the epi layer is only several microns or less in thickness). The total effect is a translucent wafer.

## 18.7 NONSILICON DEVICES

### 18.7.1 Light Emitting Diodes (L.E.D.'s)

There are a growing number of solid state, semiconductor devices manufactured using the same or similar processes as are used to fabricate silicon devices. In general the nonsilicon wafers are selected for a specific property that silicon does not have.

Perhaps the most familiar device is the *light emitting diode* (L.E.D.). This device takes advantage of the production and release of photons from an operating diode. The photons are seen as light. The material most used for this type of device is gallium phosphide (GaP).

The device is composed of multiple diodes in an array. Current is directed to selected diodes to operate them in the reverse bias mode. The reverse current causes the emission of photons as light. In a display different diodes are turned on in patterns to create letters, numbers or symbols.

Different colored displays are created by doping the wafer with specific dopants.

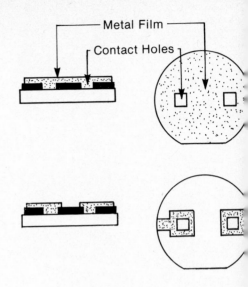

**Fig. 18.16   Formation of Thin Film Metal Conductor**

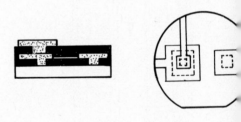

**Fig. 18.17   Dual Level Maturation**

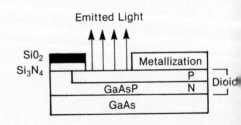

**Fig. 18.18   L.E.D. Structure**

### 18.7.2 Acoustic Wave Devices

*Acoustic wave devices* are nonsilicon devices used in communications systems, particularly microwave applications. In the circuit they function to convert electromagnetic waves to acoustic waves. To do this the wave is propagated along the surface of a semiconductor material such as $Be_{12}GeO_{20}$. Solid state circuitry formed on the surface converts the wave back into a usable electrical form.

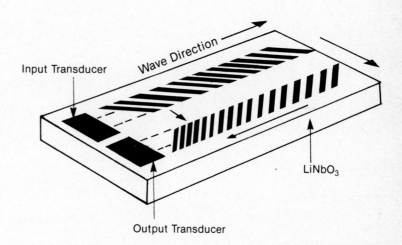

**Fig. 18.19   Accoustic Wave Device**

# Integrated Circuit Formation

Chapter 19.

# INTRODUCTION

A semiconductor circuit is a collection of individual electrical components formed and connected in and on the chip surface. The devices are resistors, diodes, capacitors and transistors. Of the four, the transistor is the "heart" of the circuit. Its electrical functioning makes possible the operation of the circuit.

Microchip processes are designed and sequenced to fabricate the transistor structure. The other devices are created along with the more complicated transistors.

A circuit designer can work with one of several transistor structures. The two most popular are bipolar and MOS. Early circuits were almost entirely bipolar-based structures. During the 70's, improved cleanliness in processing and materials made the economic manufacturing of MOS circuits possible. By the late 1980's, MOS technology will dominate the industry.

The electrical operation of individual bipolar and MOS transistors was described in Chapter 18. This chapter will explain the fabrication, structural and circuit differences of the two technologies.

## 19.1 BIPOLAR CIRCUIT CONSTRUCTION

Bipolar transistors can be structured in either an alloy or double diffused format. The latter, however, is the only one that can be "integrated" into a circuit. Using planar technology, bipolar transistors can be formed very close to each other.

All major bipolar circuits use double diffused transistors which are formed in an epitaxial layer deposited on the silicon wafer. The epi layer serves two functions in the circuit. One is as the collector region of the transistor. And second, oppositely doped from the substrate, it allows easy isolation of the separate components with the addition of a deep diffused "fence" (see 19.1.2).

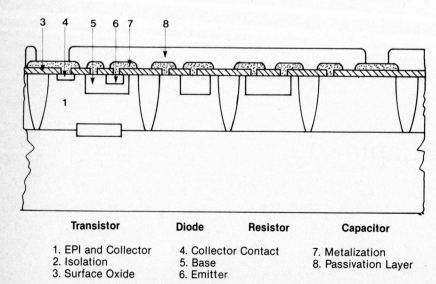

| Transistor | Diode | Resistor | Capacitor |
|---|---|---|---|
| 1. EPI and Collector | 4. Collector Contact | 7. Metalization | |
| 2. Isolation | 5. Base | 8. Passivation Layer | |
| 3. Surface Oxide | 6. Emitter | | |

**Fig. 19.1   Bipolar Structures**

### 19.1.1 Epitaxial/Collector Region

The collector region of the transistor has the highest resistivity of the three regions. In fact, high performance transistors require a resistivity level difficult to achieve during silicon crystal growing. However, controlled high resistivity epitaxial films can be grown on a wafer to function as the collector region.

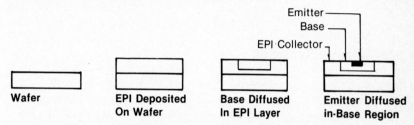

**Fig. 19.2  Epitaxial Collection Region**

### 19.1.2 Diffused Isolation

The requirement of isolation in the formation of two transistors is illustrated in figure 19.3 below. The two transistors being formed in the same epi layer share a common collector, an unacceptable electrical situation. Similarly, the diodes, resistors and capacitors formed in the epi surface would be "shorted" to each other through the epi layer.

The solution to the problem lies in growing an epi layer of the opposite conductivity type from the wafer, diffusing the narrow region through the epi layer down to the substrate. The conductivity type of the isolation diffusion is the same as that of the wafer.

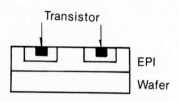

Isolated EPI
Wafer with
Two Transistors

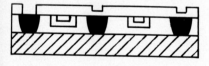

**Fig. 19.3
Formation of Adjacent
Transistors in an EPI Layer**

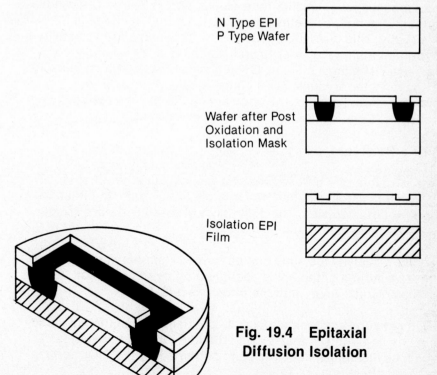

**Fig. 19.4   Epitaxial
Diffusion Isolation**

Figure 19.3 demonstrates the result with the more popular NPN bipolar structure. At the conclusion of the isolation diffusion step "islands" of epi regions have been "fenced off" electrically from each other. Currents generated in the isolated region will not cross the diffused junction into other regions. This isolation scheme is known as either *diffused isolation* or *junction isolation.*

### 19.1.3 Dielectric Isolation

In high radiation environments, such as outer space or in the vicinity of atomic weapons, diffused junctions are not sufficient to maintain the proper isolation. The radiation creates holes and electrons that "cross" the junction, causing leakage.

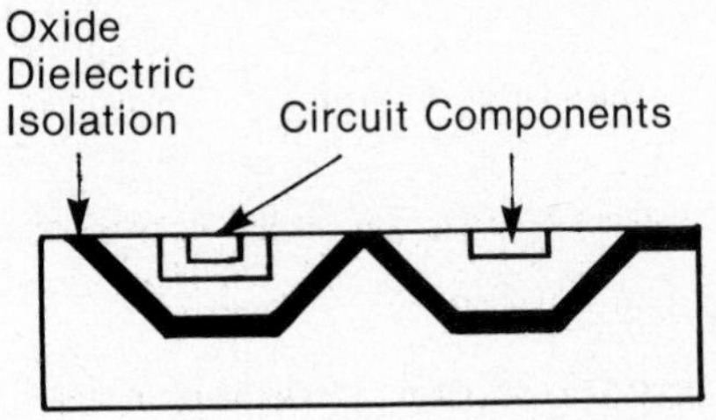

Circuits destined for use in a high radiation environment are isolated by a different method. Prior to epi growth, grooves are etched in the wafer and the surface is oxidized. The silicon oxide layer grown will eventually function as the isolating layer. Its excellent dielectric properties prevent radiation-induced leakage currents. The isolated wafer is shown in Figure 19.4. An epi layer is grown on the grooved side of the wafer. After epi, the original wafer is ground down to the oxide-isolated pockets. Normal bipolar circuit components are formed in the isolated pockets.

Oxide Dielectric Isolation →     Circuit Components →

**Fig.19.5   Dielectric Isolation**

### 19.1.4 Subcollector Region

The structure shown in Figure 14.3 would not meet the electric performance requirements for a bipolar circuit. Current flowing through the high epi collector region is limited by the high resistivity. This problem is resolved by diffusing a low resistivity region into the wafer prior to epitaxial growth. The completed transistor sits on top of this low resistivity region, which is called a *subcollector* or *buried layer.* Since it does not touch the collector base junction, the original need of the low resistivity epi collector is maintained.

### 19.1.5 Resistors

The structure of a diffused resistor was explained in Chapter 18. Diffused resistors can be formed in bipolar circuits, at either the base or diffusion step. The majority of diffused resistors are put in at the base step.

Higher resistivity resistors can be formed from the epitaxial layer itself. A portion of the epi is sectioned off by the isolation diffusion and "wired" into the circuit as a resistor.

High radiation environments cause problems to junction-isolated circuits and diffused resistors. Fortunately thin film resistors, (such as nichrome), deposited and patterned on the $SiO_2$ surface, are less affected by radiation.

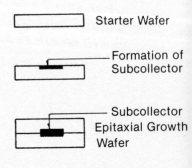

Starter Wafer

Formation of Subcollector

Subcollector Epitaxial Growth Wafer

**Fig. 19.6
Formation of a Subcollector**

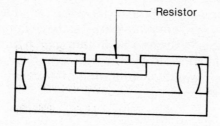

Resistor

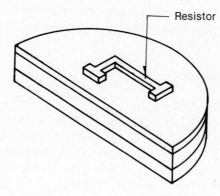

Resistor

**Fig. 19.7
Diffused Resistors**

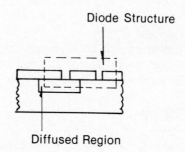

Diode Structure

Diffused Region

**Fig. 19.8   Junction Diode**

### 19.1.6 Diodes

Diodes are one-junction devices and exist at every PN junction. They can be formed from any of the diffusions.

In bipolar circuits, most diodes are formed between the base and collector junction.

A frequently used diode is formed from a completed bipolar transistor. The base and collector are shortened to form one half of the diode, while the emitter region forms the other. The structure is called an *emitter base diode.*

### 19.1.7 Collector Contact

The high resistivity collector results in an unacceptably high contact resistance with the aluminum wiring. A lower resistance contact is formed during the emitter diffusion step.

At emitter masking, an additional opening in the top side oxide is made over the collector region. During emitter diffusion, the dopants diffuse into the region, creating a low resistivity area. Subsequently, a contact hole is opened up in this region, forming a low resistance contact. In NPN transistors, the region is called an N+ contact, due to the higher concentration of dopant.

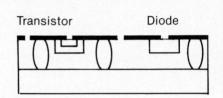

**Fig. 19.8    Base/Collector Diode**

### 19.1.8 Capacitors

Dielectric capacitors are usually formed between the top side metal and the region diffused at the emitter step. Junction capacitors are also formed from either base or emitter junctions, taking advantage of the natural capacitance associated with the depletion region of a biased junction.

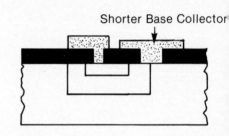

**Fig. 19.9    Emitter Base Diode**

### 19.1.9 PNP Bipolar Transistors

High performance, discrete bipolar transistors are fabricated in either NPN or PNP configurations. Integrated circuit fabrication favors NPN transistor construction. When a PNP transistor is required in the circuit, it is usually fashioned along the surface, rather than vertically into the wafer. Its regions are formed at the same time that the NPN structures are being diffused.

These lateral PNP transistors are formed by using the base diffusion as the collector and emitter, and the emitter diffusion as the base.

Vertical PNP transistors can be fashioned using the P-type substrate as the collector, the epi as the base, and a base diffusion section as the emitter.

### 19.1.10 Gold Doping

Certain circuits based on bipolar technology require fast switching characteristics. One limit on switching is the time required for an electron in motion in the NPN transistor base region to come to rest after the transistor is turned off. The time can be reduced by creating gold "traps" in the device. Gold is diffused into the structure, usually along with the base, and captures or traps a moving electron as soon as the power is switched off.

### 19.1.11 Metallization and Passivation

Once the bipolar components are formed in the epitaxial layer, the circuit is completed by processing it through conventional metallization and passivation sequences. The complete structure is shown in Table 19.1.

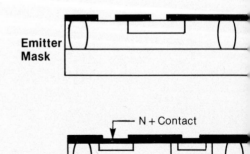

**Fig. 19.10    Collector Contact**

### 19.1.12 Diffused Conductors

It is not always convenient to connect all of the components using the top side metal layer. Additional "wiring" is often formed in the wafer surface using the lower resistivity emitter

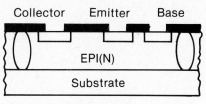

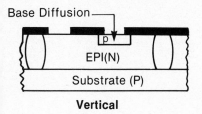

## Fig. 19.11
## Lateral and Vertical
## PNP Transistors

diffusion. These "underpasses" are designed with a short length and wide width to maintain a low resistance.

### 19.1.13 I²L Transistor Structure

Faster circuits are a never ending goal of integrated circuit design. Using conventional bipolar structures, circuit speed can be improved by "wiring" together the various bipolar into logic cells. T.T.L. and E.C.L. are two popular cell types.

Another circuit design, I²L, is based on a structural change in the basic bipolar device. I²L stands for *integrated injection logic.* The device structure includes a lateral PNP transistor, using the standard bipolar transistor base as the collector of the lateral transistor. This results in faster "injection" of the current into the base, increasing circuit speed.

The circuit performance of I²L is compared to conventional circuits in Chapter 20.

## 19.2 MOS CIRCUIT CONSTRUCTION

In Chapter 18, the various types of MOS and FET devices were explained. Their formation in an integrated circuit form is different from bipolar technology. MOS circuit technology eliminates two major steps required in bipolar technology -- the epi layer and isolation diffusion.

The MOS fabrication process starts with an incoming wafer that is processed through oxidation and goes directly to masking. If the circuit is based on metal or silicon gate structures, the first mask is the source/drain. CMOS circuits first go through the P-well doping sequences.

### 19.2.1 Resistors, Diodes and Capacitors

Like their bipolar cousins, MOS integrated circuits require resistors, diodes and capacitors. These components are also formed as the MOS transistor structure is fabricated. The MOS circuit designer is limited in choice of resistor and diode values by having only the source drain diffusion available.

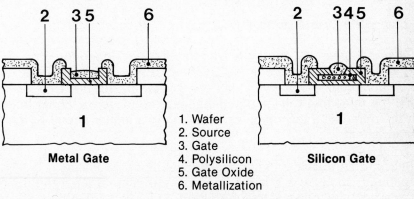

1. Wafer
2. Source
3. Gate
4. Polysilicon
5. Gate Oxide
6. Metallization

*Not Shown: Passive Layer*

## Fig. 19.12  MOS Structure

## 19.2.2 Field Doping

In both bipolar and MOS technology, the area of the circuit that does not contain active devices is called the *field.* A particular problem arises over the field in MOS circuits. Metal conductors running on top of the field oxide automatically form a capacitor with the silicon below. If the voltage on the conductors becomes high enough, the "field capacitor" will create charge in the underlying silicon and cause shorted devices.

There are two solutions to the problem. Both insure that the inescapable capacitor does not operate at the voltage level of the current in the conductors. One solution is to grow a thick field oxidation, in the range of 15,000 Angstroms. The second solution involves another doping sequence. After an initial oxidation, the field area is exposed by a masking step. The field area is then doped by a diffusion step to a level which prevents it from storing charge at the operating voltage.

## 19.2.3 Gate Oxide

An MOS gate oxide is the thinnest oxide encountered in semiconductor structures. The thinner the gate, the less voltage is required to activate (turn on) the transistor. Gate oxides range in thickness from 200 to 1200 angstroms. This oxide must be extremely clean and uniform, as must the surface below it.

## 19.2.4 Gate Doping

The goal in an MOS transistor design is for one turned on by the lowest possible gate voltage. The thickness and/or the doping in the gate region are structure parameters controlling the gate voltage. Prior to the development of ion implantation techniques, the gate doping level was that of the wafer. Thermal diffusion does not provide the doping control required to alter the gate resistivity. Ion implantation does, however. The gate can be doped directly (after being exposed to a masking step) or through the gate oxide.

Development of this reliable gate doping process also allows the selection of a starting wafer resistivity that eliminates the need for an extra thick field oxide or field doping.

## 19.2.5 Gate Construction

The metal gate MOS structure was the first developed for commercial devices, and is the simplest of the MOS structures. From a circuit perspective, it suffers several drawbacks. One is that the threshold voltage of a metal gate transistor is higher than in the other MOS technologies, resulting in a higher circuit power requirement.

A second drawback is the operating speed of this device. Operating circuit speed is a function of the time required to turn on the transistor and to fully turn it off. The effect in an entire MOS circuit is termed *access time.* The access time is affected by

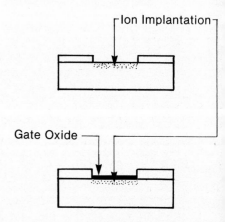

**Fig. 19.13 MOS Gate Doping**

the some overlap of the gate region into the adjacent source and drain regions. The overlap is due to the *alignment tolerance.* During the transistor operation, the overlap region gives rise to a capacitance that slows down the transistor turn on-and-off time.

Practical metal gate transistors require a field doping step to insure that there will be no charge induced in the field surface. This requirement increases the cost of fabrication.

## 19.3 SILICON GATE TECHNOLOGY

The development of reliable silicon gate processes in the mid–1970's boosted MOS technology into serious competition with both bipolar circuits and core memory. The first advantage of a silicon gate is the reduction of the threshold voltage. As a consequence of the use of silicon rather tnan aluminum as the gate electrode (see Chapter 18).

A second advantage is the increased speed of the transistor and of the circuit. In the fabrication sequence, the gate region is formed before the source and drain. This technique allows the source/drain regions to be perfectly aligned to the gate, minimizing any overlap capacitance. Use of an ion implanted source drain eliminates the capacitance due to the absence of a side diffusion. This structure is called a *self-aligned gate.*

## 19.4 COMPLIMENTARY MOS

The development of CMOS technology will push MOS into the leadership position. CMOS allows more powerful circuit operation than either N-channel or P-channel circuits. This factor, combined with a lower power consumption and increased speed, has made CMOS the favored technology for the manufacture of microprocessors. Complimentary MOS(CMOS) is an MOS Circuit formed with both N Channel and P Channel Devices.

Unlike the simpler metal gate processing, CMOS requires more process steps than a bipolar process. The process comparison at

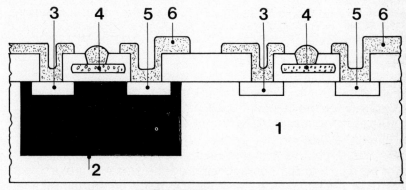

1. Wafer
2. Source
3. Gate
4. Polysilicon
5. Gate Oxide
6. Metallization

**Fig. 19.14   CMOS Structure**

the end of this session illustrates a basic CMOS process. Many process variations prevail and, in most cases, make CMOS the most complicated and involved technology in the industry.

CMOS circuits inevitably employ the latest process technology, including silicon nitride gates, ion implantation, LPCVD, Class 10 process environments, projection and stepping imaging, reactive ion etching, and dual level metallization.

## 19.5 MMOS

MMOS (memory MOS) is a structure that addresses the problem of volatile memory. In a standard RAM memory circuit, the information must constantly be "refreshed" in the array. If the refresh current stops, or the power to the chip is terminated, the individual memory cells turn off and return to their electrical rest positions, losing the stored information.

Nonvolatile memory is a memory device structure that retains its information during power shutdown. A ROM memory circuit is such a structure, having the required information permanently designed into the chip. Another approach is MMOS. In the MMOS structure, a silicon nitride layer is added between the gate oxide and metal.

During operation, the silicon nitride retains the gate charge. This structure reduces the need for constant refresh, resulting in a more nonvolatile memory. The lifetime of the charge is finite, however, and will eventually bleed away.

MMOS transistors require a higher operating threshold voltage, have reduced speed and suffer reduced device performance due to surface current leakage. By forming the circuit components on the sides of the grooves, the problems associated with surface contamination and damage of the original surface were eliminated.

The drawback to this approach is the difficulty encountered in patterning the components "down" in the grooves. MMOS has not fulfilled its promise as an integrated circuit technique, but lives on as a structure suited for MOS discrete power transistors.

## 19.6 VMOS

VMOS stands for *V-groove MOS technology*. Invented in the late 1970's, this technology held great promise as a method for significantly increasing MOS circuit density.

The process requires that V-shaped grooves be etched in the wafer surface and form components on the sides of the grooves. Density is increased as a consequence of the greater surface area.

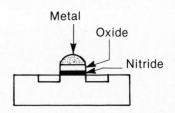

**Fig. 19.15   MMOS Structure**

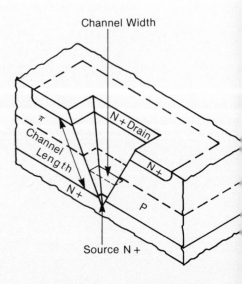

**Fig. 19.16   VMOS Structure**

## 19.7 HMOS AND OTHER MOS

HMOS simply stands for *high density MOS,* indicating higher levels of integration. It does not necessarily denote a particular device structure or processing technique.

MOS device development has produced many variations on the basic structures. Some are of enough significance to warrant a separate name. The reader is cautioned to examine these names to ascertain whether they are major structure changes, simply variations on basic structures, or trade names of particular manufacturers.

## 19.8 DUAL LEVEL METALLIZATION

Higher density of components on a chip requires more current carrying capability in the metal conduction system. At high levels of integration, the chip designer runs out of area to lay down all of the required conduction strips on the wafer surface.

One solution to this problem is dual level metallization. The first layer is applied by the standard metallization and passivation sequence. Contact holes (or VIA's) are then etched in the passivation layer to allow contact with the underlying metal system. A second metal layer is deposited and patterned on top of the passivation layer. A final passivation layer completes the dual level system.

This technique requires planar surfaces as the intermetallic layers to minimize step coverage problems with the second metal layer. Polyimide and highly phosphorus-doped oxide films are used for this intermetallic layer. Both can be flowed on the wafer surface to create a planar surface.

## 19.9 COMPARISON OF BIPOLAR AND MOS CIRCUITS

Bipolar technology has reigned over the semiconductor industry for more than thirty years. Many factors, including early development, contribute to its industry dominance. Bipolar transistors, due to their formation below the wafer surface, are less prone to contamination. With the lack of clean materials, equipment and facilities in the 1950's, it is not surprising that bipolar technology received the largest share of development activity and became the favored technology.

Less sensitivity to contamination was not the only factor, however. Early semiconductor circuits had to compete or interface with existing electrical components that operated at higher voltage and current values. Bipolar transistors and bipolar circuits operate at voltages compatible with other electrical devices. Switching speed of bipolar transistors is faster than the simpler MOS transistors. The original computers relied on solid state circuits for logic and core for memory. It was therefore logical that the faster bipolar circuits would be used for computer memories.

MOS circuit parameters became desirable after the invention of integrated circuits and the need for greater computer memory.

Jack Kilby's development of the first integrated circuit in 1959 opened an era characterized by jamming more and more components onto a chip. MOS, with no need for an isolation structure, allows a higher component density than bipolar technology. Higher density, coupled with simpler processing, made MOS circuits a natural replacement for the core memories of earlier computers.

A core memory is based on "donuts" of ferrite materials strung on the intersection of wires. Passing current down the proper X and Y lines magnetized the donut at that intersection, creating the on-off condition required of memories.

A third wire threaded through the array was used to sense the magnetic state of the donut.

Core memories possessed the attributes of the other pre-solid state electronic components:

1. Large Size
2. High Power Requirements
3. Reliability Problems
4. Slow Access and Read Times

With all of the obvious advantages of solid state devices, industry observers in the 1960's predicted the immediate demise of core memory. Surprisingly, the final switchover did not occur until the 1970's when solid state memory devices finally reached competitive cost levels. MOS circuitry was a natural for this purpose because it was cheaper than bipolar to produce, due to fewer processing steps and higher density.

A third factor favoring MOS memory development was the absence of a high current power requirement for operation. The lower power requirements and output of MOS circuits were ideal.

In contrast to bipolar circuits, MOS circuits are slower and exhibit higher leakage. In the earlier days of the industry, these factors prevented MOS from being a candidate for logic circuits. Fortunately, these factors did not apply to memory circuits.

By the early 1980's, these original differences in the two technologies (power, speed, density, cost, logic and memory application) began to blur. The development of hand-held calculators required logic and memory on one chip. One result was the CMOS-based microprocessor which places MOS in the lead through the 1980's.

MOS power handling capacity has increased, and speed and leakage parameters now approach those of bipolar. On the down side, the initial MOS advantage of fewer process steps is gone. MOS processes have increased, and for advanced devices, exceed those of bipolar. The improvement in circuit performance has come as the result of better processing through the advanced imaging, etching, doping and metallization processes.

MOS technology, through the development of CMOS devices and the microprocessors, now stands on its own circuit merits, rather than as a poor cousin to bipolar technology. In fact, development of bipolar and MOS devices on the same chip promises the final mating of the unique advantages of each technology. Table 19.2 compares bipolar and MOS circuits. Each structure will continue to be used where its unique properties are best utilized.

**Table 19.1   Comparison of Bipolar and MOS Technologies**

| Parameter | Bipolar | MOS |
|---|---|---|
| Component Density | | Higher |
| Operating Power | Higher | |
| Switching Speed | Higher | |
| Current Conduction By: | Holes and Electrons | Hole or Electron |
| Isolation of Components | Required | Not Required |
| Current Flow | In Bulk | Along Surface |
| Oxide Layers | Min. 5K Å | Min. 0.2K Å |
| Cleanliness Requirements | Med.—High | High |
| Current Flow Control | Current | Voltage |
| General Circuit | Power Logic | Memories |

# Solid State Circuits Technology

Chapter 20.

# INTRODUCTION

Over 60% of the units produced by the semiconductor industry are in the form of integrated circuits. The number of individual circuits that can be created using the solid state technology described in this text seems endless. A circuit catalog from a major I.C. producer like National Semiconductor or Motorola is the same size as the New York City phone book. I.B.M. estimates that by 1990 their internal circuit catalog wil list 50,000 separate circuits!

Becoming familiar with I.C. circuits is not as awesome a task as the high numbers imply. Thousands of circuits are created from a few standard designs and fall into only three function categories: logic, memory, and logic and memory.

The major functional circuit categories and the major circuit designs are explained in this chapter. In the last section, we looked at the future in I.C. circuitry from the perspective of the industry today. What the circuits will actually be like in 2010 can only be imagined, just as in 1950 no one predicted the megabit RAM or the microprocessor.

## 20.1 I.C. CIRCUIT BASICS

Both logic and memory circuit operation are based on the processing of data in binary notation. The binary system is a way of representing any number with just two digits -- a zero and a one. It is actually an accounting system that keeps track of the place and value of the components of a number. Let's illustrate by expressing isome numbers as the sums of their components.

The number one is equal to 1 + 0. The number three can be expressed as the sum of 2 + 1. The number seven can be expressed as the sum of 4 + 2 + 1 and ten = 8 + 2.

There is a relationship, however, between the digits chosen to express the numbers 1,3,7 and 10. Note that the digits chosen can be expressed as powers of 2.

$$1 = 2^0$$
$$2 = 2^1$$
$$4 = 2^2$$
$$8 = 2^3$$

The basis of binary notation is that every number can be represented by a combination of powers of two. Twenty-five can be expressed as the sum of 16 ($2^4$) plus 8 ($2^3$) and 1 ($2^0$).

Translating numbers into binary notation is easily accomplished by establishing a grid with each column representing a power of 2. The actual number is represented by a string of zeros or ones that indicate the presence of the particular powers of 2 that make up that number.

| | 32 $2^5$ | 16 $2^4$ | 8 $2^3$ | 4 $2^2$ | 2 $2^1$ |
|---|---|---|---|---|---|
| Number | | | | | |
| 1 | 0 | 0 | 0 | 0 | 0 |
| 7 | 0 | 0 | 0 | 1 | 1 |
| 18 | 0 | 1 | 0 | 0 | 1 |
| 33 | 1 | 0 | 0 | 0 | 0 |

**Fig. 20.1   Binary Notation**

| 8 | 4 | 2 | 1 |
|---|---|---|---|
| 0 | 1 | 1 | 1 |

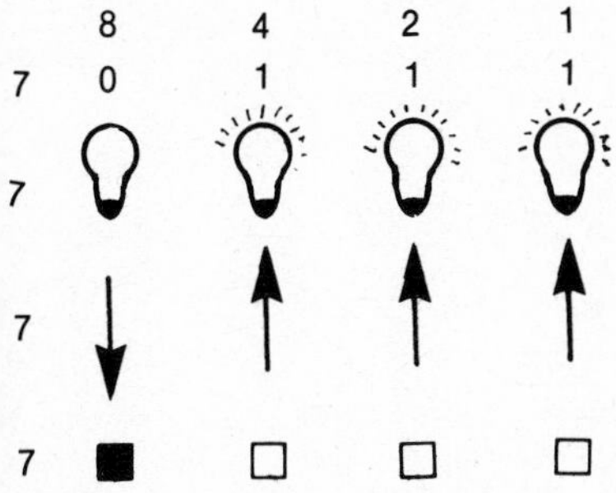

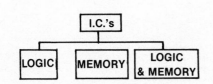

**Fig. 20.2    Binary Representation of the number 7**

Binary notation has been known for centuries. Buckminister Fuller, in his book *SYNERGISTICS,* has an amusing account of the use of binary coding by the ancient Phoenicians to keep track of cargo amounts. He claims that the Phoenician sailors were considered stupid because they could not count in the system of the day, when actually they were accurately keeping track of large amounts of cargo with only two "numbers."

Binary notation is used in computers and I.C. circuits due to the ease of number representation by only two conditions. In the discussion above, binary coding was represented by the numbers zero or one. In the physical world, binary numbers can be represented by any system that has two conditions. Figure 20.2 shows several different ways to code the number 7. The last row represents binary coding by the off/on states of a transistor.

Inside a circuit the numbers are coded, stored and manipulated by either having transistors "on" or "off" in the correct sequence. The smallest piece of information in a circuit is called a "binary digit" or "bit."

The binary coding system is simple. The problem of how the coded numbers could be added, subtracted and multiplied was solved by George Boole, a nineteenth century mathemetician. He developed a logic system capable of handling numbers in binary notation. Until the development of computer logic, his *Boolean Logic* (or *Boolean Algebra*) was an academic curiosity.

Chips and computers are designed to handle a specific size binary number or word. An eight-bit machine manipulates numbers with eight binary *bits* at a time. A 32–bit machine can handle a number composed of 32 binary bits. Every eight bits is known as a *byte.* Thus, a megabyte storage capacity can hold eight million bits of information.

Within a solid state integrated circuit there are a number of functional areas. Each chip, regardless of the circuit function, has an input and encode section where the incoming signals are "coded" into a form that the circuit can understand. The majority of the circuit area contains the circuitry required to perform the circuit function, either memory or logic. After the data is manipulated by the circuit, it goes to a decode section where it is changed back into a form that is usable by the machine's output mechanism. The circuit output section actually sends the data to the outside world.

Although this is an overly simplified explanation of a circuit, it illustrates the fact that the interior of a chip is composed of definite separate functional areas. In many circuits these areas perform the same functions as the main parts of a computer.

**Fig. 20.3    I.C. Circuit Functions**

Circuit types fall into three broad categories: logic, memory, and logic and memory (microprocessors).

Logic circuits perform a specified logical operation on the incoming data. For example, pushing the " + " key on a calculator instructs the logic portion of the chip to add the numbers presented to it. An on-board automobile computer goes through a logical operation to direct the signal from a sensor indicating an open door to light up the correct warning light on the dashboard.

Memory circuits are designed to store and give back data, in the same form in which it is entered. Pushing the $\pi$ key on a calculator activates the memory part of the circuit where its value is stored. The value 3.14... is displayed on the screen. Every time that key is activated that value is displayed.

In 1972, Intel Corporation introduced the first practical microprocessor -- a circuit that performs both logic and memory functions. Microprocessors can be programmed to perform many different circuit functions. To accomplish this they contain logic and memory circuitry as well as the necessary encode, decode, input and put sections. The microprocessor has made possible the one-chip electronic calculator, the digital watch and the personal computer.

The microprocessor has been dubbed "a computer on a chip." While it contains all of the functional areas of a computer, it is not truly a complete computer. Even simple computers require vast amounts of memory capacity. Within a personal computer, a microprocessor functions as the *central processing unit (CPU)*. Additional memory chips have to be included in order to make the computer of practical use.

Actually, every I.C. circuit contains both logic capability and memory sections. For example, the logic circuitry of a calculator must have certain constants stored in a memory section in order to perform calculations. And memory circuits must have some logic functions to direct the flow of electrons and holes to the right parts of the circuit for storage.

## 20.2 LOGIC CIRCUITS

Logic circuits fall into two main categories: analog and digital. Analog logic circuits were the earliest circuits developed. An analog circuit has an output that is proportional to the input. Digital circuits on the other hand, feature a predetermined output in response to a variety of inputs.

A wall light dimmer is an analog device. Turning the control varies the voltage to the dimmer, which in turn varies the brightness of the light. A standard on-off light switch is a digital device. Only two brightness conditions are possible: on or off.

Most audio circuits are of the analog type. Changing the level setting of the volume produces a proportional change in the sound coming out of the speaker.

Analalog circuits were the first type designed in integrated form. The home computer hobby kits of the 1950's were analog type. These simple circuits were based on Ohm's Law (R = V/I). The circuit contains a resistance meter and a means for generating a current and measuring a voltage. The three quantities are related

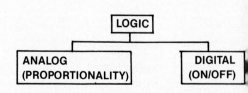

**Fig. 20.4  Logic Circuit Types**

by Ohm's Law. Any other three variables similarly related can be represented by the resistance, voltage and current. Varying one changes the other two. The circuit thus becomes a computer for solving any equation of the form A = B/C.

The accuracy of analog circuits is dependent on the precision of the relationship between the input and the output. In the simple computer illustrated, accuracy is dependent on the precision of the components in the circuit, the clarity of the meters for setting the input and reading the output, and the immunity of the circuit to outside "noise." Unless the circuit contains a section to regulate incoming voltage levels, a change in the line voltage would alter the output, and hence the accuracy.

Both simple and complex analog circuits are vulnerable to variations in the incoming signal and to internal noise. Analog circuits are also dependent on precise control of the resistor values. Unfortunately, diffused resistors cannot be fabricated with a resistance variation from design value better than 3-5%, which is unacceptable for many applications.

Greater resistance precision is gained by the use of matched resistor pairs, in which the effective resistance in the circuit is the difference between two resistors. This difference can be controlled with better precision.

Ion implantation also provides the analog circuit designer with a tool for producing resistors with a higher degree of control. Many analog circuits feature thin film resistors to achieve the required precision.

The growth and popularity of digital circuits is based on their ability to produce a set output. If a 5 volt signal is absolutely required to operate a device, this can be achieved by designing a digital circuit that produces a 5 volt signal every time, regardless of the input variation or internal electrical noise.

Digital circuits, however, do not respond as fast as linear circuits. The term used in electronics is *real time response.* In some applications, such as airplane controls, real time response is mandatory. Recent development in digital circuit speed is speeding the encroachment of digital circuitry into this traditional use of analog circuits.

A major advantage of digital circuits over analog circuits is in general purpose computers. Analog circuits are more difficult to design to respond to a general range of problems. All modern general purpose computers are based on digital circuits.

### 20.2.1 Analog Circuits

The most popular use for analog circuits is in amplifiers. They are designed in a variety of configurations, for many different applications. All have the same basic principle -- the incoming signal or pulse is amplified. Audio circuits require amplification of a weak signal from the record tone arm or other input in order to produce the level required to operate a speaker.

The real time aspect of analog circuits also makes them real world circuits. Wherever there is a real world measurement such as temperature or movement, analog circuits are used. Even when the majority of the circuitry in a system is digital, analog circuits are part of the interface with the outside world.

Most analog amplifier circuits are of the differential operational type. These circuits produce an output voltage amplified from and proportional to the difference of two input signals. Bipolar technology is favored for these circuits because bipolar circuits are modular electrical current devices and are better suited to the applications required of analog circuits.

The output signal of an analog device can have a "one-to-one" relationship with the input signal. These circuits are called *linear*. If the input is changed, the out-put changes linearly. So many analog circuits are of linear design that the two terms are often used interchangeably. However, there are non-linear circuits, many featuring a logarithmic relationship between the input and output.

## 20.2.2 Digital Circuits

Digital circuitry is built around the logic gate. A gate allows passage through a barrier. The size and design of the gate influences the amount of passage allowed. A room with many "in" doors and only one "out" door is a gate. Many people can enter the room but their exit is restricted because only one door is provided.

The gate can also be operated in reverse, allowing people to enter through only one door, and leave through many.

Electronic digital logic gates perform similar functions but with electrical signals. There are three major gate functions: "and," "or," and "invert." In a digital circuit they perform the necessary logic operation by the dictates of Boolean logic. A discussion of their incorporation in logic design is beyond the scope of this text. However, it is necessary to know that these gates are constructed from individual solid state components.

The logic gates that can be constructed from the components are titled after the first letters of the components that are wired together to make up the gate. The major ones are:

RTL  Resistor-Transistor Logic
DTL  Diode-Transistor Logic
TTL  Transistor-Transistor Logic
ECL  Emitter Coupled Logic
DCTL  Direct Coupled Transistor Logic

**Integrated Injected Logic**

Integrated injected logic is another approach to constructing a logic gate. In this arrangement, a bipolar transistor is operated in the reverse mode, with the emitter as collector and collector as emitter.

An advanced gate design is formed with the bipolar transistor constructed with a Schottky diode (sometimes called a clamp) between the base and collector. This arrangement results in a faster circuit.

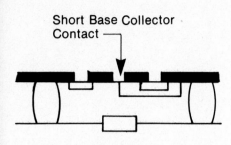

**Fig. 20.5**
**Schottky Clamped Transistor**

Short Base Collector Contact

### Gate Arrays

Using any of the logic gate approaches above, hundreds of thousands of different logic circuits can be constructed. The industry has matured to the point that a vast number of standard circuits are available, many of which are variations on a basic circuit. Basic circuits are designed to allow variations, with only moderate changes, during the fabrication process.

At the end of the fabrication process, only the components (or gates) required to form the particular logic circuit variation are "wired" into the circuit. This can be done with a contact mask which contains contact holes only for the required components. At the metal mask only the right components are wired together. A second method is to wire up only the required gates at the metal mask.

The electronics industry has many requirements for custom circuits. The user has several different customizing approaches at his/her disposal. One approach is to specify a variation of a basic circuit as described above.

At the other end of the spectrum is the totally custom designed circuit. This approach is expensive and lengthy, and is not geared for experimenting with different circuits in the design stage of a project. Custom designed circuits are not cost-effective in quantities of less than 100,000.

The gate array is a compromise solution to the problems of custom circuit, moderate cost and fast delivery. These circuits are designed with a standard number of gates. This gate section is called the *array* and the circuit is known as a *gate array.* Working with the basic design, the customer can instruct the fabrication department to wire together only the gates required to produce their custom circuit logic function.

The result is faster turn-around and moderate cost. The cost per logic function of gate arrays is higher than that of a custom circuit produced in production quantities. The larger gate section required to allow many different circuits results in a larger chip. This larger chip size leads to a higher manufacturing cost per chip and/or a lower yield.

### Programmable Array Logic (PAL)

Each of the three systems described requires the user to have the chip manufacturer do the "customizing." This requirement can result in delivery or scheduling problems and generally forces the user to buy a minimum quantity of parts.

Monolithic Memories, Inc. addressed this problem with the introduction of their PAL™ line of circuits in 1978. PAL stands for Programmable Array Logic. MMI applied the programmable fuse technology used in their memory products to logic circuits. The result was a field programmable (customizing) logic circuit.

This approach is similar to the standard gate array. But in this case, a fuse connects each logic gate into the circuit. The user programs the circuit by blowing the fuses at the unneeded gates, thus removing them from the circuit.

In his book *SOUL OF A NEW MACHINE*, Tracy Kidder related the story of a Data General project team's decision to design a 16–bit computer using the newly introduced MMI circuits. The ease of programmability and shortened delivery time is credited with allowing the computer to be brought to market in record time.

## 20.3 MEMORY CIRCUITS

Around 1960, industry forecasters began predicting that solid state circuit memory would overtake the traditional core memory. The advantages of solid circuits were their reliability, size and speed, neither of which core memories had. This prediction was made every year until the early 1970's, when solid state memories finally did surpass core memory. The factor which prolonged the life of core was the cost comparison of the two techniques.

Memory chips favor MOS structures. Because there isn't an isolation requirement, components can be placed closer to one another than in bipolar structures. However, MOS transistors force the current to flow nearer the surface than do bipolar devices. During the 1960's, the increased cleanliness requirement for MOS processing was not reliably available. High yield MOS processing also requires accurate alignment and clean thin gate oxides. These processes were not fully developed in the earlier years. The resultant low process yields kept MOS memories more expensive than core memories.

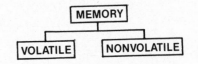

Fig. 20.6   Memory Circuit Types

With process improvements and improved MOS structures MOS has not only become the memory method of choice, but will pass bipolar circuits in volume.

While logic circuits can (and are) made in MOS technology, most MOS circuits produced are memories, with the majority incorporated into computers. They are also used in microprocessor-based products, which require auxiliary memory chips.

There are two types of memory circuits: volatile and non-volatile.

### 20.3.1 Non-Volatile Memories

A *non-volatile* memory device is one that does not lose its stored information when the playback machine loses its power. An example of this is a phonograph record. If power to the record player is lost, the songs are not lost from the record itself.

## ROM

In integrated circuits, the ROM design is the principle non-volatile circuit. ROM stands for *Read Only Memory.* Information is coded permanently into the ROM during the manufacturing process. The sole function of this circuit is to give back the prestored information.

Other circuits have read/write capability. That is, they can receive and store information from the operational input device (keyboard, magnetic tape, floppy disk, etc.).

In a calculator a lot of information is stored in the ROM section of the curcuit. Every time you turn the calculator on, all of the constants are still available. And the internal instructions and constants required so that the circuit can function as a calculator are stored in a ROM section.

ROM circuits are like logic circuits in that they number in the hundreds of thousands. Although there are many standard types, the industry also uses many custom ROM circuits. The choices offered to the user in selecting a standard or custom chip are similar to those available with logic circuits.

The user can buy a standard circuit, specify a variation on a standard basic circuit, design a total custom circuit, or buy a PROM, EPROM or EEPROM.

## PROM

PROM stands for *Programmable Read Only Memory.* A PROM is the memory equivalent of a PAL. Every memory cell is connected into the circuit through a fuse.

The user programs the PROM to his own memory circuit requirements by blowing fuses at the unwanted memory cell locations. After programming, the PROM is changed to a ROM, and the information is permanently coded in the chip.

## EPROM

For some applications, it is convenient to change the information stored in the ROM without having to replace the whole chip. EPROM chips (*Electronically Programmed ROM*) are designed for this use. A specially designed memory cell fulfills the memory function by storing charge in the transistors required to be "on" in the circuit. This structure has the ability to drain off the charge (erasing the memory) by shining ultra violet light on the chip. Reprogramming of the chip takes place by removing it from the circuit and putting in new memory information with an external programming machine. A typical EPROM can be reprogrammed up to ten times.

## EEPROM

The next level of convenience in memory design is the ability to program and reprogram the chip in its socket in the machine.

This convenience is available with the EEPROM, standing for *Electronically Erasable PROM.* Programming and erasing results from the build-up of charge in the selected memory cells and their erasure with an electric pulse, induced from outside, but with the chip in place.

**Bubble Memory**

*Bubble memories* are solid state devices which do not use a transistor-based memory cell to store information. The substrate of a bubble memory (usually garnet) has hundreds of thousands of tiny magnetic regions called "bubbles."

The bubbles can be programmed -- directionally oriented -- within the substrate by an electrical current flowing in a surface circuit. Two orientation directions are possible: up and down, or north and south. (Remember that only two conditions are required for binary information coding.)

The memory information is stored in the substrate as a string of north and south pole magnetized "bubbles." Retrieval occurs by moving the bubbles past a structure which senses the pole of each bubble.

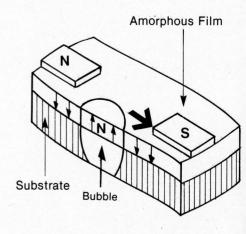

This is a serial format type of information retrieval. Gaining access to the first data put in  memory requires printing out ALL of the information in memory. A phonograph record, without a mechanism to lift the tone arm, would also be a serial memory device. Listening to the song recorded on the inside would necessitate listening to the entire record.

Bubble memories are capable of tremendous storage capability due to the small size of the individual bubbles. In fact, the storage capacity is similar to that of traditional bulk computer storage techniques such as disks and magnetic tapes. The major drawback of bubble memory use is the slowness of information retrieval. However, bubble memories are used where speed is not a critical factor. Telephone systems and lap computers are both utilizing these memories.

**Fig. 20.7  Bubble Memory Device**

Bubble memories are a non-volatile, read/write memory. They retain the information without power and new information can be entered into them for either permanent or temporary storage.

**20.3.2 Volatile Memories**

Semiconductor circuit and computer design involves the constant evaluation of trade-offs. In the case of memory, non-volatile memory provides protection against power loss, but these memories are frequently slow and not very dense (bits of storage per square centimeter).

More important, none of the circuits described above (with the exception of bubble memories) has a write capability, an essential feature in operating a computer. New information, such as a change in pay status, must be conveniently entered into the computer and stored temporarily while the new check is being written. Memory must also be easily erasable so the computer can next process new information or a completely new program.

## RAM

**The circuit used for this purpose is the** *Random Access Memory,* or RAM. "Random" refers to the ability of the computer to directly retrieve any information stored in the circuit. Unlike a serial memory, the RAM design allows the chip to give back only the information asked for by the computer. This feature allows faster retrieval and makes the RAM the principle memory circuit in computers.

RAMs come in two principle designs: static and dynamic. A dynamic memory design often called a *DRAM* for Dynamic RAM is used in great quantities in computer memories. The memory cell design is based on only one transistor and the information is stored in it by a charge built up in the gate region. Unfortunately, the charge drains away very rapidly. To combat this problem, the memory information must be reinputted to the circuit on a constant basis. The term for this function is *refresh.* The refreshing of the circuit occurs many thousands of times per second.

Dynamic RAMS are vulnerable to both power loss and interruption, or problems with the refreshing circuit.

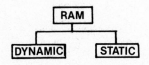

Fig. 20.8   RAM Cell Designs

Static memories are based on a cell design that does not need a refresh function. Once the information is put into the chip, it will stay as long as the power remains on. The penalty paid for this lesser degree of volatility is loss of space. The larger cell design makes static memories less dense than DRAM's.

The DRAM, executed in MOS or CMOS technology, has become the bellwether circuit of the I.C. world. The need for faster and denser memory has motivated memory designers to push the limits of process technology. RAM memory capacity is measured by the number of bits that can be stored. A 1K RAM has a capacity of 1024 bits of information; 1024 is a power of 2. The industry rounds off to the nearest thousand. A 64K bit RAM actually has a capacity of 65,536 bits of information.

RAM Capacity is expanding rapidly, with megabit memories (one million) expected to be produced in quantities by the end of the decade. Each step upward in RAM capacity places greater pressure on wafer processing and yield improvement. The nature of the semiconductor chip business is exemplified by the 64K RAM. Introduced by IBM in 1977, the chips were soon available in the merchant market, priced at over $100.00 per circuit. By 1983, competition and yield immprovements had lowered the price to under $6.00 per circuit!

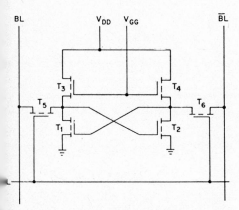

Fig. 20.9   Static RAM Schematic

## 20.4 THE NEXT GENERATION

Higher Levels of Integration

The industry is moving toward a higher level of integration through the reduction of the components on the chip. There are a number of limits affecting size the levels which can be reached. First are the limits imposed by optical lithography. It is predicted that this technology will allow feature size down to the sub-micron dimension due to better process tools and control and improved clean rooms.

Production imaging into the sub-micron range will require use of either X-rays or E-beams. Both of these technologies require development of higher reliability photoresist, which will enable feature size to be brought down to 0.04 microns.

The physical limit setting the bottom floor on device size and operation is 0.004 microns, the smallest size on which semiconductor devices will operate by the same physical laws as layered components. Below that size, conventional semiconductor physics do not apply.

Of more immediate concern are yield limits, especially as the individual circuits grow in size. Presently, the technology exists to cover an entire wafer with individual circuits. However, the yield of a one wafer circuit would be virtually zero, due to the presence of defects. Many circuits fail due to only one defect. A number of approaches are available to overcome the fatal influence of one small defect on an otherwise functioning die.

### Redundancy

*Redundancy* is the inclusion of extra circuit components in the design. If one or more of the components don't work, there are others available that do. The trade-off for redundancy is larger chip size. Also, extra circuitry is required within the main circuit to detect the functioning and nonfunctioning components and direct the selection of a functioning component.

Although this approach to higher yield has been discussed for years, it hasn't yet become a mainstay of circuit design.

### Wafer Scale Integration

*Wafer Scale Integration* is a novel approach to integration aimed at the full utilization of all the functioning areas on a wafer. The surface of a wafer using WSI is not covered by individual die. Instead, the wafer contains sections that are the functional segments of a circuit.

For example, consider a super circuit requiring ten logic chips and twenty memory chips. The conventional approach requires manufacturing enough wafers to deliver the required number of chips.

The failed chips on the wafers are usually inoperable due to a single or relatively few defects that prevent one of the sections of the circuit from performing. Even failed chips have areas or subsections that DO function. In the conventional chip approach, vast areas of the chip that contain working subsections are thrown away.

In WSI, the wafer surface is covered with individual circuit subsections rather than complete circuits. For example, in the super circuit above, the WSI wafer would have all of the subsections plus extras required to make the ten logic and twenty memory sections. Die sort testing at the end of the process would be performed to identify the subsections that are working. The metallization layer connects only the working subsections into the super circuit.

The result is a supercircuit that uses all of the functioning parts of the wafer surface. Other benefits include faster speed due to the lower number of package connections and lower cost resulting from eliminating individual packages.

The drawbacks to WSI include longer processing time to form both logic and memory functions on the same wafer, and reliability problems stemming from high heat levels which the more dense circuit generates.

## Josephson Junctions and Cryogenics

The next generation of solid state circuitry may have already been identified by the discovery of super-conductivity and the Josephson junction. Super-conductivity is a dramatic lowering of electrical resistance in semiconductor materials that takes place at very low temperatures. The temperatures required are those of liquid helium (–273° C).

The Josephson junction is formed by a thin insulator between two superconductors. At the low temperatures, electrons move through the barrier with little or no resistance. Externally supplied fields to the junction allow control of the current.

A number of Josephson junction based devices have been developed in laboratories. IBM is the leader in this technology. Problems yet to overcome in commercializing this technology for large scale very fast computers include developing metallization systems that can withstand the low temperatures and submicron imaging.

## Electro/Mechanical Solid State Devices

Semiconducting devices can respond to and produce effects other than electric signals. Optoelectrical devices have been available for years. These devices produce a current in response to light, or produce light from the result of a current crossing a junction (LED's).

Other semiconductor devices react to the physical strain of the crystal by producing a current.

Solid state technology, which has transformed the world since the discovery of the first transistor in 1947, continues to expand and offer the world exciting and revolutionary innovations. It is hard to contemplate the near and far future without considering the influence of this marvelous technology.

# Glossary

# GLOSSARY

**ACCEPTOR:** an impurity that can make a semiconductor P-type by accepting valence electrons, thereby leaving "holes" in the valence band. The holes act like carriers of positive charge.

**ALLOY:** in semiconductor processing, the alloy step causes the interdiffusion of the semiconductor and the material on top of it, forming an ohmic contact between them.

**ALUMINUM (Al):** the metal most often used in semiconductor technology to form the interconnects between devices on a chip. It is usually deposited by evaporation.

**ANGLE LAP:** a method of magnifying the depth of a junction by cutting (lapping) through it at an angle away from the perpendicular.

**ANGSTROM:** a unit of length. An angstrom is one ten-thousandth of a micron ($10^{-4}$ micron).

**ANNEAL:** a high temperature processing step (usually the last one), designed to minimize surface effects in devices by relieving stress or annealing the wafers.

**ANTIMONY (Sb):** a Group V element that is an N-type dopant in silicon. It is often used as the dopant for the buried layer.

**ARSENIC (As):** an N-type dopant often used for the buried layer predeposition.

**BASE:** 1. The control portion of an NPN or PNP transistor. 2. The P-type diffusion done using boron that forms the base (1) or NPN transistors, the emitter and collector of lateral PNP transistors, and resistors.

**BEAM LEAD (for integrated circuits):** a deposited metal lead, usually of gold, which projects beyond the edge of the semiconductor chip. Used for both mechanical and electrical contact of the chip.

**BIPOLAR TRANSISTOR:** a transistor consisting of an emitter, base and collector, whose action depends on the injection of minority carriers into the base by the emitter and the collection of these minority carriers from the base by the collector. Sometimes called NPN or PNP transistor to emphasize its layered structure.

**BOAT:** 1. Pieces of quartz joined together to form a supporting structure for wafers during high temperature processing steps. 2. A teflon or plastic assemblage used to hold wafers during wet processing steps.

**BOAT PULLER:** a mechanical arrangement to push a boat loaded with wafers into a furnace and/or withdraw it at a fixed speed.

**BONDING PAD:** the relatively rectangular, or square areas of metallization that are probed or attached to when access to devices or circuits is desired.

**BORON (B):** the P-type dopant commonly used for the isolation and base diffusion in standard bipolar integrated circuit processing.

**BORON TRICHLORIDE (BCl$_3$):** a gas that is often used as a source of boron for doping silicon.

**BUFFER:** an additive that prevents the rapid change of the chemical activity of an acid or base solution by keeping the number of ions capable of reacting essentially constant even as the solution is used.

**BURIED LAYER:** the N+ diffusion in the P-type substrate done just prior to growing the epitaxial layer. The buried layer provides a low resistance path for current flowing in a device. Common buried layer dopants are antimony and arsenic.

**CCD (Charge Coupled Device):** A semiconductor device whose action depends on the storage of electric charge within a semiconductor by an insulated electrode on its surface, with the possibility of selectively moving the charge to another electrode by prior manipulation of voltages in the electrode.

**CHANNEL:** a thin region of a semiconductor that supports conduction. A channel may occur at a surface or in the bulk. They may indicate contamination problems or incomplete isolation if not wanted, but are essential for the operation of MOSFET's and SIGFET's.

**CHARGE CARRIER:** a carrier of electrical charge within the crystal of a solid-state device, such as an electron or hole.

**CHIP:** one of the individual circuits on a wafer.

**CHROME:** a metal often used to fabricate masks. Chrome does not wear out as fast as emulsion, so chrome masks last longer.

**COLLECTOR:** along with the emitter and base, one of the three regions of the bipolar type of transistor.

**CONTACT:** the regions of exposed silicon that are covered during the metallization process to provide electrical access to the devices.

**CONTAMINATION:** a general term used to describe unwanted material that adversely affects the physical or electrical characteristics of a semiconductor wafer.

**CURRENT:** a measure of the number of charged particles passing a given point per unit time.

**CURVE TRACER:** a piece of electrical test equipment that displays the characteristics of a device visually on a screen.

**DEPLETION LAYER:** the region in a semiconductor where essentially all charge carriers have been swept out by the electric field which exists there.

**DEVELOPMENT:** a photoresist processing step in which photoresist is removed from areas not defined by the masking and exposure step.

**DIBORANE (B$_2$H$_6$):** a gas that is often used as a source of boron for doping silicon.

**DIE:** see "Chip."

**DIELECTRIC:** a material that conducts no current when it has a voltage across it. Two dielectrics encountered in semiconductor processing are silicon dioxide and silicon nitride.

**DIFFUSION:** a process used in semiconductor production which introduces minute amounts of impurities into a substrate material such as silicon or germanium and permits the impurity to spread into the substrate. The process is very dependent on temperature and time.

**DIODE:** a two-terminal device that allows current to flow in one direction but not in the other. A diode is present at the intersection of a P-type and an N-type region of a semiconductor.

**DIP (Dual In-Line Package):** A rectangular circuit package, with leads coming out of the long sides and bent down to fit into a socket.

**DONOR:** an impurity that can make a semiconductor N-type by donating extra "free" electrons to the conduction band. The free electrons are carriers of negative charge.

**DOPANTS:** an element that alters the conductivity of a semiconductor by contributing either a hole or an electron to the conduction process. For silicon, the dopants are found in Groups III and V.

**DOPING:** the introduction of an impurity (dopant) into the crystal lattice of a semiconductor to modify it electronic properties -- for example, adding boron to silicon to make the material more P-type.

**DRAIN:** along with the source and gate, one of the three regions of a unipolar or field effect transistor (FET).

**DRY OXIDE:** thermal silicon dioxide grown using oxygen.

**ELECTRON:** a charged particle revolving around the nucleus of an atom. It can form bonds with other atoms or be lost, making the atom an ion.

**ELECTRON BEAM (E-beam):** a type of evaporation that uses the energy of a focused electron beam to provide the required energy.

**EMITTER:** 1. The region of a transistor that serves as the source or imput end for carriers. 2. The N-type diffusion usually done using phosphorus which forms the emitter of NPN transistors, the base contact of PNP transistors, the N+ contact of NPN transistors, and low value resistors.

**EPI:** see "Epitaxial."

**EPITAXIAL (Greek for "arranged upon"):** the growth of a single crystal semiconductor film upon a single crystal substrate. The epitaxial layer has the same crystallographic characteristics as the substrate material. The N-type layer of silicon deposited on the substrate and buried layer is epitaxial silicon.

**ETCH:** a process for removing material in a specified area through a chemical reaction.

**EVAPORATION:** a process step that uses heat to evaporate a material from a source and deposit it on wafers. Both electron beam and filament evaporation are common in semiconductor processing.

**FAB:** see "Wafer Fab."

**FET (Field-Effect Transistor):** A transistor consisting of a source, gate and drain, whose action depends on the flow of majority carriers past the gate from source to drain. The flow is controlled by the transverse electric field under the gate. (See Unipolar Transistor.)

**FILAMENT:** a coiled piece of wire that is loaded with a material to be evaporated and heated by passing current through it.

**FOUR-POINT PROBE:** a piece of electrical equipment used to determine the sheet resistivity of a wafer.

**FURNACE:** a piece of equipment containing a resistance heated element and a temperature controller. It is used to maintain a region of constant temperature with a controlled atmosphere for the processing of semiconductor devices.

**GATE:** along with the source and drain, one of the three regions of the unipolar or field-effect transistor (FET).

**GROWN JUNCTION:** P/N junction made by controlling the type of impurity in a single crystal while it is being grown from a melt.

**HYBRID INTEGRATED CIRCUIT:** a structure consisting of an assembly of one or more semiconductor devices and a thin-film integrated circuit on a single substrate, usually of ceramic.

**HOLE:** the absence of a valence electron in a semiconductor crystal. Motion of a hole is equivalent to motion of a positive charge.

**HYDROFLUORIC ACID (HF):** a strong acid used to etch silicon dioxide. It is often diluted or buffered before it is used.

**HYDROGEN ($H_2$):** a gas used in semiconductor processing primarily as a carrier gas for high temperature reaction steps such as epitaxial silicon growth.

**INTEGRATED CIRCUIT (I.C.):** an electrical circuit consisting of several to many thousands of devices in a single chip of a semiconducting material.

**INGOT:** material prepared by solidification from a melt.

**INTEGRATED CIRCUIT:** a circuit in which many elements are fabricated and interconnected by a single process on a single chip of semiconductor material, as opposed to a "nonintegrated" circuit in which the transistors, diodes, resistors, etc. are fabricated separately and then assembled.

**ION:** an atom that has either gained or lost electrons, making it a charged particle (either negative or positive).

**ION IMPLANTATION:** introduction into a semiconductor of selected impurities in controlled regions, via high-voltage ion bombardment, to achieve desired electronic properties.

**ISOLATION MASK:** the second mask used in standard bipolar integrated circuit fabrication. Boron is diffused into silicon in regions etched during the isolation photoresist process and electrically separates or isolates regions of silicon.

**ISOPROPYL ALCOHOL:** a solvent often used in semiconductor processing for final rinsing and drying.

**JUNCTION:** the interface at which the conductivity type of a material changes from P-type to N-type or vice versa.

**JUNCTION DEPTH:** the depth of a junction down in the wafer.

**JUNCTION TRANSISTOR:** a bipolar transistor constructed from interacting P/N junctions. The term is used to distinguish junction transistors from other types, such as field-effect and point-contact transistors.

**LASER (Light Amplification by Stimulated Emission of Radiation):** In the laser, excited electrons give up their excitation in step with the light that is passing by to add energy to the transmitted light. Some lasers can generate or amplify extremely pure colors, in very narrow beams, often with very high intensity.

**LEAKY:** a much used term implying the presence of an unwanted current when a voltage is applied between two points.

**LED (Light-Emitting Diode):** a semiconductor device in which the energy of minority carriers in combining with holes is converted to light. Usually, but not necessarily, constructed as a P/N junction device.

**MAJORITY CARRIER:** the mobile charge carrier (hole or electron) that predominates in a semiconductor material -- for example, electrons in an N-type region.

**MASK:** a glass plate covered with an array of patterns used in the photomasking process. Each pattern consists of opaque or clear areas that respectively prevent or allow light through. The masks are aligned with existing patterns on silicon wafers and used to expose photoresist prior to etching with silicon dioxide or a metal. Masks may be emulsion, chrome, iron oxide, silicon, or a number of other materials.

**MESA:** a device structure fabricated by selective etching which leave flat portions of the original surface ("mesas") projecting above the neighboring regions. The mesa technique is often used to limit the extent of the electronically active material to the area of the mesa.

**MICRON:** a unit of length. One micron is one millionth of a meter ($10^{-6}$ meter).

**MINORITY CARRIER:** the nonpredominant mobile charge carrier in a semiconductor -- for example, electrons in a P-type region.

**MOSFET:** a field-effect transistor containing a metal gate over thermal oxide over silicon.

**NEGATIVE RESIST:** photoresist that remains in areas that were not protected from exposure by the opaque regions of a mask while being removed in regions that were protected by the develop cycle. A negative image of a mask remains following the develop process. Waycoat and Microneg are two common negative resists.

**NITRIC ACID ($HNO_3$):** a strong acid often used to clean silicon wafers or etch metals.

**NITROGEN ($N_2$):** a gas that seldom reacts with other materials. It is often used as a carrier gas for chemicals in semiconductor processing.

**NPN TRANSISTOR:** a transistor which has a base of P-type silicon sandwiched between an emitter and a collector of N-type silicon.

**N-TYPE:** a semiconductor material in which the majority of carriers are electrons and therefore negative. N-type dopants in silicon are Group V elements, in which the fifth outer electron is free to conduct current.

**OXIDE:** see Silicon Dioxide.

**OXIDE MASKING:** use of an oxide on a semiconductor to create a pattern in which impurities are diffused or implanted.

**OXYGEN ($O_2$):** a gas used in semiconductors to oxidize silicon, to form vapor deposited oxide, and for other processing steps.

**PASSIVATION:** treatment of a region of a device to prevent deterioration of electronic properties through chemical action or corrosion. Usually passivation protects against moisture or contamination. Layers of silicon dioxide or silicon nitride are often used for passivation.

**PHOSPHINE ($PH_3$):** a gas that is often used as a source of phosphorus for doping silicon.

**PHOSPHORUS (P):** the N-type dopant commonly used for the sinker and emitter diffusions in standard bipolar integrated circuit technology.

**PHOSPHORUS OXYCHLORIDE ($POCl_3$):** a liquid that is often used as a source of phosphorus for doping silicon.

**PHOTORESIST:** the light-sensitive film spun onto wafers and "exposed" using high intensity light through a mask. The exposed photoresist can be dissolved off the wafer with developers, leaving a pattern of photoresist which allows etching to take place in some areas while preventing it in others.

**PLANAR STRUCTURE:** a flat-surfaced device structure fabricated by diffusion and oxide masking, with the junctions terminating in a single plane. The structural planarity is often advantageous for photoresist processing.

**P/N JUNCTION:** within a crystal, an interface between a P region that conducts primarily by holes and an N region that conducts primarily by electrons.

**PNP:** semiconductor crystal structure consisting of an N-type region sandwiched between two P-type regions, as commonly used in bipolar transistors.

**POSITIVE RESIST:** photoresist that is removed in areas that were not protected from exposure by the opaque regions of a mask while remaining in regions that were protected by the develop cycle. A positive image of the mask remains following the develop process. AZ–1350 is a common positive resist.

**POLYCRYSTALLINE SILICON (poly):** silicon composed of many crystals. Raw silicon comes in ingots of poly prior to crystal growth. Poly may be deposited epitaxially (either accidentally of on purpose) by depositing too fast, at too low a temperature, or by depositing on a layer of silicon dioxide.

**PREDEPOSITION (predep):** the process step during which a controlled amount of a dopant is introduced into the crystal structure of a semiconductor.

**P-TYPE:** semiconductor material in which the majority carriers are holes and therefore positive. P-type dopants in silicon are Group III-A elements, in which the absence of a fourth outer electron manifests itself as conduction by a positively charged hole.

**PVX (Doped Silox):** a chemically deposited layer of phosphorus-rich silicon dioxide. PVX (a shortened name for phosphorus-doped vapor-deposited oxide) can be used for scratch protection, but is often used with a layer of vapox.

**QUARTZ:** another name for silicon dioxide. Because of its high temperature resistance, quartz is used in many processing steps in integrated circuit fabrication.

**REACTOR:** a piece of equipment used for the deposition of a layer of material used in semiconductor processing. Common types of reactors are epitaxial reactors, vapox reactors, and nitride reactors.

**SCHOTTKY BARRIER:** a potential barrier formed between a material and a semiconductor. The term usually refers to a barrier which is high enough and thick enough to serve as a rectifier but which avoids the slowing-down effect that results from injection of charge in P/N junction rectifiers.

**SEMICONDUCTOR:** an element such as silicon or germanium, intermediate in electrical conductivity between the conductors and the insulators, in which conduction takes place by means of holes and electrons.

**SHEET RESISTANCE:** a measurement with dimensions of $ohms/cm^2$ that tells the number of N-type or P-type donor atoms in a semiconductor.

**SIC (Silicon Integrated Circuit):** An integrated circuit where all the elements such as transistors, diodes, resistors and capacitors are successively fabricated in or on the silicon and interconnected.

**SILICON (Si):** the Group IV element used for fabricating diodes, transistors, and integrated circuits.

**SILICON DIOXIDE ($SiO_2$):** a passivating layer that can be thermally grown or deposited on silicon wafers. Thermal silicon dioxide is commonly grown using either oxygen ($O_2$) or water vapor ($H_2O$) at temperatures above 900° C.

**SILICON NITRIDE ($Si_3N_4$):** a passivation layer chemically deposited on wafers at temperatures between 600° and 900° C. It protects devices against contamination once it is applied.

**SILICON TETRACHLORIDE ($SiCl_4$):** a gas that reacts with hydrogen to produce silicon and hydrogen chloride gas. It is often used to deposit epitaxial silicon.

**SLUG:** see "Buried Layer."

**SOLAR CELL:** large-area diode in which a P/N junction close to the surface of a semiconducor generates electrical energy from light falling on the surface.

**SOLID STATE:** along with gas and liquid, one of the three states of matter.

**SOLID STATE ELECTRONICS:** designation used to describe devices and circuits fabricated from solid materials such as semiconductors, ferrites, or films, as distinct from devices and circuits making use of electron tube technology.

**SOURCE:** along with the gate and drain, one of the three regions of a unipolar or field-effect transistor (FET).

**SPUTTERING:** a method of depositing a film of material on a desired object. A target of the desired material is bombarded with RF-excited ions which knock atoms from the target and deposit them on the object to be coated.

**STEAM OXIDE:** thermal silicon dioxide grown by bubbling a gas (usually oxygen or nitrogen) through water at 98° – 100° C.

**SUBCOLLECTOR:** see "Buried Layer."

**SUBSTRATE:** the underlying material upon which a device, circuit, or epitaxial layer is fabricated.

**SULFURIC ACID ($H_2SO_4$):** a strong acid often used to clean silicon wafers and to remove photoresist.

**SURFACE STATES:** extra donors, acceptors or traps, usually undesired, which may occur on a semiconductor surface because of crystal imperfections or contamination and which may vary undesirably with time.

**SUSCEPTOR:** the flat slab of material (usually graphite) that wafers are heated on during high temperature deposition processes such as epitaxial growth or nitride deposition.

**TCE (Trichloroethylene):** a solvent used for wafer and general cleaning.

**THERMAL OXIDE:** on silicon semiconductor devices, an oxide fabricated by exposing the silicon to oxygen at high temperatures. The resulting interface is outstandingly free of ionic impurities and defects (surface states).

**THERMOCOUPLE:** a device to measure the temperature in a furnace of a reactor. It is made by welding two wires together at a point. Heat generates a voltage between the two materials that is proportional to the temperature.

**THIN-FILM INTEGRATED CIRCUIT:** a circuit consisting of patterns of tantalum or other materials laid down on a substrate of glass or ceramic, typically larger than silicon integrated circuits. Sometimes designated "FIC."

**TRANSISTOR:** a semiconductor device that uses a stream of charge carriers to produce active electronic effects. The name was coined from the electrical characteristic of "transfer resistance." As compared with electron tubes, transistors are usually advantageous because of their longer lifetime and greater efficiency, reliability and compactness.

**TUBE:** 1. See Furnace. 2. A cylindrical piece of quartz with fittings on one or both ends. It is placed in a furnace to provide a contamination-free and controlled atmosphere.

**UNIPOLAR TRANSISTOR:** a transistor such as an FET whose action depends on majority carriers only.

**VLF HOOD:** a work station with vertical laminar air flow to keep dirt out.

**VOLTAGE:** the force applied between two points to try to cause charged particles (and hence current) to flow.

**WAFER:** a thin, usually round slice of a semiconductor material, from which chips are made.

**WAFER FAB:** the operations in which the circuit or device is put in and on the wafer.

**WAFER SORT:** the step at which integrated circuits are tested to see whether or not they work. Probes contact the pads of the circuit and they are measured by putting in an electrical signal and seeing if the correct one comes out.

# Index